BTEC National IT Practitioners

Book 2

Specialist units

Steve Farrell
Trevor Heathcote
Sue Jennings
Diane and Jon Sutherland
Judith Tope

A PEARSON COMPANY

Contents

How to use this book

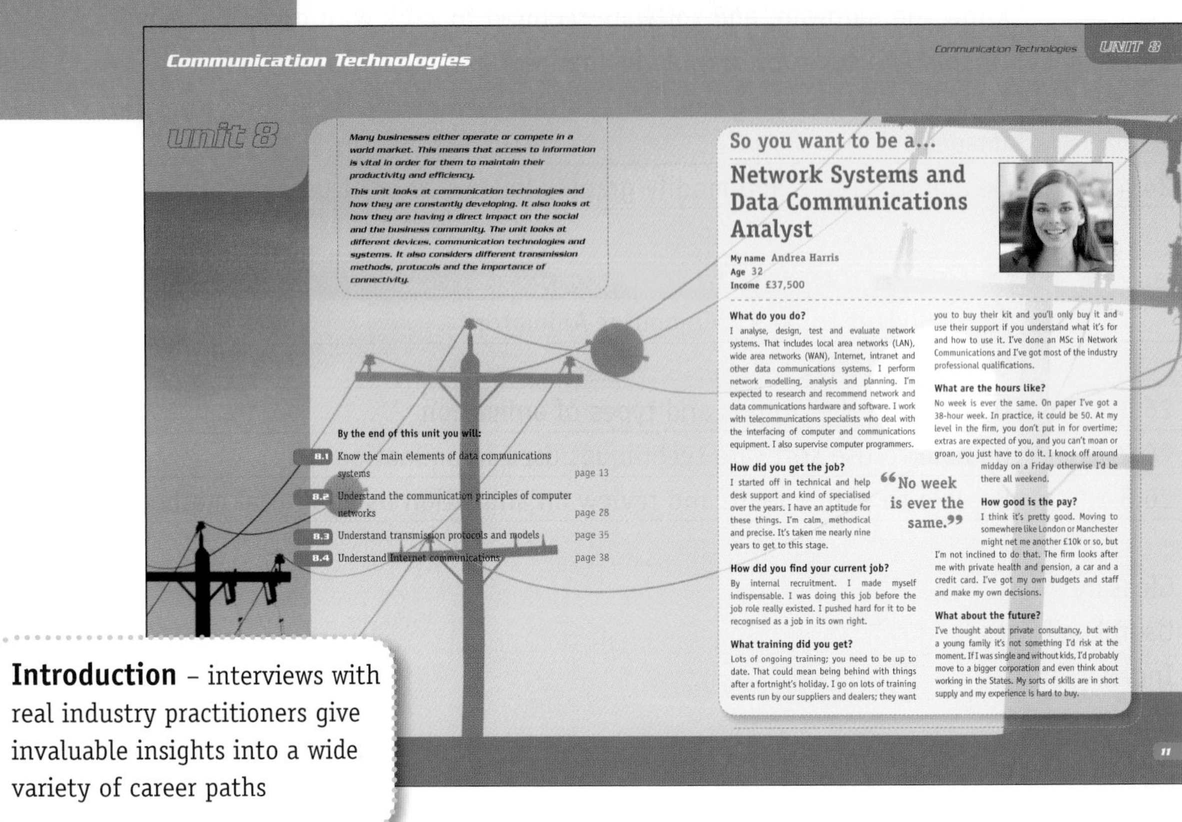
Communication Technologies

Communication Technologies UNIT 8

unit 8

Many businesses either operate or compete in a world market. This means that access to information is vital in order for them to maintain their productivity and efficiency.

This unit looks at communication technologies and how they are constantly developing. It also looks at how they are having a direct impact on the social and the business community. The unit looks at different devices, communication technologies and systems. It also considers different transmission methods, protocols and the importance of connectivity.

By the end of this unit you will:

So you want to be a...

Network Systems and Data Communications Analyst

My name Andrea Harris
Age 32
Income £37,500

What do you do?
I analyse, design, test and evaluate network systems. That includes local area networks (LAN), wide area networks (WAN), Internet, intranet and other data communications systems. I perform network modelling, analysis and planning. I'm expected to research and recommend network and data communications hardware and software. I work with telecommunications specialists who deal with the interfacing of computer and communications equipment. I also supervise computer programmers.

How did you get the job?
I started off in technical and help desk support and kind of specialised over the years. I have an aptitude for these things. I'm calm, methodical and precise. It's taken me nearly nine years to get to this stage.

How did you find your current job?
By internal recruitment. I made myself indispensable. I was doing this job before the job role really existed. I pushed hard for it to be recognised as a job in its own right.

What training did you get?
Lots of ongoing training; you need to be up to date. That could mean being behind with things after a fortnight's holiday. I go on lots of training events run by our suppliers and dealers; they want you to buy their kit and you'll only buy it and use their support if you understand what it's for and how to use it. I've done an MSc in Network Communications and I've got most of the industry professional qualifications.

What are the hours like?
No week is ever the same. On paper I've got a 38-hour week. In practice, it could be 50. At my level in the firm, you don't put in for overtime; extras are expected of you, and you can't moan or groan, you just have to do it. I knock off around midday on a Friday otherwise I'd be there all weekend.

"No week is ever the same."

How good is the pay?
I think it's pretty good. Moving to somewhere like London or Manchester might net me another £10k or so, but I'm not inclined to do that. The firm looks after me with private health and pension, a car and a credit card. I've got my own budgets and staff and make my own decisions.

What about the future?
I've thought about private consultancy, but with a young family it's not something I'd risk at the moment. If I was single and without kids, I'd probably move to a bigger corporation and even think about working in the States. My sorts of skills are in short supply and my experience is hard to buy.

11

Introduction – interviews with real industry practitioners give invaluable insights into a wide variety of career paths

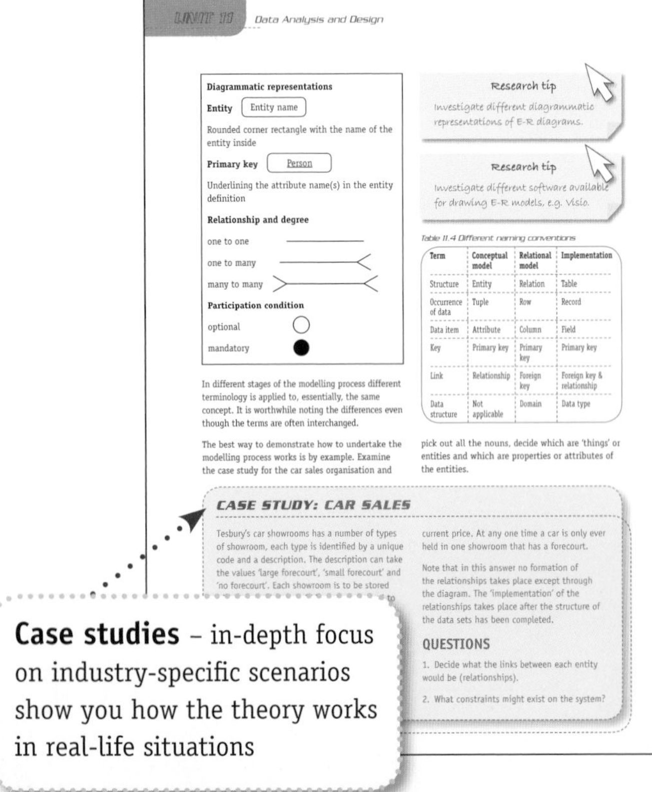
UNIT 11 Data Analysis and Design

Diagrammatic representations	
Entity	Entity name
Rounded corner rectangle with the name of the entity inside	
Primary key	Person
Underlining the attribute name(s) in the entity definition	
Relationship and degree	
one to one	
one to many	
many to many	
Participation condition	
optional	○
mandatory	●

Research tip
Investigate different diagrammatic representations of E-R diagrams.

Research tip
Investigate different software available for drawing E-R models, e.g. Visio.

Table 11.4 Different naming conventions

Term	Conceptual model	Relational model	Implementation
Structure	Entity	Relation	Table
Occurrence of data	Tuple	Row	Record
Data item	Attribute	Column	Field
Key	Primary key	Primary key	Primary key
Link	Relationship	Foreign key	Foreign key & relationship
Data structure	Not applicable	Domain	Data type

In different stages of the modelling process different terminology is applied to, essentially, the same concept. It is worthwhile noting the differences even though the terms are often interchanged.

The best way to demonstrate how to undertake the modelling process works is by example. Examine the case study for the car sales organisation and pick out all the nouns, decide which are 'things' or entities and which are properties or attributes of the entities.

CASE STUDY: CAR SALES

Tesbury's car showrooms has a number of types of showroom, each type is identified by a unique code and a description. The description can take the values 'large forecourt', 'small forecourt' and 'no forecourt'. Each showroom is to be stored ...

current price. At any one time a car is only ever held in one showroom that has a forecourt.

Note that in this answer no formation of the relationships takes place except through the diagram. The 'implementation' of the relationships takes place after the structure of the data sets has been completed.

QUESTIONS

1. Decide what the links between each entity would be (relationships).
2. What constraints might exist on the system?

Case studies – in-depth focus on industry-specific scenarios show you how the theory works in real-life situations

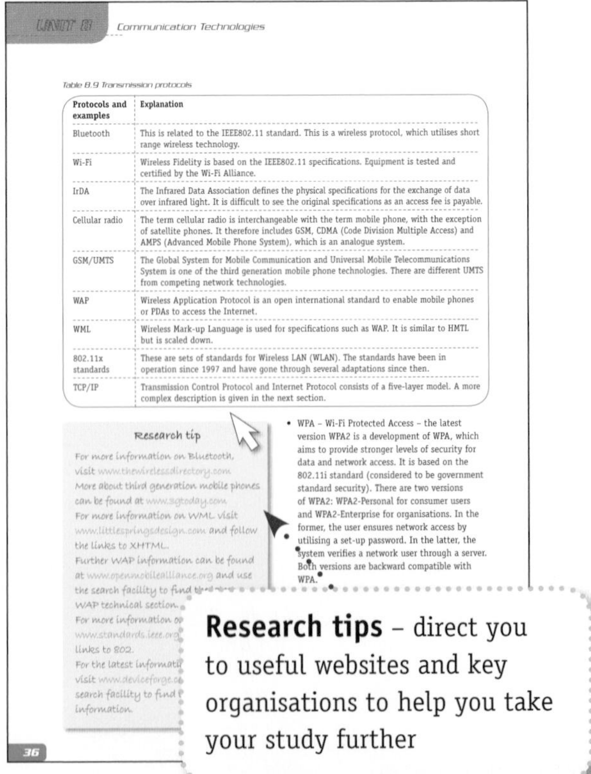
UNIT 8 Communication Technologies

Table 8.9 Transmission protocols

Protocols and examples	Explanation
Bluetooth	This is related to the IEEE802.11 standard. This is a wireless protocol, which utilises short range wireless technology.
Wi-Fi	Wireless Fidelity is based on the IEEE802.11 specifications. Equipment is tested and certified by the Wi-Fi Alliance.
IrDA	The Infrared Data Association defines the physical specifications for the exchange of data over infrared light. It is difficult to see the original specifications as an access fee is payable.
Cellular radio	The term cellular radio is interchangeable with the term mobile phone, with the exception of satellite phones. It therefore includes GSM, CDMA (Code Division Multiple Access) and AMPS (Advanced Mobile Phone System), which is an analogue system.
GSM/UMTS	The Global System for Mobile Communication and Universal Mobile Telecommunications System is one of the third generation mobile phone technologies. There are different UMTS from competing network technologies.
WAP	Wireless Application Protocol is an open international standard to enable mobile phones or PDAs to access the Internet.
WML	Wireless Mark-up Language is used for specifications such as WAP. It is similar to HMTL but is scaled down.
802.11x standards	These are sets of standards for Wireless LAN (WLAN). The standards have been in operation since 1997 and have gone through several adaptations since then.
TCP/IP	Transmission Control Protocol and Internet Protocol consists of a five-layer model. A more complex description is given in the next section.

Research tip
For more information on Bluetooth, visit www.thewirelessdirectory.com
More about third generation mobile phones can be found at www.3gtoday.com
For more information on WML visit www.littlespringsdesign.com and follow the links to XHTML.
Further WAP information can be found at www.openmobilealliance.org and use the search facility to find ...
WAP technical section.
For more information ...
www.standards.ieee.org ...
links to 802.
For the latest informati...
visit www.deviceforge.c...
search facility to find ...
information.

- WPA – Wi-Fi Protected Access – the latest version WPA2 is a development of WPA, which aims to provide stronger levels of security for data and network access. It is based on the 802.11i standard (considered to be government standard security). There are two versions of WPA2: WPA2-Personal for consumer users and WPA2-Enterprise for organisations. In the former, the user ensures network access by utilising a set-up password. In the latter, the system verifies a network user through a server. Both versions are backward compatible with WPA.

36

Research tips – direct you to useful websites and key organisations to help you take your study further

Grading criteria – learning outcomes and grading criteria at the beginning of every unit, so you know right from the start what you need to do to achieve a pass, merit or distinction

UNIT 11 Data Analysis and Design

Grading criteria

The table below shows what you need to do to gain a pass, merit or distinction in this part of the qualification. Make sure you refer back to it when you are completing work so that you can judge whether you are meeting the criteria and what you need to do to fill in gaps in your knowledge or experience.

In this unit there are five evidence activities that give you an opportunity to demonstrate your achievement of the grading criteria:

page 56 P1, P2, P4, M1
page 66 P3, P5, M2
page 70 P6, M3
page 70 P7, D2
page 70 M4, D1

To achieve a pass grade the evidence must show that the learner is able to...	To achieve a merit grade the evidence must show that, in addition to the pass criteria, the learner is able to...	To achieve a distinction grade the evidence must show that, in addition to the pass and merit criteria, the learner is able to...
P1 describe the advantages and disadvantages of the specified database types, using examples	M1 explain the benefits of the logical data modelling process	D1 evaluate the effectiveness of the data modelling process in producing an efficient data model to meet user requirements
P2 describe the advantages and disadvantages of the specified analysis and design methodologies, using examples	M2 explain the constraints developed in a logical data model to meet specified user requirements	D2 evaluate a model produced against an initial brief, and suggest improvements to enhance the model to meet user requirements.
P3 identify and describe potential modelling constraints that could arise from a logical data model, using examples	M3 justify the requirements for all types of test required to ensure a logical data model is efficient and effective	
P4 describe the concepts involved in logical data modelling	M4 justify the purpose of complete and accurate technical documentation for a logical data model and associated testing.	
P5 produce a data model to meet specified user requirements		
P6 produce a test strategy and test plan for normal situations for a data model		
P7 implement a logical data model.		

44

Examples – industry-specific examples show you what the theory looks like in practice

Think – questions help you reflect on your learning and to think about how it could be applied to real-life working practice

UNIT 11 Data Analysis and Design

Table 11.3 Rental example data (1NF)

CD id	customer code	date of rental	date of return	customer name	customer date of birth	CD title	CD rating	rental cost per day
1	99	01-Oct	03-Oct	freddie	04/04/1993	doom	12	£3.00
2	98	01-Oct	03-Oct	billy	05/01/1989	doom 2	18	£4.00
3	97	02-Oct	05-Oct	mohammed	06/02/1993	less doom	pg	£2.00
4	96	02-Oct	05-Oct	jamila	07/01/1985	happiness	U	£1.00
5	99	03-Oct	07-Oct	freddie	04/04/1993	scare 1	12	£3.00
6	98	03-Oct	08-Oct	billy	05/01/1989	scare 2	18	£4.00
1	97	04-Oct	07-Oct	mohammed	06/02/1993	doom	12	£3.00
2	96	04-Oct	06-Oct	jamila	07/01/1985	doom 2	18	£4.00
3	99	05-Oct	10-Oct	freddie	04/04/1993	less doom	pg	£2.00
4	98	05-Oct		billy	05/01/1989	happiness	U	£1.00

Example

Repeat the normalisation process for the following relation in 1NF:

Rental activity (CDid, customercode, startdateofrental, returndate, customername, customerdateofbirth, rentalcostperday, CDrating, costperday)

An aspect that has not been introduced through normalisation as yet is that of constraints that might be applied to the data and to the processing. This is done in LDM and assists the developer in moving forward with the system development.

Think Just for interest look at the data in the table for the rental activity exercise and see if you can spot any potential constraints that could be applied.

EVIDENCE ACTIVITY

P1 – P2 – P4 – M1

You have seen the post of junior database analyst with a small software consultancy, Manford

Presentation 1 will be delivered in the morning session, after which a shortlist will be drawn up for applicants to attend the second stage of the interview process during which presentation 2 will be delivered.

Obviously you need to prepare both presentations in preparation for the whole interview process. You should develop PowerPoint slides with notes pages for the panel to collect during the day.

Presentation 1

You should demonstrate your knowledge and understanding of different database types. The interviewing panel wants to know the difference between a flat file database, a relational database and a network database. In order to support your knowledge give an example of each, state situations where each type might be suitable for use. You should also give an overview of the pros and cons of each type of database listed above. **(P1)**

Presentation 2

You should show your knowledge and understanding of analysis and design methodologies. The interview panel wants to know the pros and cons of each of logical data modelling (LDM) and the normalisation approach **(P2)**. You should support your knowledge with an example of how each might be used. You should also give details of the different concepts, constraints, stages and outcomes of LDM **(P4)** and ... LDM produces an effective model in any

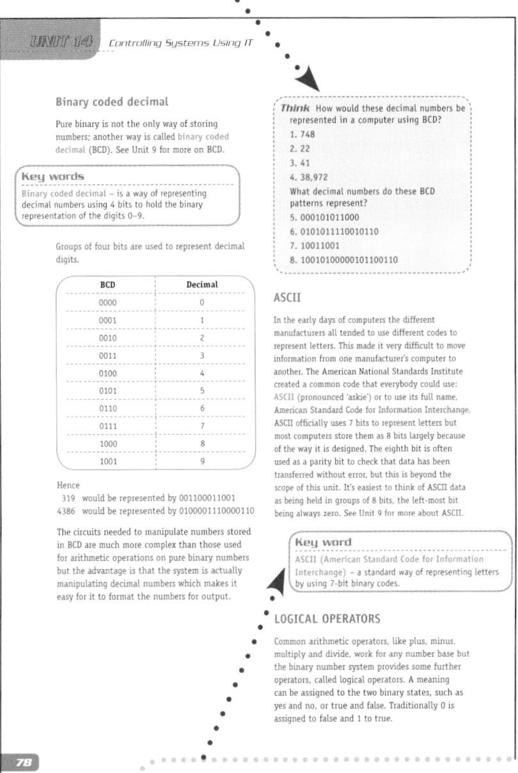
UNIT 14 Controlling Systems Using IT

Binary coded decimal

Pure binary is not the only way of storing numbers; another way is called binary coded decimal (BCD). See Unit 9 for more on BCD.

Key words

Binary coded decimal – is a way of representing decimal numbers using 4 bits to hold the binary representation of the digits 0–9.

Groups of four bits are used to represent decimal digits.

BCD	Decimal
0000	0
0001	1
0010	2
0011	3
0100	4
0101	5
0110	6
0111	7
1000	8
1001	9

Hence
319 would be represented by 001100011001
4386 would be represented by 0100001110000110

The circuits needed to manipulate numbers stored in BCD are much more complex than those used for arithmetic operations on pure binary numbers but the advantage is that the system is actually manipulating decimal numbers which makes it easy for it to format the numbers for output.

Think How would these decimal numbers be represented in a computer using BCD?
1. 748
2. 22
3. 41
4. 38,972
What decimal numbers do these BCD patterns represent?
5. 000101011000
6. 0101011110010110
7. 10011001
8. 100101000000101100110

ASCII

In the early days of computers the different manufacturers all tended to use different codes to represent letters. This made it very difficult to move information from one manufacturer's computer to another. The American National Standards Institute created a common code that everybody could use: ASCII (pronounced 'askie') or to use its full name, American Standard Code for Information Interchange. ASCII officially uses 7 bits to represent letters but most computers store them as 8 bits largely because of the way it is designed. The eighth bit is often used as a parity bit to check that data has been transferred without error, but this is beyond the scope of this unit. It's easiest to think of ASCII data as being held in groups of 8 bits, the left-most bit being always zero. See Unit 9 for more about ASCII.

Key word

ASCII (American Standard Code for Information Interchange) – a standard way of representing letters by using 7-bit binary codes.

LOGICAL OPERATORS

Common arithmetic operators, like plus, minus, multiply and divide, work for any number base but the binary number system provides some further operators, called logical operators. A meaning can be assigned to the two binary states, such as yes and no, or true and false. Traditionally 0 is assigned to false and 1 to true.

78

Evidence activities – short activities are spread throughout the unit giving you the opportunity to demonstrate your achievement of the grading criteria in small steps

Key words – easy to understand definitions of key industry terms

Track your progress

This master grid can be used as a study aid. You can track your progress by ticking the level you achieve. The relevant grading criteria can also be found at the start of each unit.

To achieve a pass grade the evidence must show that the learner is able to...	To achieve a merit grade the evidence must show that, in addition to the pass criteria, the learner is able to...	To achieve a distinction grade the evidence must show that, in addition to the pass and merit criteria, the learner is able to...
Unit 8		
P1 identify and explain types of communication devices	M1 explain techniques that can be used to reduce errors in transmissions	D1 critically compare the OSI seven layer model and the TCP/IP model
P2 explain the principles of signal theory	M2 explain why particular transmission media are chosen in particular situations	D2 choose and justify the choice of a particular access control method for a given situation
P3 describe communication protocols used and explain why they are important	M3 explain and implement direct communication between two networked devices	D3 compare and evaluate the effectiveness of the transfer of data over both wireless and wired networks
P4 describe different methods of electronic communication and transmission media used		
P5 identify and describe the roles of network components and how they are interconnected		
P6 describe the features of networks and the communication services they offer		
P7 describe the nature of internet communication and the associated system requirements		
Unit 11		
P1 describe the advantages and disadvantages of the specified database types, using examples	M1 explain the benefits of the logical data modelling process	D1 evaluate the effectiveness of the data modelling process in producing an efficient data model to meet user requirements
P2 describe the advantages and disadvantages of two analysis and design methodologies, using examples	M2 explain the constraints developed in a logical data model to meet specified user requirements	D2 evaluate a model produced against an initial brief, and suggest improvements to enhance the model to meet user requirements
P3 identify and describe potential modelling constraints that could arise from a logical data model, using examples	M3 justify the requirements for all types of test required to ensure a logical data model is efficient and effective	
P4 describe the concepts involved in logical data modelling	M4 justify the purpose of complete and accurate technical documentation for a logical data model and associated testing	
P5 produce a data model to meet specified user requirements		
P6 produce a test strategy and test plan for normal situations for a data model		
P7 implement a logical data model		

To achieve a pass grade the evidence must show that the learner is able to...	To achieve a merit grade the evidence must show that, in addition to the pass criteria, the learner is able to...	To achieve a distinction grade the evidence must show that, in addition to the pass and merit criteria, the learner is able to...
Unit 14		
P1 describe how data can be represented in control systems	M1 compare analogue and digital signals and explain the need for signal conversion	D1 design a control system for a given user need that uses different types of sensors
P2 describe using examples types of control systems	M2 explain the principles and uses of proportional control	D2 critically evaluate the design and performance of a control system
P3 describe the characteristics of digital and analogue control systems	M3 propose and explain potential improvements to a control system	
P4 demonstrate the operation of different sensors and output devices		
P5 explain the stages of control loop operations		
P6 assemble, implement and review a control system for a given purpose		
Unit 18		
P1 describe, using examples, why different types of programming languages have been developed	M1 compare and contrast two different types of program languages	D1 justify the language used for two different circumstances
P2 describe, with examples, the benefits of having a variety of data types available to the programmer	M2 justify the choice of data types used in a programmed solution	D2 evaluate a programmed solution and suggest potential further extensions
P3 write and test the functionality of a number of internally documented programs that demonstrate the features available in a given language	M3 adapt and improve a programmed solution based on formal testing and review	
P4 describe the features of a programming language		
P5 design and create a working programmed solution based on a defined set of requirements		
P6 document, test and review a programmed solution		
Unit 24		
P1 describe hardware and software used to create and edit graphics	M1 compare the limitations of at least two different hardware devices and two different software packages utilised for the capture, manipulation and storage of graphics	D1 justify the following in connection with the production of graphic images to meet a client and user need: software and tools used, file format, image resolution, colour depth
P2 identify two graphics related hardware upgrades to an existing system and describe the potential benefits when working with graphic images	M2 demonstrate the use of two advanced techniques in graphics manipulation	D2 evaluate the impact of evolving output media on the designing and creation of graphic images
P3 define and document a client and user need for three related graphic images	M3 demonstrate the impact that file format, compression techniques, image resolution and colour depth have on file size and image quality	

To achieve a pass grade the evidence must show that the learner is able to...	To achieve a merit grade the evidence must show that, in addition to the pass criteria, the learner is able to...	To achieve a distinction grade the evidence must show that, in addition to the pass and merit criteria, the learner is able to...
Unit 24 (*contd*)		
P4 create and review three original graphic images to meet a defined user need		
P5 capture existing images using a scanner and a digital camera and edit them to meet a given user need		
P6 explain potential legal implications of using and editing graphical images		
Unit 26		
P1 describe how persistence of vision is used in animation	M1 compare two different animation formats	D1 evaluate one software package or technique that is used to create animations
P2 describe three applications for animations	M2 compare two different specialist software package or programming techniques used to create computer animation	D2 evaluate the tools and techniques used to create finished animations.
P3 describe the features, advantages and limitations of animated GIFs and one other animation format	M3 adapt and improve animations based on formal reviews	
P4 describe two different types of animation techniques	M4 explain particular techniques that are used to minimise the file size of animations	
P5 describe the special factors that need to be taken into account when creating animations for the web		
P6 design, create and review animations for particular purposes that use both vector and bit map graphics		
P7 design, create and review animations for particular purposes that are designed to be incorporated into web pages.		

Research Skills

Before you start your research project you need to know where to find information and the guidelines you must follow.

Types of information

Primary Sources

Information you have gathered yourself, through surveys, interviews, photos or observation. This information is only as good as the questions and people you ask. You must get permission before you use someone's photo or include an interview in your work.

Secondary Sources

Information produced by somebody else, including information from the internet, books, magazines, databases and television. You need to be sure that your secondary source is reliable if you are going to use the information.

Information Sources

The Internet

The internet is a useful research tool, however, not all the information on the internet is accurate; anyone can set up a webpage, so when using the internet ask yourself if you can trust the information you find.

Acknowledge your source! When quoting from the internet always include author name (if known)/document title/URL web address/date site was accessed.

Books, Magazines and Newspapers

Information in newspapers and magazines is up to date and usually researched thoroughly. Books have a longer shelf life than newspapers so make sure you use the most recent edition.

Broadcast Media

Television and radio broadcast current news stories and the information should be accurate. Be aware that some programmes offer personal opinions as well as facts.

Acknowledge your source! When quoting from books, magazines, journal or papers, always include author name/title of publication/publisher/year of publication.

Plagiarism

Plagiarism is including in your own work extracts or ideas from another source without acknowledging its origins. If you use any material from other sources you must acknowledge it. This includes the work of fellow students.

Storing Information

Keep a record of all the information you gather. Record details of book titles, author names, page references, web addresses (URLs) and contact details of interviewees. Accurate, accessible records will help you acknowledge sources and find information quickly.

Internet Dos and Don'ts

Do ✓

- check information against other sources
- keep a record of where you found information and acknowledge the source
- be aware that not all sites are genuine or trustworthy

Don't ∅

- assume all the information on the internet is accurate and up to date
- copy material from websites without checking whether permission from the copyright holder is required
- give personal information to people you meet on the internet

unit 8

Many businesses either operate or compete in a world market. This means that access to information is vital in order for them to maintain their productivity and efficiency.

This unit looks at communication technologies and how they are constantly developing. It also looks at how they are having a direct impact on the social and the business community. The unit looks at different devices, communication technologies and systems. It also considers different transmission methods, protocols and the importance of connectivity.

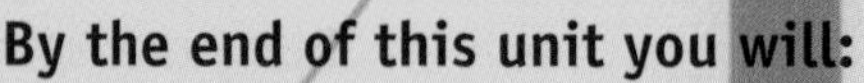

By the end of this unit you will:

So you want to be a...

Network Systems and Data Communications Analyst

My name Andrea Harris
Age 32
Income £37,500

What do you do?

I analyse, design, test and evaluate network systems. That includes local area networks (LAN), wide area networks (WAN), Internet, intranet and other data communications systems. I perform network modelling, analysis and planning. I'm expected to research and recommend network and data communications hardware and software. I work with telecommunications specialists who deal with the interfacing of computer and communications equipment. I also supervise computer programmers.

How did you get the job?

I started off in technical and help desk support and kind of specialised over the years. I have an aptitude for these things. I'm calm, methodical and precise. It's taken me nearly nine years to get to this stage.

How did you find your current job?

By internal recruitment. I made myself indispensable. I was doing this job before the job role really existed. I pushed hard for it to be recognised as a job in its own right.

What training did you get?

Lots of ongoing training; you need to be up to date. That could mean being behind with things after a fortnight's holiday. I go on lots of training events run by our suppliers and dealers; they want you to buy their kit and you'll only buy it and use their support if you understand what it's for and how to use it. I've done an MSc in Network Communications and I've got most of the industry professional qualifications.

What are the hours like?

No week is ever the same. On paper I've got a 38-hour week. In practice, it could be 50. At my level in the firm, you don't put in for overtime; extras are expected of you, and you can't moan or groan, you just have to do it. I knock off around midday on a Friday otherwise I'd be there all weekend.

"No week is ever the same."

How good is the pay?

I think it's pretty good. Moving to somewhere like London or Manchester might net me another £10k or so, but I'm not inclined to do that. The firm looks after me with private health and pension, a car and a credit card. I've got my own budgets and staff and make my own decisions.

What about the future?

I've thought about private consultancy, but with a young family it's not something I'd risk at the moment. If I was single and without kids, I'd probably move to a bigger corporation and even think about working in the States. My sorts of skills are in short supply and my experience is hard to buy.

Grading criteria

The table below shows what you need to do to gain a pass, merit or distinction in this part of the qualification. Make sure you refer back to it when you are completing work so that you can judge whether you are meeting the criteria and what you need to do to fill in gaps in your knowledge or experience.

In this unit there are seven evidence activities that give you an opportunity to demonstrate your achievement of the grading criteria:

page 15	P1
page 20	P2
page 25	P3
page 27	P4, M1
page 34	P5, M2
page 37	P6, D1
page 41	P7, M3, D2, D3

To achieve a pass grade the evidence must show that the learner is able to...	To achieve a merit grade the evidence must show that, in addition to the pass criteria, the learner is able to...	To achieve a distinction grade the evidence must show that, in addition to the pass and merit criteria, the learner is able to...
P1 identify and explain types of communication devices	**M1** explain techniques that can be used to reduce errors in transmissions	**D1** critically compare the OSI seven-layer model and the TCP/IP model
P2 explain the principles of signal theory	**M2** explain why particular transmission media are chosen in particular situations	**D2** choose and justify the choice of a particular access control method for a given situation
P3 describe communication protocols used and explain why they are important	**M3** explain and implement direct communication between two networked devices.	**D3** compare and evaluate the effectiveness of the transfer of data over both wireless and wired networks.
P4 describe different methods of electronic communication and transmission media used		
P5 identify and describe the roles of network components and how they are interconnected		
P6 describe the features of networks and the communication services they offer		
P7 describe the nature of Internet communication and the associated system requirements		

8.1 Know the main elements of data communications systems

COMMUNICATION DEVICES

Data communications systems are computer systems that transmit data over communications lines, including telephone lines or cables.

Inside a computer, data may need to move a few thousandths of an inch (such as in a single IC chip) or several feet in the case of the back plane (a board that connects several connectors in parallel to each other) of a main circuit board. When small distances are involved, the digital data can be transmitted directly using electrical signals over copper conductors. Faster computers are an exception, but for the most part, circuit designers are not really worried about the shape of the conductor, nor the fact that the signal transmission is analogue.

Often data needs to be sent further, sometimes over huge distances, which makes transmission more problematic. Signals often experience electrical distortion as they travel through long conductors. The major problems tend to occur once the data enters another device; distortion or noise can become such a problem that the data is actually lost.

Data communication is concerned with the transmission of digital messages to different devices (external to the source of the message). An external device can be any independently powered circuitry outside the main chassis of the sending computer. Usually, the permissible transmission rate is directly proportional to the signal power and inversely proportional to the channel 'noise'. Data communication tries to speed up the transmission rate, using the lowest possible power, whilst generating the least amount of noise.

Wired devices

Both wired and wireless devices are integral parts of computer systems. Without them, there would be neither computer networks nor the ability to communicate from one computer to another.

Devices need to be capable of being networked (with at least one of the devices being a computer). Many wired devices are used as integral communication methods within an organisation's own network. These devices are a relatively short distance from the transmitting computer and are usually connected up as part of the network with conventional cabling.

Data Terminal Equipment (DTE)

DTE can be any piece of equipment connected to the end of a telecommunications link. It is used to convert the user information into signals ready for transmission, or it converts those signals back into user information. The user information can be any type of data that is being transferred across a functional interface between a transmitting source and a destination, via a telecommunications system.

Research tip

IBM introduced the term DTE (and DCE). For more information on IBM visit their website at www.ibm.com
The purpose of the DTE is to work as a functional data station operating as a data source (or **data sink**). It therefore provides the data communication control in line with the **link protocol**.

Key words

Data sink – a device implementing the event interface to receive incoming events.
Link protocol – the way in which data is transmitted from one node to another. The link protocol makes sure that the bits that have been received are the same as the bits that were sent.

DTE can be either a single piece of equipment or a sub-system of interconnected pieces of equipment. Collectively or individually, they perform all of the necessary functions in order to allow the users to communicate. In this sense, the user actually interacts with the DTE, or the DTE itself can be the user.

A DTE tends to be a terminal or a computer that is emulating a terminal. A DTE also tends to be male (and the DCE female). A typical example would be a computer as the DTE and the DCE being a modem.

Generally, the DCE provides the internal clocking and it is the function of the DTE to ensure that it synchronises on the clock (or the external clocking).

Example

DTE devices tend to transmit on pin connector 3 and then receive on pin connector 2. DCE devices, on the other hand, are the reverse of this. Hence a PC-to-PC connection that uses an Ethernet can also be called a DTE-to-DTE connection. This is usually an Ethernet connection using a crossover cable. When a straight cable is used, then there is a PC-to-DCE connection (which usually means that a hub or a switch is being used).

Data Circuit-Terminating Equipment (DCE)

DCE is also known as either Data Carrier Equipment or Data Communications Equipment. The DCE converts the signal and carries out the coding at the end of the network between the line itself and the DTE. Sometimes, the DCE is part of a single piece of equipment that also includes the DTE; in other cases, it is a separate piece of equipment. The DCE is most commonly associated with the RS232 interface, but it is also present in a number of different interfaces.

Wireless devices

As for wired devices, they tend to be limited to fairly local networks. Wireless devices are designed to make use of the Internet and mobile telephone technology. In other words, they are main components used in telecommunications and the use of wide area networks and other technologies such as **Bluetooth**.

Key word

Bluetooth – this is an industry specification for wireless personal area networks. Bluetooth allows the connection and exchange of information between devices including mobile phones and laptops.

Third Generation (3G) cellular phones

3G cellular telephones transmit information in separate but related packets before it is transmitted and then reassembled at the receiving end.

These cellular telephones are capable (at the moment) of achieving speeds of up to 2 megabits per second. The new generation phones offer the user new technologies and applications that were not available with older format mobile cellular networks, largely because there were limitations in the data transmission speed. Examples of new applications include the ability to browse the Internet and to remotely access and control home or office equipment and appliances (home automation).

Wireless Personal Data Assistant (PDA)

These are handheld personal computers that were originally designed to operate as personal organisers. They are sometimes called pocket or palmtop computers.

They are capable of acting as a:

- calculator
- clock
- device that can send and receive emails, audio and video
- word processor and spreadsheet (and other similar applications)
- address book
- global positioning system
- web browser.

Think It is now becoming increasingly difficult to distinguish between a 3G mobile and a PDA. To what extent do you think these two devices sit comfortably as a single device?

The latest models are also known as smart-phones and are also powerful portable media players. A PDA can access the Internet, extranets and intranets using Wi-Fi or wireless wide area networks. Most of the later models also have a touch screen.

Key word

Wi-Fi – this is a system that allows connection to the Internet. Wi-Fi networks broadcast radio waves that can be received by devices.

Wireless laptop

Laptops are also often called notebooks. From relatively modest beginnings (in terms of power and functionality), they are as powerful and more versatile than many desktop machines. All the latest models have in-built Wi-Fi technology. Their bright flat-screen panels and full-sized keyboards, along with a number of ports that allow the connection of a variety of peripherals, typify laptops.

Key features of modern laptops are:

- built-in Wi-Fi technology (for example Intel® Centrino™ mobile technology)
- thin and light-weight designs that do not require a compromise as far as performance is concerned
- high Wi-Fi standards in order to access public Wi-Fi hotspots, allowing high-speed access to the Internet
- Intel® Centrino™ mobile technology giving a longer battery life than in previous models.

Figure 8.1 A wireless laptop

Example

In connecting with the Internet in public hotspots, the old standard was 802.11a. Notebooks with Intel® Centrino™ mobile technology feature 802.11b or combined 802.11b and 802.11g. The 802.11b gives access up to 25 metres, the 802.11g has a shorter distance but faster connection speeds. The 802.11a is now less common as it is less flexible

EVIDENCE ACTIVITY

P1

A newly created company has employed you as their computer network manager. At present they have simply purchased a number of laptops for key users, but hope to set up a computer network that will facilitate easy communication between users and a centrally held database. There will be a requirement for the users to be able to access the database from remote locations, sometimes overseas.

At your first key meeting with the directors of the new company they have asked you to briefly identify and explain the different types of communication devices. Present this information in the form of a short report.

SIGNAL THEORY

Signal theory is an attempt to examine the theoretical aspects behind signal processing using a mathematical approach. Signal theory encompasses the study, analysis and interpretation of data transmission, as well as how signals are manipulated. As far as data communication systems are concerned, the main areas of theoretical study revolve around analogue, digital, audio, speech, imaging and video signal processing. All of these are vital parts of data communication. The primary aim of signal theory is to create signal processing systems and standards, primarily for digital signals. It is important to remember that all data that is transmitted over any type of network has to be digitised.

Digital signalling methods

Digital signalling is the transmission of binary data (in groups of 1s and 0s). It involves the conversion of analogue information into binary data in a process called digitisation. A simple example is the digitisation of a voice signal (which is analogue) into a format that can be recorded onto a CD.

Digital signal processing, therefore, means converting any signal from an analogue original to an equivalent and reliable digital form, usually using some kind of analogue-to-digital converter (known variously as an ADC, an A/D or an A to D). These are electronic circuits which convert continuous signals into digital numbers. They can be converted back using a digital-to-analogue converter (DAC).

The study of digital signal processing methods has become increasingly important, as more and more analogue signals are being digitised so that they can be distributed or shared on computer networks. Digital signal processing also involves compression, digital mobile phones, computer-generated graphics and animation, and has important applications for medical imaging.

Representing data electronically

As computers rely on digital electronics they respond to two different types of electrical state: either on or off. The easiest way to represent data, therefore, is to use those two conditions, represented by the binary numbers 0 and 1, which form the basis of binary mathematics. Binary numbers can be thought of as switches: with just two switches it is possible to represent four different numbers: 00, 01, 10, 11.

Two numbers represent a bit. Two bits would therefore give four numbers and three bits would give eight numbers. By using combinations of 0s and 1s, it is therefore possible to transform any decimal number into a binary number. One bit counts up to two numbers, two bits to four numbers, four bits to sixteen numbers, and so on.

Bits are the building blocks of data communication, followed by bytes. At higher levels of data transfer the following are used:

- a kilobyte is 1,024 bytes
- a megabyte is 1,048,576 bytes
- a gigabyte is 1,073,741,824 bytes.

This table looks at the nature of the basic electronic data types.

Table 8.1 Electronic data types

Electronic data type	Description
Bits	A bit is a binary digit with a value of either 0 or 1. It is the basic unit of data storage and data transmission.
Bytes	A byte usually consists of eight bits. Byte is actually an abbreviation for 'binary term' and a single byte is composed of eight consecutive bits that are capable of storing a single character.
Packet structures	Networks transmit data in small packets. The packets carry the information that will help it reach its intended destination. Typical packets are up to 1500 bytes. Packets are split up into three parts: the header, which includes instructions about the data being carried by the packet, including its length; the payload, which is also known as the body or data of the packet; and the trailer, also known as the footer, which tells the receiving device that it has reached the end of the packet. The cyclic redundancy check can also be found in the trailer.

Example

Data amounting to 3500 bits may actually consist of four packets. This would include:

- a header of 96 bits per packet
- a trailer of 32 bits per packet
- and three packets with 896 bits of payload and a fourth with 812 bits of payload.

Synchronous and asynchronous transmission

Serialised data does not tend to travel at a uniform rate through a channel. This means that there are bursts of data, punctuated by pauses. After a pause, the regularly spaced binary bits of data start flowing again. Packets of binary data are sent in this way, the process continuing until the entire message has been sent. The problem is that the device at the receiving end of the message must know:

- when the packet of data begins
- how long is the pause between the bits.

When the device is capable of handling this, then the receiver is known as being synchronised with the transmitter. This means that very accurate data transfer can take place. If the synchronisation is faulty, then there is a possibility that the transmission will be faulty and the data could either be corrupted or, at worst, lost.

There are two ways in which the correct synchronisation can be prepared:

- In a synchronous system, separate channels are used to transmit the data itself and the timing information. The timing channel transmits clock pulses to the receiver. When the receiver gets a clock pulse, the receiver then reads the data channel. The receiver does not then read the data channel again until it gets another clock pulse. As the transmitter is sending both the data and the clock pulse, synchronised transmission is guaranteed as the receiver only reads the data channel when it is prompted to do so by the clock pulse.
- It is possible to merge the data with the timing signal so that only one channel is used. This is particularly useful if the data is being sent using a device such as a modem. The data stream is encoded into an electrical waveform for transmission.

Think How would you identify that there is a major problem with synchronisation and what could be done to pinpoint the problem and deal with it?

Asynchronous systems do not use a separate timing channel. This means that the transmitter and the receiver have to be preset in advance. They will share the same baud rate. An accurate local oscillator is used within the receiver. This then generates an internal clock signal. Common serial protocol means that data is sent in tiny packets of 10–11 bits. Eight of these make up message information. When no data is being sent (i.e. the channel is idle), then a signal voltage sends a continuous logic 1. The receiver is waiting to hear logic 0, as this is the signal that a data packet is being sent (it is the start bit). Once the start bit is heard, the internal timer of the receiver starts to generate its own clock pulses. The message data is then sent in groups of eight bits, bit by bit at the agreed baud rate. The packet ends with a parity bit and a stop bit.

In asynchronous systems, the packet length tends to be fairly short because this minimises the risk that the oscillators in the transmitter and the receiver will drift apart. If high-quality oscillators are used, then for the most part, synchronisation over an 11-bit period can be guaranteed. However, every time a new packet of data is sent, the oscillators reset the synchronisation, making the pause between the packets longer.

Error correction and detection

Error correction and detection is of vital importance, as computers and networks often use noisy channels and somewhat unreliable storage methods. The main purpose of detection and correction is to identify errors that have been caused by noise or other reasons and then to request that the transmitter resend data containing errors.

If a transmitter does not receive an automatic acknowledgement then it will retransmit until an acknowledgement is received that the data has been sent correctly, or the error continues to persist beyond a certain number of additional attempts. This process is known as automatic repeat request. When the data is sent, it includes a check code, which the receiver checks for errors. An acknowledgement is sent if there are no errors.

An alternative error detection and correction system is known as forward error correction. In this instance the transmitter sends the encoded data, complete with an error correcting code. The receiver decodes the data, but is not asked by the transmitter to acknowledge.

Effect of bandwidth limitation and noise

Bandwidth is measured in hertz and is a measure of frequency range. It is actually a measurement of the channel's capacity to allow information to be transmitted. More commonly, bandwidth is used to describe the data transmission rates. The greater the bandwidth channel the greater its data transmission capacity or throughput.

The term noise refers to other signals within the communication channel that are actually unrelated to the data that is being transmitted. They can have an impact on the data and reduce the throughput of the channel.

Some of the noise can be put down to electrical signals caused by radio frequency interference from a host of electrical or electronic devices.

Optical fibres can experience noise in the form of distorted light waves, caused by imperfections in the fibre itself.

All signals are limited by both bandwidth and noise, and no system can be considered capable of coping with an unlimited amount of error-free data over a noise-free infinite bandwidth. Bandwidth limitation and noise means that there is always a limit on the amount of data that can be transferred at any given time, regardless of the fact that the channel may be brand new, or sophisticated coding and decoding systems are used.

Research tip

For information on the work of Shannon and Hartley, who were the first to identify and measure the impact of limited bandwidth and noise over communication channels, go to www.bellevuelinux.org and select Shannon-Hartley Theorem Definition from the index.

Channel types

As well as the examination of signalling methods, digital data and its transmission, signal theory also considers the different types of channel. A brief outline of channel types can be found in the following table.

Table 8.2

Type of channel	Description
Telephone	Telephone channels are primarily used to carry and log voice signals. However they are able to transmit signals in a frequency range of around 300 to 3000 hertz. It is important to remember that a similar technology can deliver Broadband via ADSL, and Narrowband through exchanges that have not yet been digitised.
High frequency (HF) radio	Data communication using high frequency radio channels requires the use of an HF modem. The modem converts the data into audio for radio transmission and then a converter transforms the received audio back into data. HF radio is at a disadvantage compared with other wireless communication systems. The radio channels are quite narrow, limiting data transmission rates to 9600 bits per second. The signals are also vulnerable to interference and data loss.
Microwave	Microwaves have wavelengths between 1 and 300 gigahertz. They are electromagnetic waves. Because of their short wavelength they are used in broadcast and telecommunication transmissions, using directive antennae. Before the use of fibre optic transmissions microwave point-to-point links were used for long-distance telephone calls. Today wireless LAN protocols, including Bluetooth, use microwaves.
Satellite	Satellite data transmission can provide a cost-effective alternative to landline-based networks, as the cost does not depend on the distance between the end points. Supporters of this system believe that it is highly reliable and secure. Users will usually buy a dedicated frequency channel, with a speed from 32 kilobits per second to 100 megabits per second. The quickest speeds are ideal for ensuring file transfer, video-conferencing, Internet access and other digital services.

Other issues

Bandwidth

Bandwidth is a key determining factor in possibly limiting the throughput of data through a channel. Bandwidth is measured in hertz and is commonly used as a term to describe transmission rates. In actual fact it is important to consider the channel capacity in terms of bandwidth and how particular devices use or provide bandwidth:

- Teleprinters and other telecommunication devices for the deaf have the least bandwidth, usually not exceeding 50 bits per second
- Traditional modems are capable of 48 to 9600 kilobits per second
- ISDN systems are usually 64 kilobits per second
- Computer buses can range up to nearly 200 gigabits per second
- Computer buses for storage are 6 gigabits per second
- External computer buses are just over 3 gigabits per second
- Wireless connections are up to 16 megabits per second
- Wireless networks are over 500 megabits per second
- Mobile telephone interfaces are nearly 300 megabits per second
- Wide area networks are around 400 megabits per second
- Local area networks are at least 30 gigabits per second.

Data compression

Data compression is an important issue in signal theory. By statistically analysing typical messages it can be ascertained that certain characters are used more frequently. By analysing messages before transmission, it is possible to assign short binary codes to the frequently used characters. Decoding at the receiving end can take out the codes and restore the message to its original form.

This is the basis of data compression. It can mean significant savings in the amount of data that has to be transmitted. It is necessary to analyse the message before it is transmitted, but the time savings in transmission time (including compression and decompression) are much lower than would be the case had the message been sent without using compression.

Not all data responds the same way to compression and some data are more suitable for compression than others. Images are ideal for compression and an 80% reduction in the original size can be achieved. Other types of data, such as computer programs, will only save around 20%.

Example

In data communications, a compression method known as Huffman is often used, particularly for faxes. The bulk of a fax image of a business letter is blank paper. A tiny percentage of the surface area of the paper has any image in the form of letters or other images. It is therefore possible to send a code for a consecutive string of 1000 white pixels instead of sending a separate code for each white pixel. Data compression allows the total message length to be significantly reduced; this assumes of course that the fax does not consist of a complex image or extremely closely typed characters.

Data compression, therefore, seeks to reduce the number of bits that are required to either store or transmit information. This can be achieved in a number of different ways, but broadly speaking they fall into one of two categories:

- Lossless compression – which seeks to recover the exact original data after the compression. It tends to be used for compressing word processing files, databases and spreadsheets where there is an absolute necessity to be able to replicate the original file.
- Lossy compression – this can lead to some loss of accuracy, as a trade-off against the increase in compression. It therefore tends to be used for graphics or digitised voices, where our ability to perceive the losses is small.

The degree of compression will depend upon the amount of redundancy in the source as well as the efficiency of its extraction.

EVIDENCE ACTIVITY

P2

The directors are now happy that they understand the fundamentals of communication devices, but are distinctly confused about the particular options regarding signal theory. They are concerned in particular that sensitive data could be compromised by an ill-considered wireless network structure.

Briefly explain signal theory in the form of an oral presentation and explain how it can be error free and secure.

DATA ELEMENTS

In terms of telecommunications and data communication systems, data elements can mean a number of different things:

- they can be a named unit of data that is indivisible and may consist of data items
- they can be an identifier represented in a database
- they can be a basic unit of information
- they can be a combination of characters or bytes that relate to a particular type of information, such as a name or an address.

This section looks at various different forms of data elements, including checksums, frames and packets.

Checksum

Both noise and electrical disturbances can cause the data to be changed as it passes through a channel. The received message will be incorrect if the receiver fails to pick this up. If a data error can be detected, then a defence against these errors can be created.

Errors need to be flagged; perhaps a message can be sent to request that the data (or at least the faulty packet of data) is sent again. This is essential; otherwise the faulty data will be taken as being correct and could cause a major problem. One- or two-bit errors can be corrected by the hardware within the receiver itself; this means that the correction is made before the corrupted data even reaches its destination.

In order to achieve this, a parity bit is added to the data packet to help error detection. Using the even-parity convention, the value of the parity bit is picked so that the total number of '1' digits in the combined data (plus the parity bit) is even. When the packet is received, the parity required for the data is recalculated by the hardware and compared with the parity bit that has been received with the data. If there is a changed state, then the parity does not match and an error has been detected. If an odd number of bits have been reversed, the parity will match even though an error has occurred. In practice, a single-bit error is much more common than a multi-bit error (due to random noise). This means that error detection is fairly foolproof in most circumstances.

Here are some examples of even-parity computation:

Data	Parity bit
10110001	0
10000110	1

The other alternative is a checksum. All the packets that make up a message are added arithmetically. A checksum number is appended to the packet sequence, so that the sum of the data plus the checksum is zero. When the receiver receives the packet sequence, it can be added together with the checksum by a local microprocessor. If the total is not zero, then an error has taken place. It is improbable that the data has been corrupted during transfer if the total is zero.

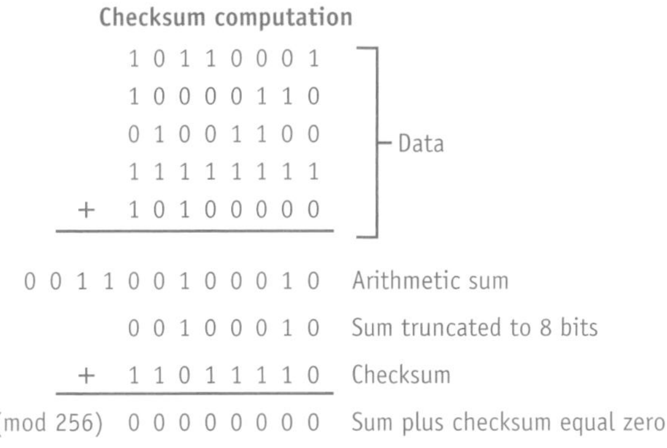

Figure 8.2 Checksum computation

If additional code is added to the packet sequence, then not only can the error be detected, but it can also be corrected. If there is a high probability that there is an error, then retransmission of the data can be requested. However, if an error-correcting code is added to the packets, then this does lessen the efficiency of the channel and there is a significant drop in the throughput along the channel.

A cyclic redundancy check (CRC) performs the same kind of function as a checksum as it is used to detect the alteration of data during either storage or transmission. This function takes as its input an unlimited-length data stream. It then produces an output of a fixed size. CRCs are useful as they are easy to analyse mathematically and they are effective in detecting common errors, particularly those caused by noise.

Think How often will retransmission be requested before the system ceases trying to receive data that still contains an error?

Frames

In networking terms a frame is a data packet which can either be of variable or fixed length. It has been encoded using a communications protocol so that it can be digitally transmitted over a node-to-node link. Usually a frame consists of:

- a header
- a bit-synchronising code (transmitted code words that attempt to ensure that no uncorrected errors are present in the stream)
- a payload (the actual information)
- a trailer (supplemental data at the end of a block of data).

Packets

Data packets are formatted blocks of data that can be transmitted on a computer network. More rudimentary computer communications networks transfer data as a series of bits, bytes or characters. Data packets allow networks to transmit longer messages in a far more efficient manner.

The first element of a data packet is the header, which has the source and destination **IP address**.

Key words

IP address – Internet protocol address that is used to identify and communicate between electronic devices on a network, including routers, printers and telephones.

The second major element of a data packet is the payload, which actually contains the main information. The third element is the trailer, which usually contains a checksum so that the packet can be checked to see if it was corrupted during transmission.

There are various different conventions regarding the three elements, as well as for formatting the data in different communication protocols. Each communication protocol has a standard set of rules, which determine how data are represented, signalled, authenticated and how any errors may be detected.

Datagrams

A datagram is very similar to a packet. A datagram is a self-contained piece of data that carries sufficient information for it to be routed from the transmitting source to its destination without a link having already been established between the transmitter and the receiver.

The term tends to be used for a number of different protocols, including User Datagram Protocol (UDP), which allows messages to be exchanged between computers on a network and uses Internet protocol. UDP is an alternative to the transmission control protocol (TCP). When it is combined with IP it is referred to as UDP/IP. The UDP uses the Internet protocol to transmit a data unit from one computer to another. However, UDP does not break up messages into packets. It does not provide sequencing of the packets that arrive. This means that the application program using a UDP has to make sure not only that the entire message has been received, but also that it has been received in the correct order. UDP is used when processing time needs to be saved when using very small data units.

Addresses

Any electronic device that is part of a computer network that utilises standard Internet protocol will have a unique IP or Internet protocol address. There are currently two versions of Internet protocol, IP version 4 and IP version 6, although IP address usually refers to IP version 4, as this is the most common.

IP version 4 has 32-bit or 4-byte addresses. Due to the growth of the Internet and the increased demand for IP addresses, there is a gradual migration over to IP version 6, which is considered to be the new standard protocol for the Internet. These addresses are 128 bits or 16 bytes wide.

The purpose of addresses as data elements is not only to identify the intended destination of the data, but also to identify the source from which it was transmitted.

Sequence numbers

Sequence numbers are rather like serial numbers that uniquely identify a particular device. Sequence numbers tend to refer to the physical device. This means that devices that have multiple names have the same sequence number.

Sequence numbers are used to keep track of the order of packets. The purpose of a sequence number is to allow the transport layer to see if any packets were lost or delivered out of sequence.

METHODS OF ELECTRONIC COMMUNICATION

Methods of electronic communication go beyond popular and conventional electronic communication methods, such as email, mailing lists and newsgroups. This section considers the ways in which networks or transmitters and receivers are connected.

Simplex, duplex and half-duplex communication

Simplex, duplex and half-duplex communication all relate to the way in which the channel operates.

Data in a simplex channel is always one way; simplex channels are not often used, as it is not possible to send back error or control signals to the transmission end of the channel.

The simplest form of simplex communication is the television or radio; it works just like a single lane in a one-way road system, as shown in Figure 8.3.

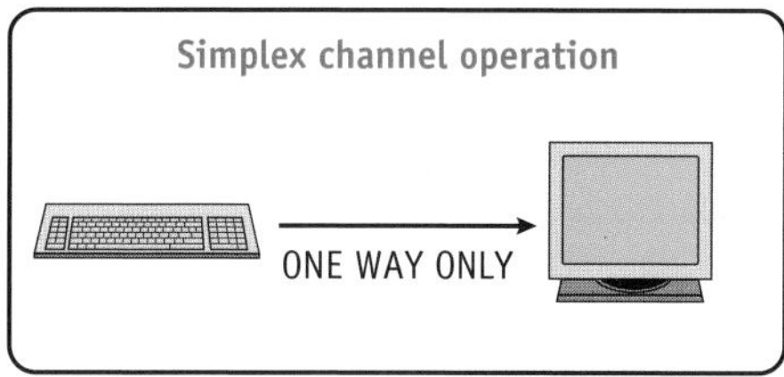

Figure 8.3 Simplex channel operation

Half-duplex channels allow data to be sent or received, but not at the same time. It can be likened to a road contra-flow system. Traffic can pass each way, but only one way at a time. Only one end of the channel can transmit at one time; the other has to receive. It is possible to undertake error detection and make a request that the sender resends the data that may have been corrupted. The Internet is a prime example of a half-duplex system as the user will request a web page and the page is downloaded before another request by the user is carried out.

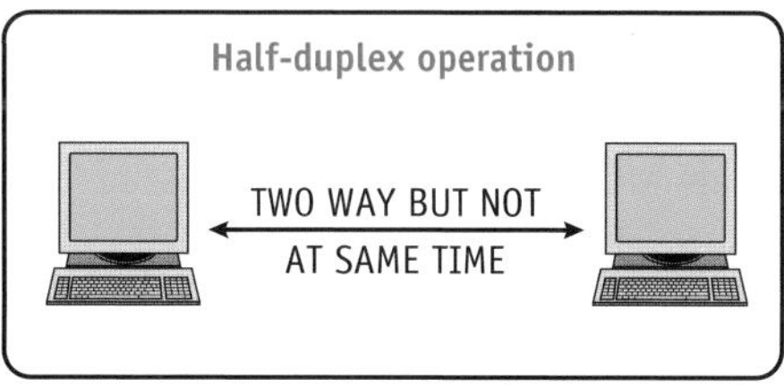

Figure 8.4 Half-duplex operation

Example

Citizen's Band radio is a prime example of a half-duplex system. A user has to press the handset and speak, then release the handset in order to hear a reply. Only one person can speak on the same channel at the same time. A verbal protocol is therefore used to determine who will speak and when.

Full-duplex communication allows data to simultaneously travel in both directions at the same time. Users do not have to switch from transmit to receive as in half duplex. Increasing numbers of businesses and home users are using full duplex. It allows full connectivity and simultaneous transmission and receiving.

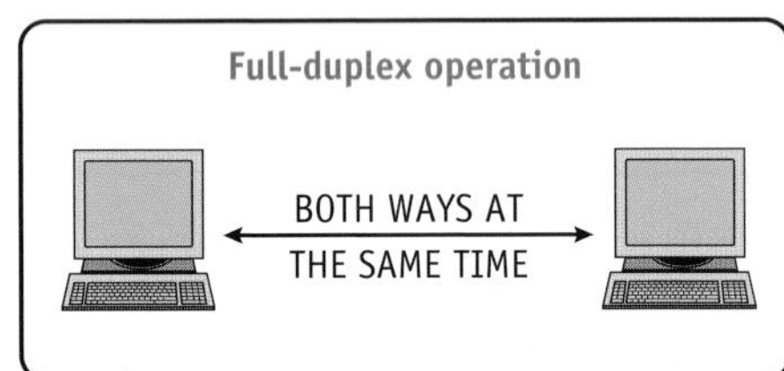

Figure 8.5 Full-duplex operation

Parallel

For many years the standard socket found on personal computers and other electronic equipment was the standard centronics port. This was a parallel port. But since 2006 the vast majority of machines and devices have instead been fitted with a universal serial bus, or USB, interface. The vast majority of printers, networks and scanners are now reliant on the USB. USBs are also used to connect non-networked printers.

USB signals are transmitted on a twisted pair of data cables, which use half-duplex differential signalling. This means that electromagnetic noise is combated. The USB is a very adaptable system that allows devices such as keyboards and mice to be connected at a relatively low speed. The majority of other electronic devices use its full speed, but it also has a high-speed data rate of around 480 megabits per second.

Serial

Just as the USB was designed to replace the parallel port, it was also intended to replace the serial port. The most common type of serial port was known as the RS232. It was originally designed to act as an interface with a modem or another communication device, such as a mouse or a keyboard.

A standard RS232 port had a limit of 20,000 bits per second, although some of the other serial ports could achieve settings of up to 115,200 bits per second.

By 2007 very few computers were still being manufactured with serial ports.

Think Why might it still be advisable for manufacturers to incorporate a serial port in modern computers?

Other

The other key methods of electronic communication are:

- Infrared – this is used for short-range data transmission, usually between a computer and peripherals or a PDA and peripherals. The devices have to conform with the IrDA (Infrared Data Association). The device uses infrared light emitting diodes to emit infrared radiation. The beam, focused through a plastic lens, is modulated to encode the data. The receiver picks up the radiation via a silicone photodiode and converts it into an electric current.

Research tip

For more information on IrDA visit www.irda.org

- Bluetooth – this is a specification for wireless personal aerial networks. The specifications are developed and licensed by the Bluetooth Special Interest Group. Bluetooth is effectively a radio standard and communication protocol that has low power consumption. It is, however, relatively short-ranged, with a maximum range of approximately 100 metres. There have been various versions of Bluetooth since the middle of the 1990s. Current technology suggests that it will increase its speed and data rate, whilst maintaining low power requirements.

Research tip

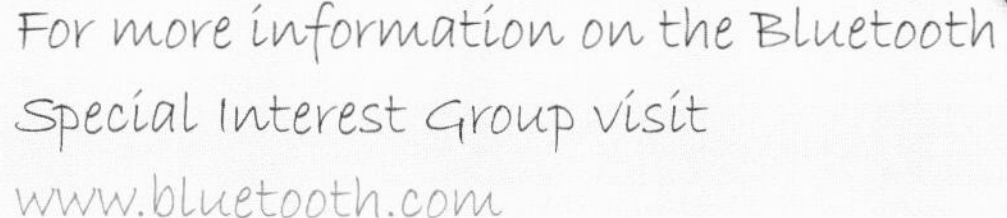

For more information on the Bluetooth Special Interest Group visit www.bluetooth.com

Figure 8.6 Wi-Fi covers many square miles

- Wi-Fi – this is a derivation of the term wireless fidelity, which was originally a brand licensed by the Wi-Fi Alliance. It is now more widely used to describe Wireless Local Area Networks (WLAN). Provided a device, including a PDA or a laptop computer, is close to an access point, full connection can be made to the Internet. These public access points are popularly known as 'hotspots'. These are wireless LANs deployed in areas where it would be inappropriate to lay cables and require wired connection.

Research tip

For more information on the Wi-Fi Alliance visit www.wi-fi.org

EVIDENCE ACTIVITY

P3

As part of your education of the board of directors, explain to them the fundamentals of communication protocols. Briefly explain why they are important. This explanation could be incorporated with the presentation on signal theory.

TRANSMISSION MEDIA

Coaxial

Coaxial cable is a two-conductor cable. One conductor forms an electromagnetic shield around the other. The two conductors are separated from one another by insulation. Coaxial cables are also known as constant impedance transmission cables. They tend to be used for transmission in two different ways:

- Base band – these use unmodulated digital signals, have single channels, the stations are connected by T connectors and there is no requirement to have modems.
- Broadband – these carry digital signals modulated onto an RF carrier (which is analogue), the stations are connected using RF modems.

Optical fibre

These are transmission media that are designed to carry digital signals in the form of pulses of light. Optical fibres tends to be constructed with:

- a core made of glass
- cladding made of glass
- a plastic coating.

In fact, optical fibre cables often contain more than one fibre; each of the fibres is individually wrapped with a plastic coating and an external coating. There are several different types of optical fibre cable:

- Step Multimode Fibre (with a bandwidth of 20 megahertz per kilometre and a core diameter of 100–250 microns)
- Graded Index Multimode Fibre (with a bandwidth of 800 megahertz per kilometre and a core diameter of 50–100 microns)
- Step Index Single Mode Fibre (with a bandwidth of 5 gigahertz per kilometre and a core diameter of 5–7 microns).

The key advantages of optical fibre cables are:

- they are immune to electromagnetic interference
- there are no electrical ground loop or short circuit issues
- they are relatively small in size and lightweight
- they have a large bandwidth for size and weight
- they are safe to use in combustible areas
- they are immune to lightning and electrical discharges
- it is possible to run longer cable runs between repeaters
- they are very flexible and have high strength.
- they are comparatively secure against signal leakage and interference.
- they do not pose an electrical hazard when cut or damaged.

Unshielded twisted pair (UTP)

UTP is copper media that were originally used in telephony; they are the standard for **horizontal wiring**. The term 'twisted pair' actually refers to the fact that the cable consists of a pair of copper wires. They usually have a diameter of 0.4–0.8 millimetres. They are twisted together and wrapped with a plastic coating. The twisting increases the electrical noise immunity. It also reduces the bit error rate (BER) of the data transmission. Commonly, a UTP cable contains from 2 to 4200 twisted pairs.

UTP offers a low-cost media that is very flexible. It is ideal for either data or voice communication. The key disadvantage is the fact that it has a limited bandwidth. This restricts its use in long-distance transmissions that require a low error rate.

> **Key words**
>
> **Horizontal wiring** – this is usually limited to around 90 metres. It includes all types of cabling from a work area or network connection to the telecommunications closet. It gets its name from the fact that it usually runs horizontally, either above the ceiling or along the floor.

Shielded twisted pair

A shielded twisted pair is usually the ordinary copper wire used to connect most home and many business computers to the telephone network. In order to reduce cross-talk or electromagnetic induction between pairs of wires, the insulated copper wires are twisted around one another.

It is important to remember that at each connection, both wires need to be connected. As many telephone sets and desktop locations need multiple connections, twisted pairs are sometimes installed in two or more pairs, all within a single cable.

Twisted pairs tend to be installed in the home environment with an extra pair so that it is possible to add another line (historically for a modem). Usually, each twisted pair is uniquely colour coded (when it is packaged in multiple pairs). This allows them to be used for different purposes such as analogue, digital or Ethernet as each of them require different pair multiples.

Higher grade twisted pairs can be used for horizontal wiring in a LAN installation as they are less expensive than using coaxial cable.

Other

Several other types of transmission media are being increasingly used as an alternative to more common methods.

Table 8.3 Transmission media

Other types of transmission media	Explanation
Infrared	Useful in indoor environments, as it does not penetrate walls and interfere with other devices in other rooms. **Free space optics** use infrared lasers and are a cost-effective alternative to using fibre optic cables.
Radio	Transmission of signals using modulated electromagnetic waves that have frequencies below that of visible light. It can be used for wireless networks and mobile communications.
Microwave	Wireless LAN protocols, including Bluetooth, use microwaves. Microwave radiation is non-ionising and has no effect at molecular level. Unlike x-rays or gamma rays it is believed not to cause any DNA damage.
Satellite	Originally used for international telephone calls. Calls were relayed from an earth station to the satellite. Mobile phones connect their signal to a satellite, however most mobile phones now use ground-based receiving and re-transmitting stations. Satellite communication technology is also used as a means to connect to the Internet using Broadband data connections.

Key words

Free space optics – this is a telecommunication system that uses light in free space to transmit data between points. They are particularly used where it is difficult to make a physical connection between the transmitting and receiving locations.

EVIDENCE ACTIVITY

P4 – M1

The board is discussing whether it might be advisable to install a cabled network for the main office, but also to have a wireless facility so that employees can take advantage of new office layout ideas, such as hot-desking, as well as being able to access the network from remote locations.

For P4, in the form of an extended email, briefly describe the different types of electronic communication and transmission media that could be used. **(P4)**

For M1, extend your email to explain how errors can be reduced in transmissions. Specifically mention any techniques that could be employed. **(M1)**

Features and benefits

There are two different types of transmission media:

- Guided or bound – which incorporates all types of transmission lines, including wires, coaxial cables and optical fibres
- Wireless or unguided – which use antennae to transmit or receive radio waves.

Transmission is the act of sending an electrical message, usually as a series of data units or digits. The transmission is despatched by the sender in the form of a signal and it incorporates data. It can be intended for mass consumption, such as radio or television, or for individual and named addresses, such as emails and telephone calls.

8.2 Understand the communication principles of computer networks

FEATURES OF NETWORKS

There are three major types of network, but there are a number of different network topologies and associated network services and software.

Types

A computer network is a series of computers that are connected together in some way using a telecommunications system, so that they can communicate with one another and share resources.

As technology has developed there is no longer a requirement for there to be a physical connection using wires between computers in a network. There are many different types of network; the following table briefly explains the three main types.

Table 8.4 Computer network types

Type	Explanation
LAN	A local area network tends to be limited to a single room or building. It is alternatively entitled a single location network. In large LANs a number of computers can be connected together as work groups. These share common sets of resources. It is possible to have LANs that are somewhat wider than a single building and may connect together an entire area, such as a university campus. Equally, utilising routers, switches and hubs, a town or the centre of a city can be connected on a single LAN. LANs can either be wired or wireless.
WAN	A wide area network is a telecommunication and data communication network that covers a broader area than a LAN and tends to utilise transmission facilities provided by telecommunications companies. WAN technology requires three layers: the physical, data link and network in order to function fully, according to the Open Systems Interconnection (OSI) basic reference model. A WAN can consist of two or more LANs. The largest WAN is the Internet.
Wireless	A wireless network is any type of network that does not rely on cabling to facilitate the transmission of data or telecommunications. It uses some form of electromagnetic wave, such as a radio wave. Within the general description of a wireless network there are wireless LANs, global systems for mobile communications (GSMs), Wi-Fi networks and other less well-known systems.

Research tip

For more information on the OSI system visit the website of the International Organisation for Standardisation at www.iso.org

Network topologies

Network topologies effectively map all of the elements incorporated as part of the network. The topology includes both the physical devices and the interconnections between them, whether they are wired or wireless. The topology also shows how data can flow around the network and how devices, applications and resources can be shared. A number of typical topologies are used, some of which can be combined to create hybrid topologies.

Star network

Each of the nodes (devices) on this type of network is connected to a central node. The central node is the hub and the other nodes are the spokes. In its simplest form there would be a single node at the centre and a small number of nodes connected to it.

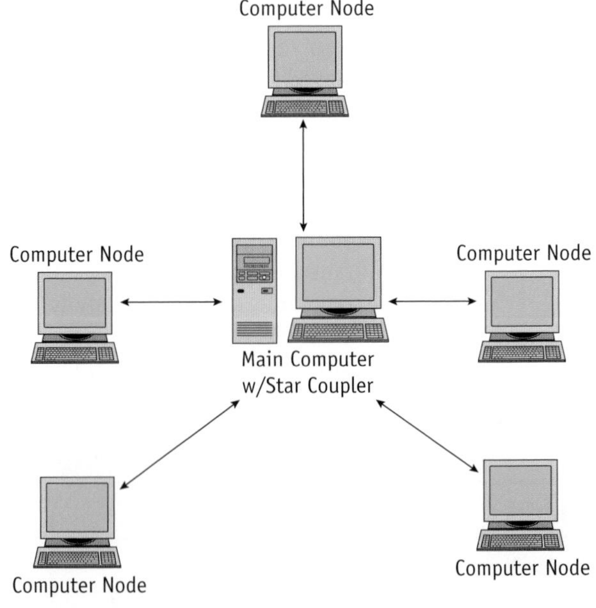

Figure 8.7 Star network

Mesh network

Each of the nodes within this type of network is connected to each of the other nodes, making it possible for data to be transmitted simultaneously from one of the nodes to all of the other nodes. This is what is known as a fully connected mesh, however most mesh topologies are only partially connected. Data transmitted between nodes within the network find the shortest path between the nodes. If they find a break or fault in the link then they seek an alternative path.

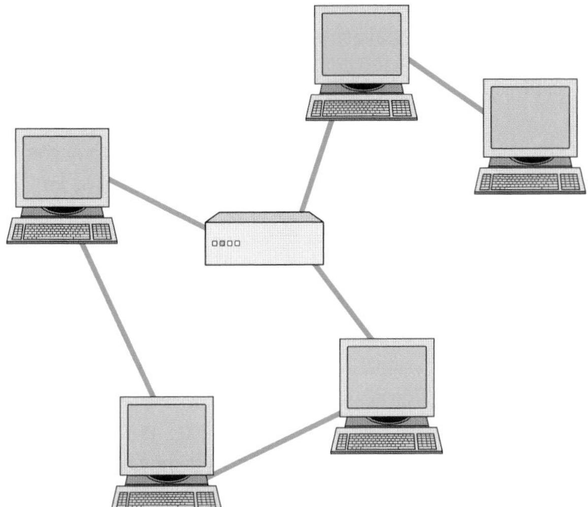

Figure 8.8 Mesh network (partially connected)

Bus network

There are two different types of bus topology, the first being called a linear bus. In this type of network the nodes are connected along a backbone or trunk. Data that is transmitted between the nodes moves to the backbone or trunk and is then transmitted along it, exiting en route to the destination node.

An alternative is the distributed bus, which has more than two end points, as additional branches have been added to the main backbone of the network.

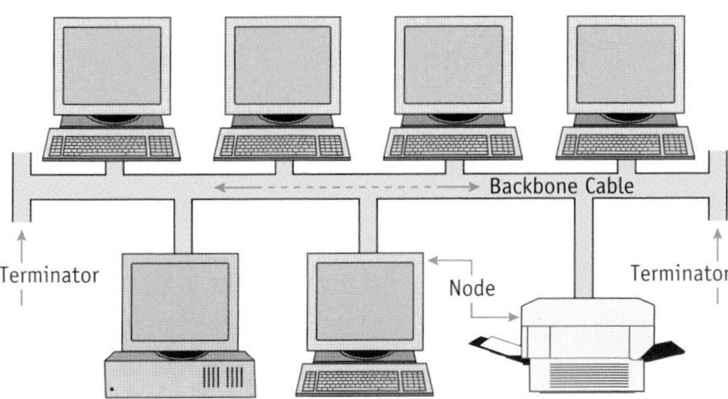

Figure 8.9 Bus network (linear)

Tree (or hierarchical) network

This type of network has a central route node, which is connected to the other nodes at a lower level in the hierarchy. Below this second level may be another series of nodes that are also connected to the central route node. The network tends to have at least three levels of hierarchy; otherwise the network would in fact be a star network.

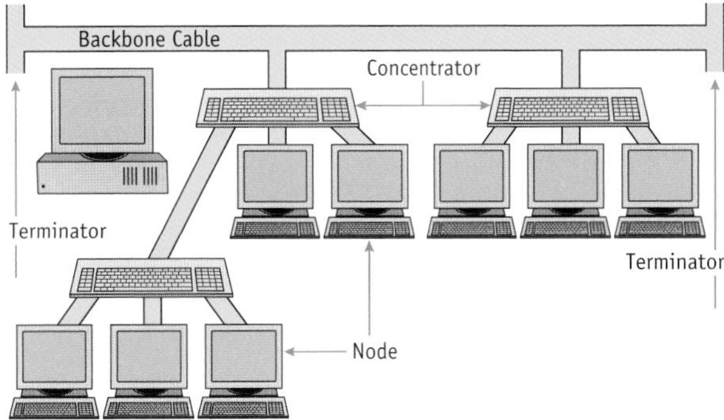

Figure 8.10 Tree network

Ring network

In this topology each node is connected to two other nodes within the network. The first and the last nodes are then connected together to create an unbroken ring. Within the ring is a file server and hub. The former provides the necessary backup and storage files and applications, whilst the hub gives access in and out of the network, to either another network or the broader network, such as the Internet.

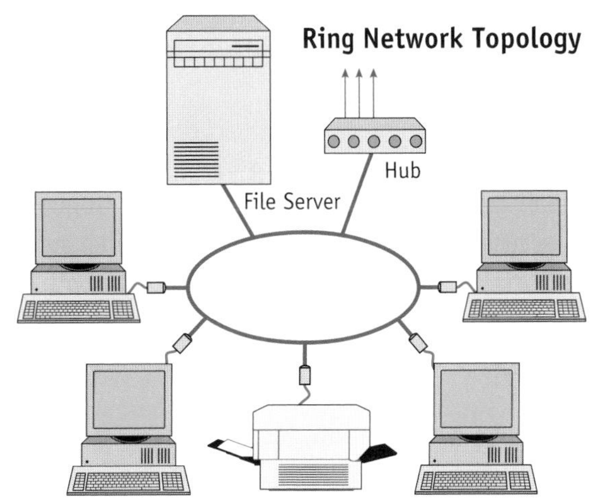

Figure 8.11 Ring network

> **Think** To what extent do you believe that the requirements of the users should determine the topology of a network, or should the topology determine how the network should be used?

Network services

Network services allow the computers on a network to share resources and gain access to the servers. At the most basic level network services would include:

- authentication
- directory services
- domain name system (DNS)
- email
- printing
- a network file system that supports the sharing of files, printers and resources.

The table on top of the next page briefly explains some of the more technical network services.

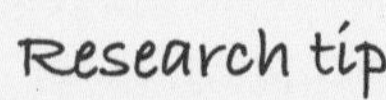

For information about ATM, visit the ATM Forum at www.atmforum.com

Network software (network operating system)

Network software, or the network operating system, controls the network, the traffic, queues and access. It also performs other functions, such as security. Typically the operating system will:

- support processors, protocols and hardware detection
- handle authentication, log on, access control and authorisation
- provide directory services
- allow file, web and print services, as well as performing backups
- support the routing.

Table 8.5 Network Services

Typical network service	Explanation
Packet switched	Designed to optimise channel capacity by determining how packets of data are routed between nodes through the network. Packets are routed using a routing algorithm; the best known is the Internet, which actually uses the Internet Protocol suite. Packet switching is often known as connectionless networking, because no connections are actually established.
ISDN	Integrated Services Digital Network is designed to allow digital transmission over ordinary telephone wires with better quality and higher speeds. It is used for voice, video and text transmission.
Multiplexed	Also known as muxing and is a process where multiple analogue message signals, or digital data, are combined into one signal. In order for the system to work a device that performs the reverse process, known as a de-multiplexer, is also required. Multiplexing is provided by the physical layer of the OSI layer model or TCP/IP.
ATM	Asynchronous Transfer Mode is a cell relay. Data is encoded into small, fixed-sized cells. ATM is different from other packet switched networks, such as Internet Protocol, as it is a connection-orientated technology. It is widely used in WANs, but not in LANs, as the Internet protocol is already well established in that field.
WAP	WAP is an international standard and a shortened version of Wireless Application Protocol. It was designed to allow Internet access from mobile phones or from PDAs. WAP requires websites to be converted into Wireless Markup Language (WML) which can then be accessed via the WAP browser.
Broadband	Broadband is a signalling method that is now often an interchangeable term with data communications or data transmission. In the former, multiple pieces of data can be sent simultaneously using Broadband. Broadband uses multiplexing in order to utilise several physical channels simultaneously.

Network connection software

There are dozens of proprietary shareware and freeware programs that consist in establishing and checking network connectivity. There are also optimisers that can improve both connection and download speeds, with the added benefit of there being fewer delays whilst the user is browsing. Network connection is dependent upon factors such as the version of Windows being run, whether connection is standard or wireless and the core network infrastructure.

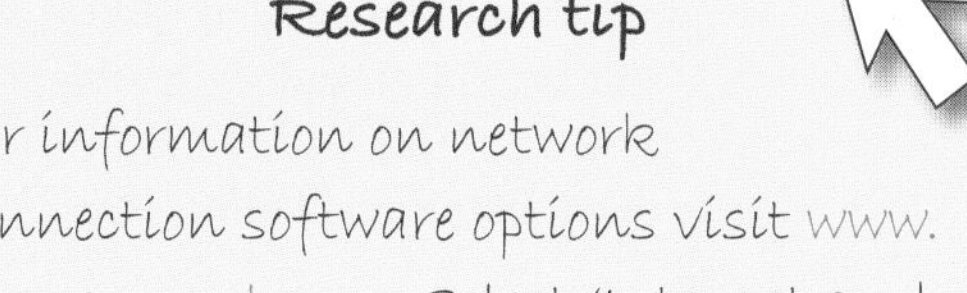

Research tip

For information on network connection software options visit www.programsurl.com. Select 'Internet and networking options' and choose from the menu on the left.

Access methods

In most systems either channel access or a multiple access method allows several computers to be simultaneously connected and to transmit data and share data and applications. Multiple access protocols are often referred to as media access control. Multiple access is based on a multiplex method, allowing several simultaneous signals to share the same channel. The following table looks at typical types of access method.

Table 8.6 Methods of access

Type of access method	Explanation
CSMA/CD	Carrier Sense Multiple Access with Collision Detection – this uses a carrier-sensing scheme. It has a transmitting data station that detects another signal whilst transmitting a frame. It then stops transmitting that frame and instead transmits a jam signal and then waits for a random time interval before trying to send the frame again.
CSMA/CA	Carrier Sense Multiple Access with Collision Avoidance – the station waiting to transmit listens to the channel for activity. If the channel is idle then the station transmits. If the channel is busy the station defers its transmission, thus achieving collision avoidance.
Token passing	A token is passed between the nodes, authorising a node to communicate. The token is a control mechanism, which gives authority to the system to either use the resources on the network or to communicate. Once the communication is over the token is passed on to the next node in sequence.

NETWORK COMPONENTS

A network consists of a number of computers connected together using a telecommunications system. Network components refer to the basic nuts and bolts of the system, in other words the major hardware that makes up the network.

Servers

The server is also known as a server application, but it can also be described as a server operating system. In effect it is a computer that accepts connections and may provide some or all of the following:

- files
- databases
- backup
- print
- mail
- web
- FTP
- application
- logon and security (including firewall).

Server computers have faster processors, and memory and more RAM. They have larger hard drives and need to be very reliable. Increasingly they are more compact. The server is a dedicated machine that has been optimised to allow a controlled and shared use of applications and resources, as well as providing the means by which connections are made within the network.

Workstation

A workstation is essentially a client computer on a LAN or a WAN. It is used to run applications and is connected to a server, which provides the data and applications that are shared with other computers. In the past it was described as a terminal; it may not necessarily have its own hard disk facility for saving documents and other files. Workstations usually have powerful microprocessors and high-quality monitors.

Network cards

A network card is a piece of hardware that is designed to allow computers to communicate via a computer network. It provides physical access, allowing the computer to be connected either using cables or wireless technology. The following table shows common network card or network adaptor types.

Table 8.7 Network cards

Type of network card	Explanation
Ethernet	This type of network card has unique serial numbers and no two cards are ever manufactured using the same address. The device, as a cable-based connection system, is quickly becoming obsolete, as it is being superseded by wireless connection.
Wireless	Technically this refers to a wireless network interface controller. It allows a radio connection between the computer and the network. The card uses an antenna to communicate via microwaves.
Token ring	The popularity of token rings is in steep decline. They have been superseded by Ethernet. It was found that token rings were not as reliable and did not have the same level of performance as Ethernets.

INTERCONNECTION DEVICES

Interconnection devices can be seen as the glue that holds a network together. They have different functions and limitations; understanding them can help in the analysis and design of networks.

Interconnection is, and will always remain, a major consideration for network managers. The problems usually come down to a combination of time and space. Another major consideration is the protocols used by the different media. For example, optic fibres will operate at a far faster speed than a twisted pair and the manager needs to find a means by which the rates can be matched. There are also cost considerations with interconnectivity as the ability to connect different networks allows the organisation to achieve a far better return on their investment.

It should not be thought that a slow network means that the network is not doing its job; it may be functional, secure and reliable, which are as important as speed in many cases.

Table 8.8 Interconnection devices

Types of interconnection devices	Explanation
Hubs	Hubs are usually used in a wired network as a means by which Ethernet cables from a variety of different devices are connected (this allows the devices to communicate with one another). Hubs are not used in networks that only have wireless connections; in these cases the routers and the adaptors communicate with one another directly (without the need to have anything in between them). Hubs are relatively straightforward devices, as they do not need to be configured. In the majority of cases, routers and modems have taken over their function.
Switches	Switches tend to be used in wired networks in order to connect Ethernet cables from a variety of devices. The switches are put into the network to facilitate the communication between the different devices. As with hubs, switches are not found in wireless networks. Users can utilise the ports at the back of a router or a modem to connect Ethernet devices, but switches still retain an importance. They can allow the connection of dozens of devices; they can keep the traffic between two devices from interfering with other devices on the same network. Switches can also control the access to the network and monitor usage. Switches mean faster communication within the network and high-end switches have modules that allow the user to tailor them to specific functions or needs for the network.
Routers	When a router is used on a network, all Internet traffic passes through it. Routers can have a number of features which, until relatively recently, had to be purchased separately (such as firewalls, modems and print servers). Most networks now use the router as the main firewall for security purposes. Routers take information that arrives through the Broadband signal via a modem, decipher it and deliver it to computers on the network. The router will also choose the best route for the data packet so that it is received at the fastest speed possible. Broadband routers can be used to connect two different computers or to connect computers to the Internet; they can also be used to facilitate a telephone connection. Wireless routers, on the other hand, create a wireless signal (the only way of preventing unauthorised use is to use a secure router).
Repeaters	A repeater receives low-level signals and retransmits them at a higher level or power, allowing an un-degraded signal to be transmitted over longer distances. It amplifies the digital signal for retransmission.
Bridges	A bridge is a term that is often used to describe the connecting of two parts of a wireless network separated by a distance. A wireless bridge could be used to connect a printer in another room. This is of great value if the user has a small network. The term bridging is a more general one and refers to the connection between two parts of a network. This is particularly the case when it is not considered desirable or necessary for every computer on the network to have the ability to send traffic to every other computer connected to the network. This can avoid distributing the traffic too widely on the network, particularly where long distances are involved.
Gateways	A gateway is a node that operates as an entrance to a network or as an exit out of that network. Gateways are therefore used to transfer data between the Internet and LANs or WANs. Gateways can be likened to routers.
Wireless devices	These can include cellular telephones and PDAs. However, in the context of a network they can also incorporate computer mice and keyboards, which can be wireless.

Think Is it possible for a network to incorporate all of these interconnection devices? Which of them may or may not be necessarily compatible or standard in a common computer network?

Example

Routers respond only to traffic specifically addressed to them; this means that security can be implemented using these devices. As they are programmable it is possible to specify alternate paths for data transmission in the event of an overloading of the circuit. Organisations tend to combine data and voice traffic within the same network. Networks are never really constructed to cope with the maximum predicted load across the whole of the network and its component parts. The simple expedient is to re-route traffic overloads to a third-party network (in most cases this will be a telecommunications provider).

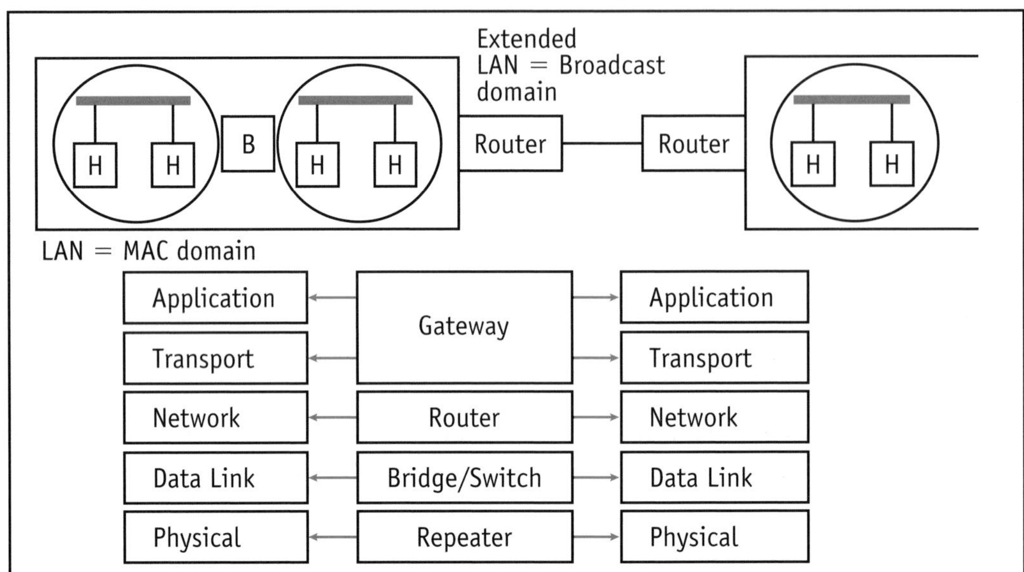

Figure 8.12 Typical interconnection devices

EVIDENCE ACTIVITY

P5 – M2

The board of directors now believe that they are in a position to authorise purchases and assign a budget to the creation of a computer network. They still, however, need some reassurance about particular network components, how they are used and why they might be necessary. In the form of an oral presentation, with examples, briefly identify and then describe the roles of the components and why they are essential. **(P5)**

For M2, the directors have responded to your email and still do not understand a sufficient amount about transmission media. They want to know why particular transmission media are used in particular situations. They are particularly confused regarding cable and wireless transmission media. Briefly respond by sending them a second email, explaining why the particular transmission media are used in particular situations. **(M2)**

8.3 Understand transmission protocols and models

MODEL

Transmission control protocol (TCP) allows connection on networks to exchange data using stream sockets. FTP, secure shell, email and the Internet all use TCP. However the Open System Interconnection (OSI) Model is a key-networking framework. Control is passed from one layer to the next. It begins at the application layer and then proceeds to the bottom layer via the channel to the next station. The seven layers of the OSI Model are:

- Layer 7 – application – supports the application and end-user processes (file transfers, email and network software services, etc.)
- Layer 6 – presentation – transforms data into a form that the application layer can accept
- Layer 5 – session – sets up, coordinates and ends exchanges and conversations between applications
- Layer 4 – transport – provides for the transfer of data between end systems or hosts and ensures data transfer
- Layer 3 – network – creates logical paths using switching and routing in order to transmit data from one node to another
- Layer 2 – data link – here data packets are encoded and decoded into bits. There are in fact two sub-layers: immediate access control, which determines how a computer gains access to data and has permission to transmit it; and logical link control, which is involved in frame synchronisation, error checking and flow control
- Layer 1 – physical – provides the means by which data can be sent and received and includes any cables, cards or other hardware.

Levels and relationship with connection devices

As described above, the OSI Model implements protocols in seven layers. Layers 1 and 3 are particularly concerned with connection devices. Layer 3, in creating virtual circuits for the transmission data, relies on switches and routers. Layer 1, which deals with the bit stream, is directly related to the hardware of the system both at an electrical and a mechanical level. Layer 1 has a direct relationship with all of the physical aspects of the network, including any network cards or cabling used by the system.

PROTOCOLS

Protocols are sets of rules that govern communication between devices. Over the years there have been several different types of protocols. The key protocols and brief explanations are included in the following table.

Wireless security protocols

Despite the fact that many computer users and network managers are rather lax about the security of their computers or networks of machines, wireless security protocols have improved considerably in recent years. Particularly vulnerable were wireless systems, with public hotspots a prime example of wireless services that did not have even the most rudimentary security. Those that do tend to have either of the following:

- WEP – Wired Equivalent Privacy – this is a security protocol for Wireless Local Area Networks (WLAN) as defined using the 802.11b standard. It is designed to provide the same level of security as a wired LAN. WLANs do not have the same kind of physical structure as a LAN and therefore are more vulnerable to attack. WEP aims to encrypt data so that it is protected as it is transmitted from one point to another. It has been found that WEP is not as secure as was originally thought. In fact, WEP is used at the two lowest levels of the OSI model (the data link and the physical layers) and, as a result, does not actually provide end-to-end security for the data.

Table 8.9 Transmission protocols

Protocols and examples	Explanation
Bluetooth	This is related to the IEEE802.11 standard. This is a wireless protocol, which utilises short range wireless technology.
Wi-Fi	Wireless Fidelity is based on the IEEE802.11 specifications. Equipment is tested and certified by the Wi-Fi Alliance.
IrDA	The Infrared Data Association defines the physical specifications for the exchange of data over infrared light. It is difficult to see the original specifications as an access fee is payable.
Cellular radio	The term cellular radio is interchangeable with the term mobile phone, with the exception of satellite phones. It therefore includes GSM, CDMA (Code Division Multiple Access) and AMPS (Advanced Mobile Phone System), which is an analogue system.
GSM/UMTS	The Global System for Mobile Communication and Universal Mobile Telecommunications System is one of the third generation mobile phone technologies. There are different UMTS from competing network technologies.
WAP	Wireless Application Protocol is an open international standard to enable mobile phones or PDAs to access the Internet.
WML	Wireless Mark-up Language is used for specifications such as WAP. It is similar to HMTL but is scaled down.
802.11x standards	These are sets of standards for Wireless LAN (WLAN). The standards have been in operation since 1997 and have gone through several adaptations since then.
TCP/IP	Transmission Control Protocol and Internet Protocol consists of a five-layer model. A more complex description is given in the next section.

Research tip

For more information on Bluetooth, visit www.thewirelessdirectory.com
More about third generation mobile phones can be found at www.3gtoday.com
For more information on WML visit www.littlespringsdesign.com and follow the links to XHTML.
Further WAP information can be found at www.openmobilealliance.org and use the search facility to find the latest WAP technical section.
For more information on IEEE802 visit www.standards.ieee.org and follow the links to 802.
For the latest information on IrDA visit www.deviceforge.com. Use the search facility to find the latest IrDA information.

- WPA – Wi-Fi Protected Access – the latest version WPA2 is a development of WPA, which aims to provide stronger levels of security for data and network access. It is based on the 802.11i standard (considered to be government standard security). There are two versions of WPA2: WPA2-Personal for consumer users and WPA2-Enterprise for organisations. In the former, the user ensures network access by utilising a set-up password. In the latter, the system verifies a network user through a server. Both versions are backward compatible with WPA.

The primary danger of not having any form of security is that open wireless connections leave the user prone to being re-directed to fake WLAN login pages, so that the hacker can then capture all of the data and keystrokes (such as passwords and financial information).

TCP/IP MODEL

Levels and relationship with connection devices

The TCP/IP model does not match the OSI model. There are five layers instead of seven; the last two layers are generally considered as one distinct layer.

Table 8.10 Connecting networks

Layer	Description
Application	Includes all the processes that involve user interaction. It determines the presentation of the data and controls the session. The terms socket and port are used to describe the path over which applications communicate (including FTP, POP, SMTP and HTTP).
Transport	There are two transport layers: the TCP ensures that the data is received as it was sent and the User Datagram Protocol makes end-to-end reliability checks.
Internet	Sometimes described as the TCP/IP layer. All of the upper and lower layer communications pass through the IP as they are passed through the TCP/IP protocol stack.
Network access	The two layers included are the data link and the physical layer. The data link deals with how the IP handles the existing data link protocols (e.g. token ring or Ethernet) by describing the pin configurations and cable requirements etc. The physical layer standards cover aspects such as RS232 and V.35 etc.

Information passes down from applications to the physical layer. Data is sent and each layer adds control information in front of that data. The control information is referred to as a header. The process of adding the header is known as encapsulation. Once the data is received, each layer then removes its own header before passing the data on to the next layer.

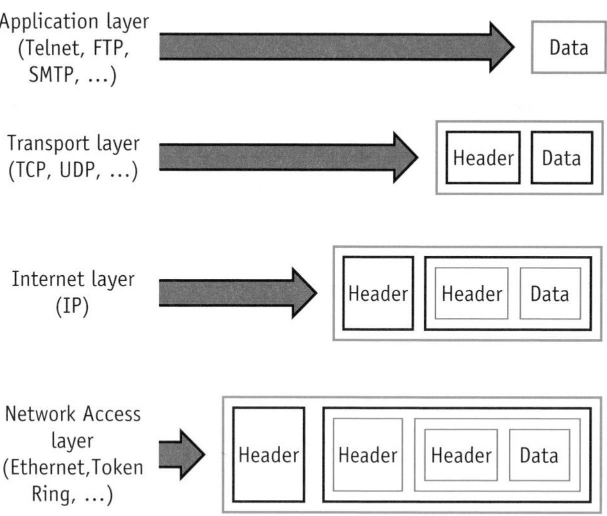

Figure 8.13 The TCP/IP model

EVIDENCE ACTIVITY

P6 – D1

Before the board of directors is happy to sign off the budget and necessary purchases they would like you to describe briefly the features of networks and the communication services that they offer. They require all of the systems to be compatible with one another and to build in a certain degree of future-proofing. In the form of a brief report, describe the features of networks and communication services. **(P6)**

For D1, respond to the finance director, who believes that he knows quite a lot about computer networks and in an effort to embarrass you has asked you to compare critically the OSI and TCP/IP models. You are not sure whether he is serious or not, but you will need to respond to him and make the critical comparison in the form of an email. **(D1)**

8.4 Understand Internet communications

INTERNET COMMUNICATION

Internet communication takes place in many forms, including email, instant messaging, message boards, file transfer and chat rooms. Communication on the Internet is used for many different purposes and has distinct business applications. In this final section, the focus is on the understanding of the fundamentals of Internet communications, including terminology and systems.

Terminology

As with many technical disciplines, Internet communication is awash with terminology. Much of this may already be familiar, at least in its basic form. The following table explains some of the key terms used.

Table 8.11 Some terms explained

Term	Explanation
HTTP	HyperText Transfer Protocol is the protocol for transferring hypertext documents that makes the use of the Internet possible. A standard web address (such as http://www.yahoo.co.uk/) is called a URL; the prefix (http) indicates its protocol.
HTTPS	This is HyperText Transfer Protocol, but with an added S, for Secure Sockets Layer. This is a protocol primarily developed for secure, safe Internet transactions.
FTP	File Transfer Protocol is the simplest and the most secure way to exchange files over the Internet. Users routinely use FTP without even knowing it (it has driven the ability to download MP3 tracks, for example).
SMTP	Simple Mail Transfer Protocol is the standard means by which email is sent over the Internet. It is a relatively straightforward text-based protocol. One or more of the receivers of the message is specified (using an email address which is then verified as existing) and then the message is transferred.

Uniform resource locator (URL)

A URL defines the protocol to be used to retrieve a resource such as an FTP or HTTP. It also determines the server on which the resource resides and where in that server's directory structure the relevant file can be located. In effect, it is the address of the file or resource. Each URL is unique to that file or resource. Most Internet users know the URL as the means of specifying a web address.

If a user fails to add the http:// before the URL, then browsers will add this automatically. Websites tend to be set up so that they send the user to a default page if they do not specify an exact directory or file name. If the user does specify the full URL, then the index.htm is usually loaded.

Worldwide web

This is another term used to describe the Internet. Some prefer to distinguish the Internet from the Worldwide Web. In this respect, the Worldwide web is the repository of information (web pages etc), whilst the Internet is the network that allows access to that information. The Internet is a network of interconnected LANs, WANs and individual computers, as well as a vast hardware and software infrastructure, which includes cabling, servers and various forms of wired and wireless connection technologies. In fact, the Internet is a network of networks, including all of the switching mechanisms, software and IP that is used to access the Worldwide Web.

Other

Internet communication is an ever-evolving phenomenon. Different uses are constantly being created or adapted. This brief look at different types of Internet communication focuses on some of the practical communication applications which are becoming increasingly familiar and popular.

Table 8.12 Internet communications

Other types of Internet communication	Explanation
Blogs	Blog is short for weblog, essentially a frequently updated journal or newsletter, written from a personal point of view. Many believe that it is a new form of web journalism.
Wikis	A Wiki is an online database, the term being derived from the Hawaiian word for fast. The most famous is the Wikipedia, which began life in 1994. It encourages readers' contributions and incorporates the ability to store and amend entries on a huge variety of topics.
Video-conferencing	This is a communication technology that incorporates both voice and video in order to connect remote users. It requires each user to have access to a microphone, Broadband connection, computer and webcam. It allows real-time conversations to take place between remote locations.
Vlogs	A vlog is essentially a weblog that uses video, accompanied by images and text. It is the natural progression and successor to the blog.

Research tip

For a basic primer on blogs visit www.blogger.com
Wikipedia can be found at www.en.wikipedia.org
For more information on video-conferencing visit www.wisegeek.com and use the search engine to find their section on video-conferencing, with links.
More information about vlogs can be found at www.01vlog.com

SYSTEM REQUIREMENTS

Networks are a combination of hardware and software. Collectively they are required to ensure not only that the network is workable and robust, but also that each device on that network is capable of sending and receiving relevant data. Compatibility, in terms of the technical features of devices, is an important consideration, as is the application of specific protocols that will facilitate rather than cause conflicts within the network.

Hardware and software system requirements for wired and mobile systems

Wired networks require physical cables, running from a router and then connecting each device on that network. The router performs the switching and routing functions and is the device that facilitates Broadband connection. The switching facilitates the data transfer and ensures that the data remains on the network, such as a request from a personal computer that a printer prints a copy of a document.

Wireless networks, on the other hand, still require a number of specific devices, but they use wireless connection in order to transmit data and instructions from one device to another. A router is still required, however this can also be wireless in that it makes a wireless connection to the Internet and also facilitates wireless connectivity to devices on the network.

Communication services

Internet communications seek to facilitate the interaction between users and the interchange of data applications and ideas. The following table outlines some of the principal communication services used.

Table 8.13 Internet communication services

Other types of communication service	Explanation
Email	This is one of the most common forms of communication and is an electronic version of a letter or a memorandum. The principal advantage over these two more traditional methods is that documents, images and other attachments can be easily added to the email and shared or distributed by the sender.
Video	There are two distinct types of video in terms of communication. The first is the passive presentation-style video, which has already been recorded. The more adaptable version is often used either for video-chatting or for video-conferencing and is in real time.
Internet	The Internet is a vast repository of information and ideas. Much of the information is accessed using search engines. These hunt for key phrases, words or terms and make suggestions as to best-match websites or pages. It is possible to share data and information either publicly or privately, the latter usually facilitated by restricting access to only internal or authorised users or viewers.

Software

The two most important pieces of software are an Internet browser (e.g. Internet Explorer) and an email software system (e.g. Yahoo or Outlook Express). Through these two pieces of software the user is able to search, view and download information stored on web pages and the email system allows them to communicate directly with other Internet users.

Configuration

This is a general term that is used to describe the way in which the computer is set up. It is also used to describe the combination of hardware components. In effect it is both the hardware and the software that make up a complete system.

Configuration management is of vital importance in a networked system, as compatibility is vital in order to ensure that conflict issues do not arise between different devices incorporated onto the network at different times. Increasingly many devices are compatible with a variety of different protocols and systems and have the advantage of being plug-and-play components, requiring little in the way of installation software.

Think What steps need to be taken in order to ensure that all devices, applications and software are compatible within any given network system?

DIRECT COMMUNICATION

One of the major advantages of Internet communications is that it facilitates instantaneous communication between users in remote locations. This has not only important leisure applications, but also vital business uses.

The following table briefly outlines four of the main ways in which users can make direct communication.

Table 8.14 Direct Internet communications

Types of direct communication	Explanation
Chat	There are two ways in which this can be primarily facilitated. The first is to use instant messaging, which recognises particular identified users as being online and allows personal messages to be typed onscreen and instantaneously sent to their computer. This is a text-based communication system. To leave a permanent trail of a chat conversation, message boards are also used, allowing registered users to involve themselves in an ongoing conversation on a particular topic by typing into a box and sending it to the message board.
Video communication	Video-conferencing is much more achievable and cost effective now that the majority of potential users have access to Broadband connections. Communication is undertaken in real time and can be achieved by a microphone and a web cam attached to a computer. Sound and vision is instantaneously transmitted via the Internet, so that an audio-visual conversation can take place with the minimum of time lag between transmission and receipt of the data.
Email	Email requires the user to have the correct email address for the intended recipient. Each email received can be logged and stored and any relevant email address added to an address book for future reference. Emails are primarily text-based, but have the adaptable facility to allow files of other formats to be attached to them.
Web phone	There are several proprietary brands of web phones that use differing technologies to facilitate instantaneous voice contact and interaction using the Internet. One of the most popular is Skype, which provides a free service between registered users, but also allows standard telephone calls to be made, for which the user has to first purchase credits.

EVIDENCE ACTIVITY

P7 – M3 – D2 – D3

The board of directors is very excited about the possibilities that a bespoke computer network can offer them. They are eager to embrace the latest in Internet communications, but do not fully understand the implications and the applications. They have asked you to describe in a brief, informal meeting, the nature of Internet communications and any associated system requirements. **(P7)**

For M3, back up your meeting with the directors by explaining and demonstrating direct communication between two network devices. So that it can be shown to other employees at a later date this should be recorded using audio-visual equipment. **(M3)**

For D2 and D3, the directors still have some concerns regarding network security and accessibility. Suggest a particular access control method that would suit the business and then justify your choice in the form of a brief presentation. Then explain and possibly demonstrate the effectiveness of data transfer using both wireless and wired networks. **(D2, D3)**

Databases are the prime technique for the development of any information system used in modern business. They are also used in e-commerce and Internet-based marketing systems. Therefore it is very important that developers of information systems have a detailed understanding of the data analysis and data structures involved in order to be able to develop functional and accurate systems which satisfy the needs of all the users of those systems.

You will gain an understanding of the analysis and design principles of a database system. You will learn about different types of databases in order to ensure that the most appropriate is used in any given situation. These could include relational, flat file, hierarchical and network structures.

You will become familiar with a range of design methodologies and the associated terminology involved in the analysis and design of a database. You will develop skills and understanding in the use of at least one methodology in order to be able to create the design for development. You will, at the end of the unit, be able to put your theories into practice and develop a database system and test it through implementation.

You will study and produce relevant documentation at the end of each of the modelling and implementation stages of the development of a database.

This unit will concentrate on the logical data modelling (LDM) methodology for the analysis and design but you will be introduced to other approaches. On completion of this unit you will be in a position to analyse and design simple models for databases in a small business environment.

By the end of this unit you will:

So you want to be an...

IT Support/Analyst

My name Mike Daniels
Age 20
Income £10,500

What do you do?

I work in the IT support department giving advice and support to users of the company computers. The company has sites all across Europe.

What responsibilities do you have?

I make sure that all the users know how to use their computers properly, that the computers they are using are working properly and that records of all user requests are maintained in a log. This helps us see which machines have recurrent faults and which users need regular training and advice. The first thing I did when I started was to redo the database that keeps the log so that it was easier for everyone to enter and query data.

> "The company may pay for me to go to university."

How did the course help?

The database units on the course helped me rework the database we keep. The hardware and software units covered help no end with supporting the users. I also design and develop databases for the end users.

How did you get the job?

With the help of my tutor at college I applied for the job. My BTEC National ITP and general educational level were sufficient entry qualifications for the post. I have a natural approach to people and so a job helping others was good for me.

What training did you get?

The first two weeks there we had 'induction' sessions to the company, its structure and organisation, as well as its practices and approaches to work. I did not need much training for the job as I already have sufficient skills but I will need some when I have been in the company longer to help me progress and get promoted.

What are the hours?

I work from 8 till 4 at the moment but some people work different shift patterns to fit in with US hours. I will have the chance to work in Europe as well so the hours will be different there obviously. I may get to learn new languages when abroad!

What's the pay?

I started last year on £9000 but when I passed the probationary period I had a raise to £10500. My supervisor earns £15000 so there's hope for me there.

What about the future?

The company may pay for me to go to university as part of their personal and career development plan for all staff. I obviously want to get promoted and also would love to go to the States to work for the company there.

Grading criteria

The table below shows what you need to do to gain a pass, merit or distinction in this part of the qualification. Make sure you refer back to it when you are completing work so that you can judge whether you are meeting the criteria and what you need to do to fill in gaps in your knowledge or experience.

In this unit there are five evidence activities that give you an opportunity to demonstrate your achievement of the grading criteria:

page 56	P1, P2, P4, M1
page 66	P3, P5, M2
page 70	P6, M3
page 70	P7, D2
page 70	M4, D1

To achieve a pass grade the evidence must show that the learner is able to...	To achieve a merit grade the evidence must show that, in addition to the pass criteria, the learner is able to...	To achieve a distinction grade the evidence must show that, in addition to the pass and merit criteria, the learner is able to...
P1 describe the advantages and disadvantages of the specified database types, using examples	**M1** explain the benefits of the logical data modelling process	**D1** evaluate the effectiveness of the data modelling process in producing an efficient data model to meet user requirements
P2 describe the advantages and disadvantages of the specified analysis and design methodologies, using examples	**M2** explain the constraints developed in a logical data model to meet specified user requirements	**D2** evaluate a model produced against an initial brief, and suggest improvements to enhance the model to meet user requirements.
P3 identify and describe potential modelling constraints that could arise from a logical data model, using examples	**M3** justify the requirements for all types of test required to ensure a logical data model is efficient and effective	
P4 describe the concepts involved in logical data modelling	**M4** justify the purpose of complete and accurate technical documentation for a logical data model and associated testing.	
P5 produce a data model to meet specified user requirements		
P6 produce a test strategy and test plan for normal situations for a data model		
P7 implement a logical data model.		

11.1 Know modelling methodologies and techniques

Databases come in a range of sizes and shapes but they all are designed to hold data which can be interrogated to provide information. Valid and reliable information can only be produced if the data held are accurate and sufficient. Part of the art of database design includes knowing about the domain of discourse (the topic on which the database will be built).

Key word

Database – a collection of information that is organised so that it can easily be accessed, managed and updated.

Think Where are your details held in a database? There is likely to be more than one system that holds information on you.

DATABASE TYPES

Flat file database

A flat file structure holds all the data in one file. It closely resembles a spreadsheet worksheet in layout when printed out. It requires a great deal of careful processing to extract relevant information and can have major problems when updating or deleting any values held in it.

Flat file databases are still used internally by many computer applications to store configuration data. Many other applications allow users to store and retrieve their own information from flat files using a pre-defined set of fields. Examples are programs to manage collections of books or appointments. Home users will create expenditure files to track where their monies are going each month.

Think What is the most common paper-based flat file database that is delivered to your doorstep each year?

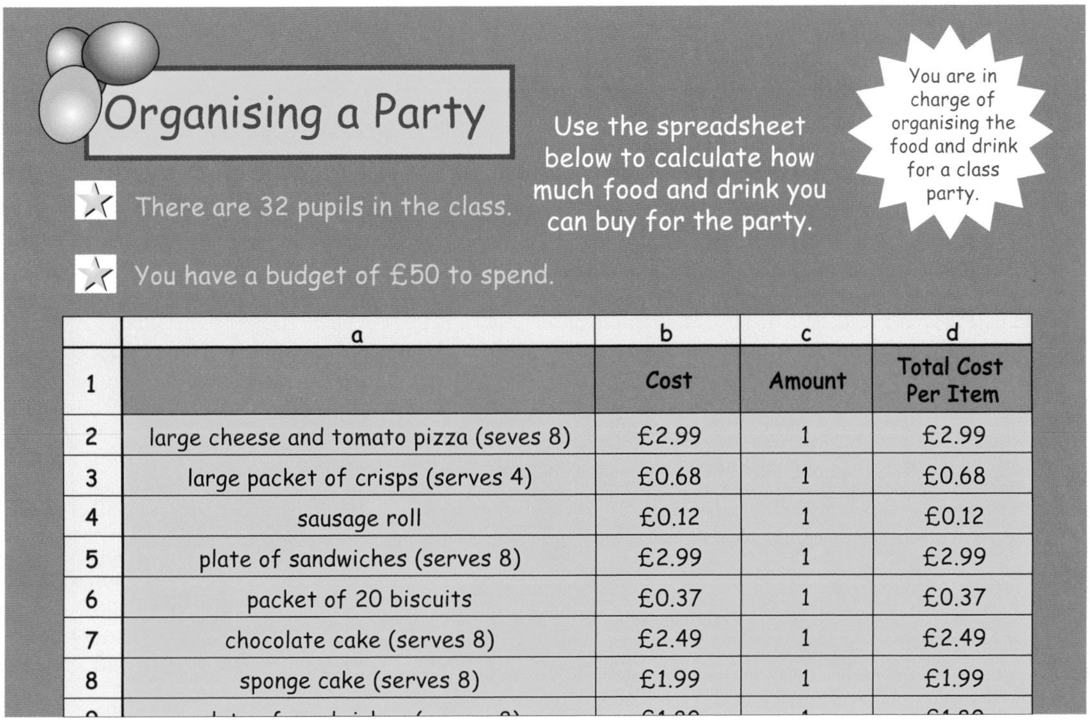

Organising a Party

There are 32 pupils in the class.

You have a budget of £50 to spend.

Use the spreadsheet below to calculate how much food and drink you can buy for the party.

You are in charge of organising the food and drink for a class party.

	a	b	c	d
1		Cost	Amount	Total Cost Per Item
2	large cheese and tomato pizza (seves 8)	£2.99	1	£2.99
3	large packet of crisps (serves 4)	£0.68	1	£0.68
4	sausage roll	£0.12	1	£0.12
5	plate of sandwiches (serves 8)	£2.99	1	£2.99
6	packet of 20 biscuits	£0.37	1	£0.37
7	chocolate cake (serves 8)	£2.49	1	£2.49
8	sponge cake (serves 8)	£1.99	1	£1.99

Figure 11.1 Example of a flat file database

A flat file database should really consist of nothing but data. In the wider connotation, the term refers to any database which exists in a single file in the form of rows and columns, with no relationships or links between records and fields except the table structure.

Flat file databases should only be used when there are only one or two columns on which the data is organised and where there is no opportunity to store the same data in more than one row. As can be seen from the diagram below this has not happened.

Hierarchical database

The hierarchical model developed from the flat file type when database developers tried to combine flat file structures together. It still has inherent problems with querying and general maintenance.

This type of database involves the structuring of data into a tree of records. Each record has a parent record with many children. It is possible to 'walk' upwards from the lowest level to the top level to query the data and extract information. However, it does not allow easy tracking across the levels. As can be seen from the diagram it easily resembles a family tree.

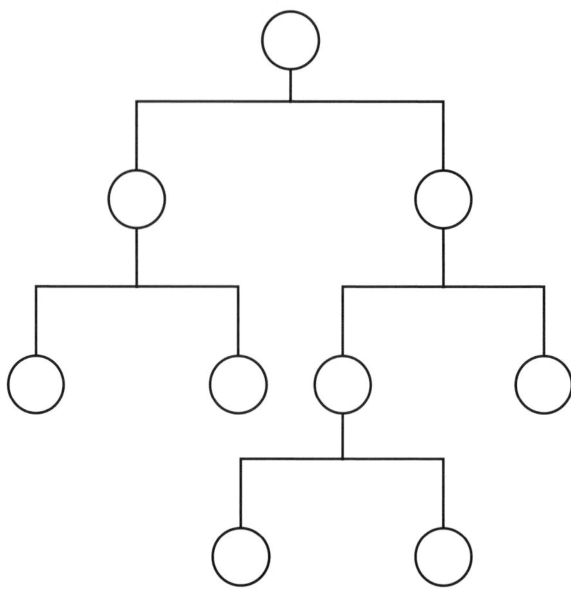

Figure 11.2 Hierarchical database

Each 'circle' represents either a parent or a child; these are called nodes. The top node is called the root. Each node is only allowed one parent, with the exception of the root; this is 'orphaned'.

Table 11.1 Hospital flat file data

hospital in patient details extract from over 1000 records!
records run from 06/04 first year to 05/04 following year

ward no.	patient id	admission date	discharge date	ward name	ward speciality	ward gender	patient name	patient date of birth	patient next of kin
g1	1212	10-Oct	12-Oct	edwards	renal	male	fred	20/09/1989	wife
g2	1213	11-Oct	19-Oct	jenkins	renal	female	joanna	01/01/1948	daughter
r1	1214	12-Oct	19-Oct	jones	cardiac	both	jamal	13/11/1991	mother
r2	1215	13-Oct	04-Feb	williams	cardiac	both	samira	03/04/1990	father
g1	1216	13-Oct	11-Nov	edwards	renal	male	moses	07/05/1960	partner
g2	1215	06-Aug	09-Sep	jenkins	renal	female	samira	03/04/1990	father
r1	1215	05-Feb		jones	cardiac	both	samira	03/04/1990	father
r2	1213	02-Nov	05-Dec	williams	cardiac	both	joanna	01/01/1948	daughter
g1	1214	06-Jul	08-Aug	edwards	renal	male	jamal	13/11/1991	mother
g2	1213	12-Dec	19-Jan	jenkins	renal	female	joanna	01/01/1948	daughter
r1	1216	19-May		jones	cardiac	both	moses	07/05/1960	partner
r2	1212	03-Apr	10-Jun	williams	cardiac	both	fred	20/09/1989	wife

A table of contents in a book is an example of a parent record and the chapters or sections in the book become the children. Within each of the chapters or sections there may be subsections (in turn, children).

Example

An example with field names is that of an American university record system:

An issue here is that it is not possible to add a new student who has not yet signed up for a course, as the course details need to be allocated first. A further issue arises if the same student wishes to sign up for several courses. Records will be duplicated for the student details. Duplication of data causes issues with update and delete just as would happen with a flat file structure.

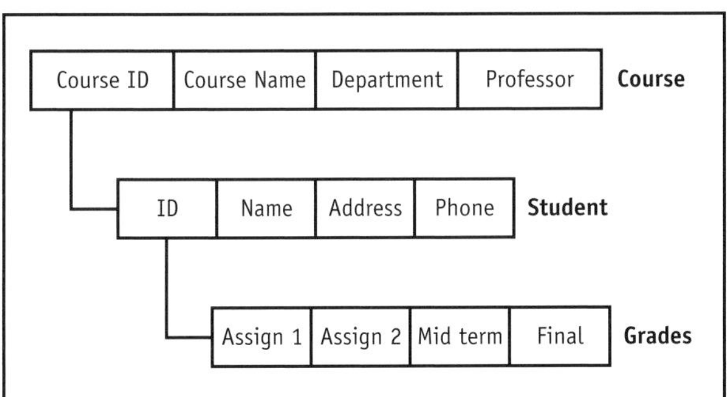

Figure 11.3 American University record system

Network database

The network model developed from the hierarchical model but this time children can have many parents. The 'walking through' the data structures to collect information has now become easier but there are still issues with insert, update and delete of records.

Research tip

Investigate the CODASYL consortium and identify its role in the development of the network database.

Although, as can be seen from the diagram, it resembles a relational model, it failed to gain popularity because the relational model was developed a couple of years later.

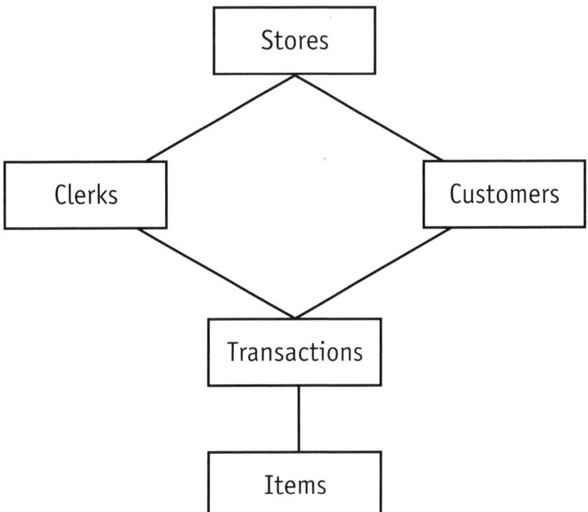

Figure 11.4 Network database

A more advanced structure can be seen in the following diagram where it looks nothing like either a hierarchical or relational structure. This is more of a 'lattice' but the problems still exist. Essentially here, it demonstrates the opportunity to link two distinct areas or topics together into one system. There are still opportunities for data duplication to happen and extraction of information to be difficult.

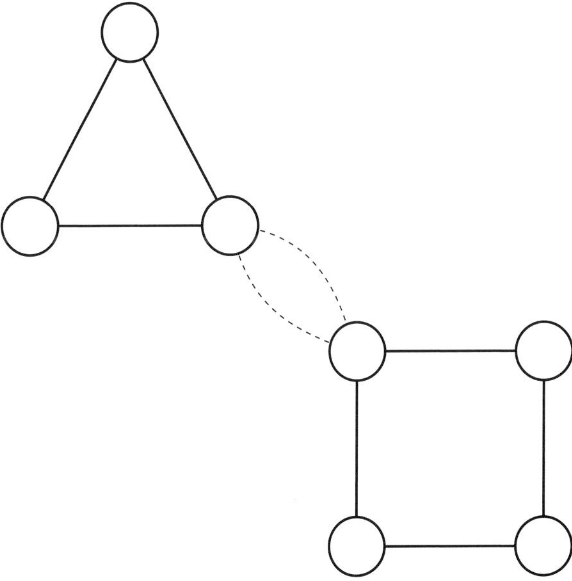

Figure 11.5 Advanced network database

Relational database

The relational type was designed to remove the problems with data redundancy, update and deletion of data contained in the flat file, the hierarchical and the network models. It contains several tables, each similar to a flat file, with relationships between the tables. Each table still contains sets of data.

There is a range of terminology in use to describe the various parts of the model – these will be described in greater detail later in this section.

It has been in existence as a model since the early 1970s but still works very efficiently today with several software packages that rely heavily on the structure. These include MSAccess, Oracle, MySQL, etc.

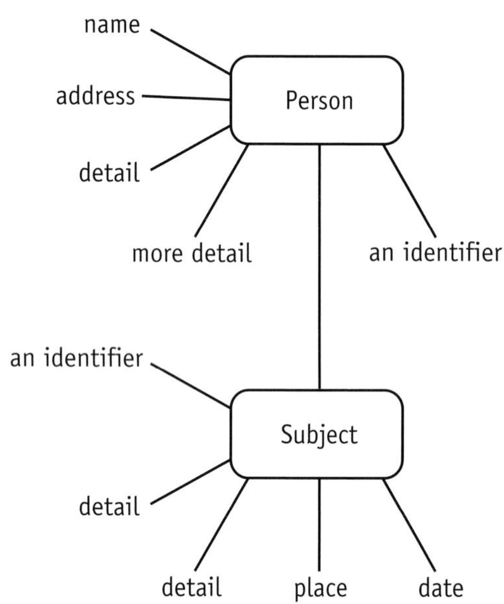

Figure 11.6 Relational database

Research tip

Investigate who developed the relational model and its underlying theories. Find out why he thought it an exemplary approach to database design.

One of the main benefits of the relational model is the ability to be able to query across the tables to find answers to questions and thus produce relevant up-to-date information. Another benefit is that there should only ever be one place where any data item need be changed. This reduces the update and delete anomalies of the flat file structure.

One disadvantage of a relational database is that it can handle only one-to-many relationships, whereas complex systems can handle many-to-many relationships. Occasionally the nature of the queries can cause relational databases to be slow to access information.

A relational database should be easy to maintain and expand as and when users, demand changes.

TASK

Prepare a table showing the advantages and disadvantages of the main features of each of the four database types discussed above, describe the differences between each type.

The concepts of the relational model are described in the next section.

MODELLING TECHNOLOGIES

Logical data modelling

Logical data modelling (LDM) is most frequently used when developing a relational model. Sometimes you will hear this referred to as conceptual modelling. A good logical data model identifies sets of data and potential relationships between these data sets. However, the relationships are not 'implemented' in the model except diagrammatically until the very end of the process.

A conceptual model is a 'map' of concepts (data sets) and their relationships. It describes aspects of a business, what data the business wishes to store, the characteristics (properties or attributes) and associations (relationships) between the concepts.

It starts off from the situation of walking into an organisation and listening to what people tell you happens in the area that will be 'databased', examining current documents, etc. As an analyst you would develop a requirements specification.

Research tip

Investigate what a requirements specification contains, who prepares one and how it might be documented. (You may have discussed this topic in the Systems Analysis unit.)

You will not know any more than that about how the data is structured or stored. It becomes like a jigsaw puzzle where you have to fit it all together in a logical, consistent manner. The benefit of this approach is that you do not need to know what sort of data is held straight away; decisions like that can come much later. A further benefit is that the final outcome from this approach should be something that could be presented to your end user for review and approval or alteration. It is certainly a useful discussion document.

The aim is to develop a group of data sets with as few data items allowed not to be empty. Wherever possible, it is expected that data items will store data at all times and not be empty (NULL). This is often very difficult and requires development at a much higher level than would be used in this course.

A true logical data model never holds values that can be calculated from others in the database. This means that, although the database might eventually, for example, produce reports showing total price, the total price would never be stored in an operational system. It would be calculated each time it was needed by multiplying quantity by item price.

Think In the games case study – check that you have not identified any data items that could be calculated from others.

Following identification of the entities and attributes (concepts and properties) it is now important to decide how these fit together to form the relationships.

In Section 11.2 you will investigate much more about how the process works. There will also be some minor changes in the notation used.

CASE STUDY: GAMES STORE

A computer games store wants to keep records about their customers, the games that are available currently, those it has in stock as well as the sales and rental records.

The concepts (data sets) in this situation will be:

- Customer
- Game
- Stock
- Sales receipt
- Rental activity

Note that each is in the singular to represent the fact that each record is only ever about one customer, one game, etc. at a time.

QUESTIONS

1. Work out what characteristics (properties or attributes) of the data sets (concepts or entities) might be stored. For example:

Customer = customer code, customer name, customer address, customer contact details, customer date of birth (Why this one? Because some games are 18-rated)

2. Think about the other four concepts (entities) involved.

Example

Use this diagram as an example and add your version of the characteristics (properties or attributes) to each of the other entities.

Now decide how many times you consider each relationship is used, e.g. one customer can have many sales receipts or one game can be held as a stock item many times. Using the notation 1 for one and ∞ for many put the correct symbol at each end of the relationship line and give the relationship a name (verb).

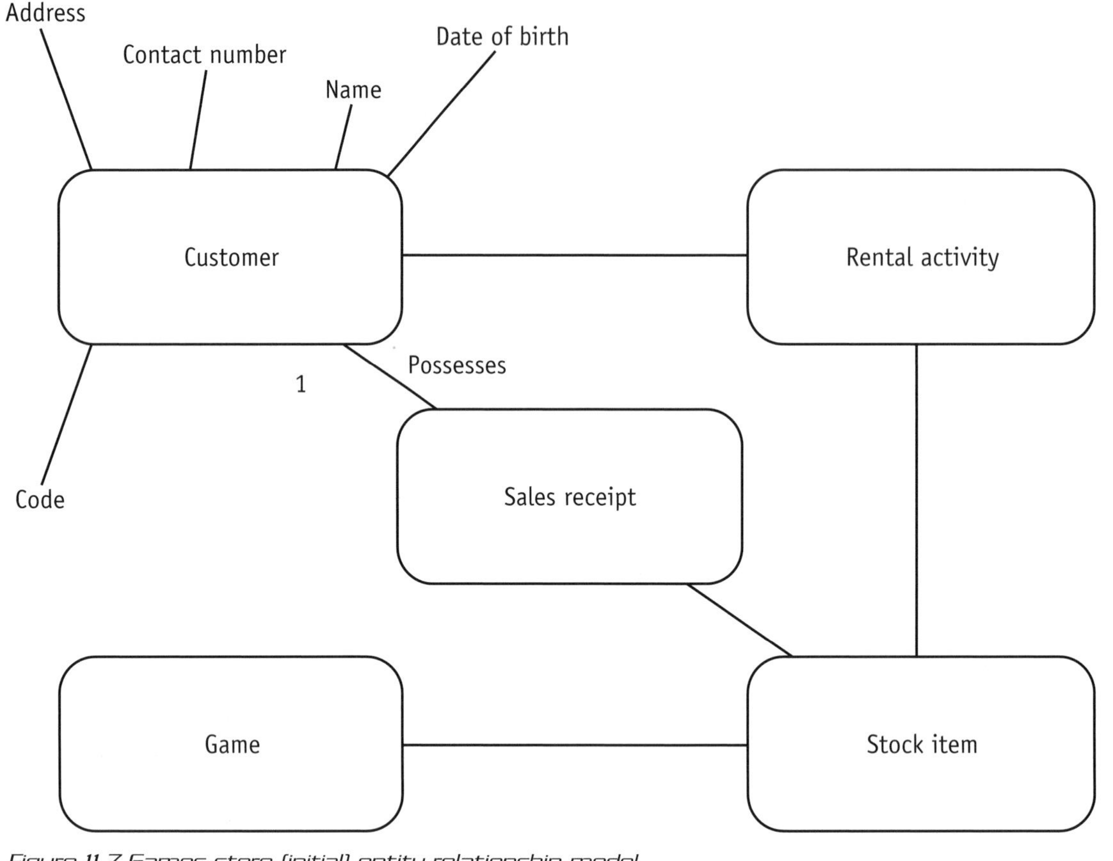

Figure 11.7 Games store (initial) entity relationship model

The model produced is a snapshot of the required system at any point in time and it is subject to change whenever users/businesses require. Therefore it must be easy to modify. It can, at certain times, relate easily to object-oriented models (OOAD, more of which later in this section).

A complex conceptual model allows for inheritance between data sets or concepts where values in one entity can be passed down to another entity. This is called the super/sub type entity structure (in OOAD this would be super/sub class structure). It is highly unlikely that, at this level, you will attempt this form of inheritance, but you need to be aware the opportunity exists.

The documentation for a logical data model comprises a list of all the data sets, relationships, a diagram that shows how the data sets link together and a list of any restrictions (constraints) in place on the system. These may be to do with data values, the way relationships are formed or may also be operational (based on what the business itself wants). This documentation is a useful tool for showing to the person who has requested the system so that they can confirm the details are correct.

Think What documentation would you present to the owner of the games store at this stage?

Data value constraints may include restricted value sets such as (pc, mainframe, hybrid) or ranges of permitted values such as 001...999). Relationship constraints include inclusive or exclusive OR, i.e. two must exist or only one can exist, mandatory, i.e. it must happen or a relationship is only allowed with a subset of values from the linking entity/concept. Operational constraints include need for passwords, restricted views for data to some personnel, restrictions on who can update certain values, etc.

> ***Think*** Are there any obvious constraints you might be able to impose on the data items in the games store case study at this stage?

The full LDM process will be examined in greater detail in Section 11.3 (page 63). Following the discovery of the entities (concepts) and their relationships a diagram can be prepared, the discoveries noted and the relationships 'implemented' by posting attributes from one entity into another. This is then called a relational model. It becomes the stage from which the database developer can create the tables and all the associated 'processing' involved.

Each entity is given a unique identifier, e.g. customer code from the games case study. These identifiers, called primary keys, are usually used to help form the relationships. Primary keys are underlined to highlight them. The attributes posted to show relationships are in italics for clarity.

> A completed example from the games case study might be as follows:
> Customer (custcode, custname, custaddress, custtelno, custdateofbirth)
> Game (gameid, gamename, description, rating)
> Rental (*custcode, gameid*, startdateofrental, returndate)
> Sales receipt (*custcode, gameid*, startdateofrental, qtybought)
> Stock item (*gameid*, priceperdayforrental, qtyinstock)

This gives all the relations necessary to progress to implementation. The final stage is to develop a data dictionary, which is a table giving details about the data to be held, the constraints that might be applied, etc. This is discussed in more detail in Section 11.3 but helps the database developer structure the tables and columns, specify permitted values and so on.

The LDM approach does not require any knowledge of how the final database might be implemented, therefore the analyst does not have to be a software specialist. It is, as its name suggests, a very logical approach to development:

1. Find the concepts (entities)
2. Find the attributes (properties) of the entities
3. Work out the relationships between the entities
4. Document the findings including diagram, definitions, relationships and data dictionary.

> ***Think*** Identify the strengths and weaknesses of the LDM approach.

Object-oriented analysis and design (OOAD)

Having looked at logical or conceptual data modelling it is important to examine in general the process involved in OOAD – which, at this stage, could be seen to be very similar. The diagram overleaf shows how the OOAD structure is put together.

The object-oriented approach started with programming in mind rather than database development. The developed systems still rely quite heavily on a large amount of coding instead of macros, queries, etc., that would be found in a relational database system.

An object-oriented system is based on objects and the collaboration between the various objects. So far this sounds much like concepts (entities) and their relationships. Each object represents some entity of interest in the system being modelled, and is characterised by its class, its state (data elements or attributes), and its behaviour. Various models can be created to show the static structure, dynamic behaviour and run-time deployment of these collaborating objects.

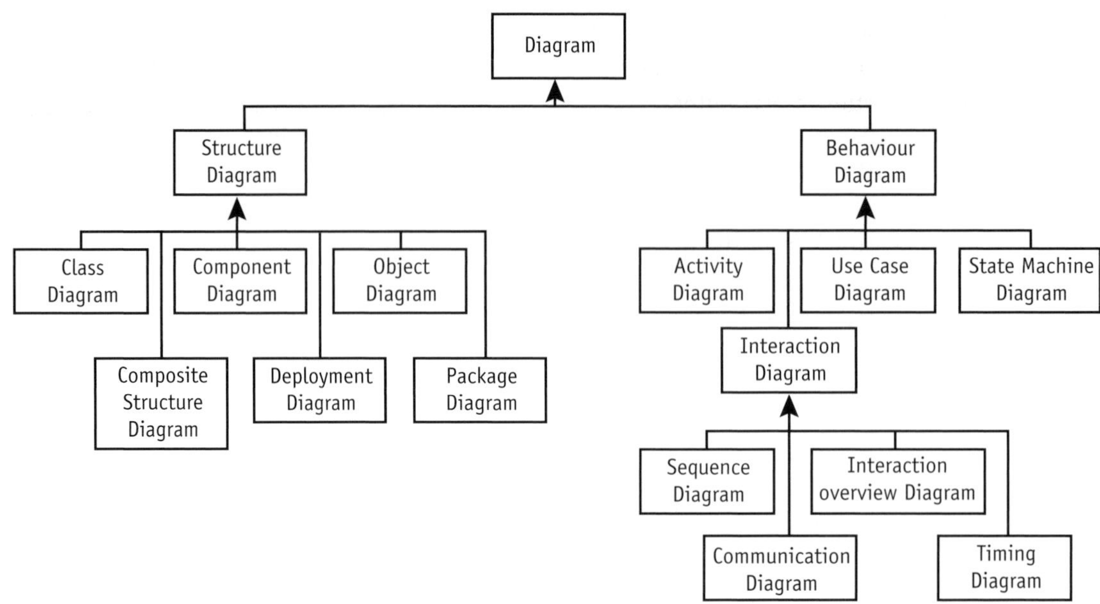

Figure: 11.8 Wikimedia Unified Modelling Language diagram

Definitions

Class
An object or data set used to group data elements together. For example:
Student
Course

Attribute
Property or characteristic of the class. For example:
Student name
Course title

Method
Operations carried out on classes. For example:
Add a student

Association
Relationship between objects. For example:
Many students attend many courses

Actor
A role involved (or it may be) in the database created. For example:
Teacher
Administrator

Use case
Description of how actor will interact with the system being developed. For example:
Produce course student list

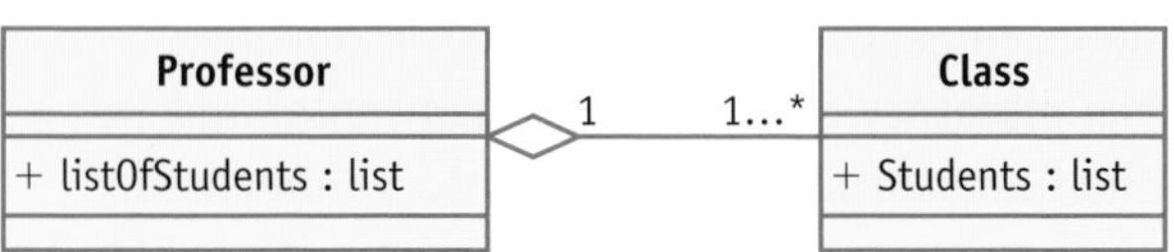

Figure 11.9 Professor – class relationship diagram

Inheritance from one level to the next is common in OOAD but is effected through the relationships in LDM.

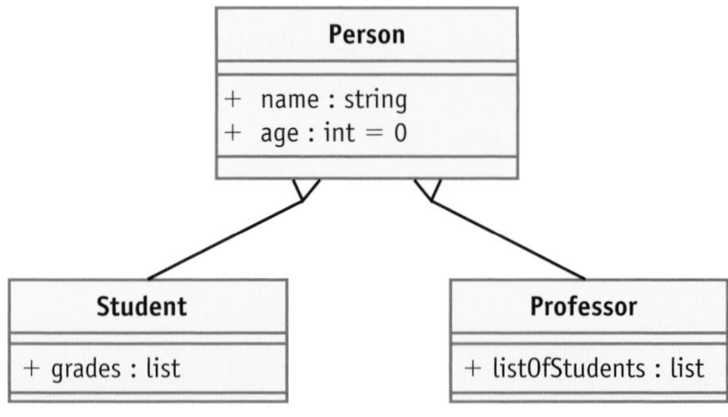

Figure 11.10 Inheritance diagram

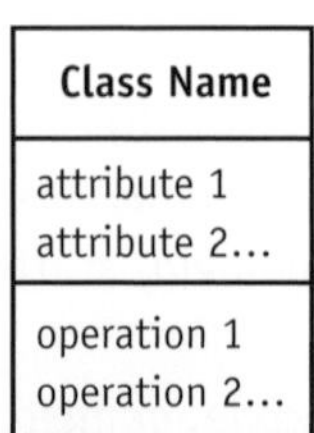

Figure 11.11 Person inheritance diagram

One advantage that OOAD has over LDM is that it also shows the actions or operations that may take place on the data or the objects (this time called classes) and also what happens in the relationships (this time called associations). The data elements are still called data properties or attributes.

The process also holds information on the people who might interact with (use) the system (actors). Each interaction is called a use case. Use cases, stated simply, allow description of sequences of events that, taken together, lead to a system doing something useful. Use cases are very beneficial in the development of systems through OOAD techniques.

An actor is often thought of as a role, rather than an actual person. A single person in the real world can be represented by several actors if they have several different roles and goals with regards to a system. In relational modelling the users have 'views' and queries created for their use. A similar process happens for 'actors' through the use case structure. The diagram shows a simple approach for the school structure.

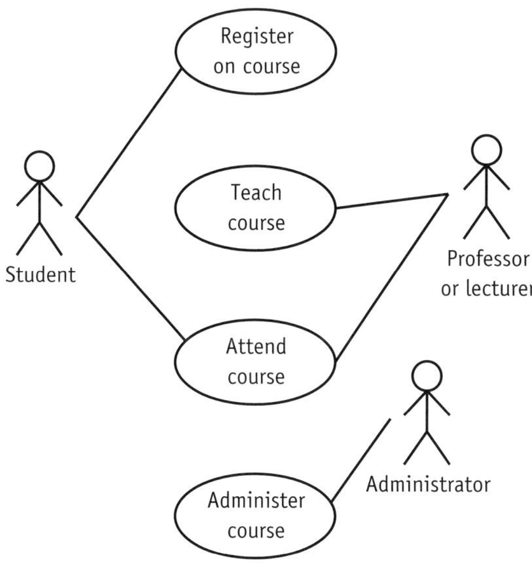

Figure 11.12 Actors diagram

Research tip

Investigate the benefits and limitations of use cases.

Think Having done the research on use cases decide how any user can best interact with the development of an OOAD model.

Research tip

Investigate the different software to support relational databases and object-oriented databases

Normalisation

Definitions

1NF – first normal form
A table is in first normal form if it has a unique identifier and a set of other attributes.

2NF – second normal form
A table must be in 1NF AND all other attributes are fully functionally dependent on the unique identifier.

3NF – third normal form
A table is in third normal form if it is in 2NF AND there are no transitive dependencies, i.e. there is no relationship between the attributes that do not form the primary key.

The process of normalisation starts when the developer knows all about the data to be stored in the database. The output from the normalisation process should be exactly the same as the final output from the logical modelling technique. The modelling process requires knowing about the domain of discourse (i.e. what the topic is about) and also being able to follow a set of rules. The most difficult part is getting to know the data and being able to present the details in a suitable format. Conventionally, the data are presented in a flat file format:

If Table 11.2 (on p. 54) does not have a unique identifier then it is in 0NF (zero normal form, conventionally a flat file structure). However, if it is given a definition such as:

Inpatient (<u>wardno, patientid, admissiondate</u>, dischargedate, wardname, wardspecialism, wardgender, patientname, dob, nok)

then it becomes a first normal form (1NF) relation because it is now a database table with a unique identifying key (underlined, <u>wardno, patientid, admissiondate</u>, showing that a patient can only be in one ward on a particular date).

Table 11.2 Hospital flat file data

hospital in patient details extract from over 1000 records!
records run from 06/04 first year to 05/04 following year

ward no.	patient id	admission date	discharge date	ward name	ward speciality	ward gender	patient name	patient date of birth	patient next of kin
g1	1212	10-Oct	12-Oct	edwards	renal	male	fred	20/09/1989	wife
g2	1213	11-Oct	19-Oct	jenkins	renal	female	joanna	01/01/1948	daughter
r1	1214	12-Oct	19-Oct	jones	cardiac	both	jamal	13/11/1991	mother
r2	1215	13-Oct	04-Feb	williams	cardiac	both	samira	03/04/1990	father
g1	1216	13-Oct	11-Nov	edwards	renal	male	moses	07/05/1960	partner
g2	1215	06-Aug	09-Sep	jenkins	renal	female	samira	03/04/1990	father
r1	1215	05-Feb		jones	cardiac	both	samira	03/04/1990	father
r2	1213	02-Nov	05-Dec	williams	cardiac	both	joanna	01/01/1948	daughter
g1	1214	06-Jul	08-Aug	edwards	renal	male	jamal	13/11/1991	mother
g2	1213	12-Dec	19-Jan	jenkins	renal	female	joanna	01/01/1948	daughter
r1	1216	19-May		jones	cardiac	both	moses	07/05/1960	partner
r2	1212	03-Apr	10-Jun	williams	cardiac	both	fred	20/09/1989	wife

It should be noted that, at this stage of the development process, each of the tables is conventionally called a relation.

There is a major problem with this structure:
– there is a lot of data duplication! As can be seen the details of ward g1 are in the table 3 times, those for patient 1215 3 times and so on. This will cause many anomalies, but this is first normal form because it meets the following rules:

1. No top to bottom ordering of the rows
2. No left to right ordering of the columns
3. No duplicate rows
4. Each cell contains only one data value (or is capable of storing a value)
5. No hidden components such as identifiers.

Date, C. J. 'What First Normal Form Really Means' pp. 127–128

There are differing views on this version of IMF, such as that promoted by E. F. Codd, which argues that repeating groups should be excluded. However, in this book, Date's concepts are being followed.

Important terms

If ward 'r1' were to be deleted records for the associated patients would also be lost (**deletion anomaly**)

If 'samira' were to change her next of kin it would have to be done in each of the three records for her – one might get omitted (**update anomaly**).

A new ward cannot be added as there are no associated patient records (**insertion anomaly**).

Definitions

Candidate key

A unique identifier for any record in a relation – commonly called a primary key (there are higher definitions for this but these are outside the realm of this course). For example:
WardNo

Superkey

A set of attributes that uniquely defines a record, could be a candidate key, often called a complex primary key. For example:
wardno, patientid, admissiondate

Non-key attribute

An attribute that plays no part in any key field. For example:
Dischargedate

Functional dependency

For each value of attribute X there is exactly one value in attribute Y. For example:

PatientId maps to patientname
or
PatientId ← patientname

Transitive functional dependency
An indirect functional dependency where attribute X maps to attribute Y and attribute Y maps to Attribute Z – thus giving:
Attribute X maps to attribute Z

Determinacy diagram
Can be used to represent various aspects of normalisation pictorially. For example:

Figure 11.13 Determinacy diagram

Higher levels of these exist and will become obvious through the text.

From the data in the relation it is possible to decide on the functional dependencies that apply in this case.

Starting with patients
PatientId ← patientname
PatientId ← patient date of birth
PatientId ← patient next of kin

And then Ward
Ward No. ← ward name
Ward No. ← ward specialism

And that leaves:
Ward No, PatientId, AdmissionDate ← Discharge Date

A discharge date for any patient from any ward who was admitted on a given date must depend on all the attributes in the key field. Discharge date can have null fields if the patient is still in the ward; this makes it a nullable field. In the advanced theories this would not be allowed but at this level of study it is alright to ignore nullable fields as it does not go into higher levels of normalisation. Nor would it be feasible in this instance to be able to record any inpatient records until after the patient was discharged.

Example

Draw the simple determinacy diagrams that could be achieved with the above functional dependencies (FDs)

Think Are there any transitive functional dependencies in this example?

There are no transitive dependencies (TFDs) in this example. It is unlikely that, at this level of study, you will find instances of transitivity. Transitive states come in much larger systems that you will be asked to develop in the working environment. You may just come across TFDs if the model that you are looking to develop contains relationships that are situations where one potential primary key depends on another potential primary key.

Once the functional dependencies have been discovered the 2NF relations can be prepared. The technique is to look to see where the left-hand side of the mappings contains exactly the same attributes (which will become primary keys) and join all the other attributes together.

So, in the hospital example, the 2NF relations are:
Ward (<u>wardno</u>, wardname, wardspecialism)
Patient (<u>patientId</u>, patientname, dob, nok)
Inpatient (<u>wardno, patientId, admissiondate</u>, dischargedate)

It is convention to leave the name of the original relation in 0 or 1NF holding the same primary key attribute(s) as shown above.

As there are no TFDs and there is no interrelation between any of the attributes in the complex primary key of Inpatient, the three relations listed above are in 3NF.

The final stage of normalisation is to draw the diagram that represents the relationships between the relations:

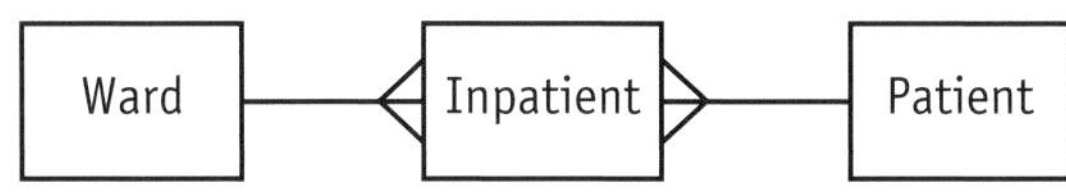

Figure 11.14 Hospital relational diagram

You may question why the relationships have been drawn with crow's feet? The initial table shows us that each ward has many records in the Inpatient table as does each patient. Hence the relationships are 1:M (one to many) and the crow's foot represents many.

Table 11.3 Rental example data (1NF)

CD id	customer code	date of rental	date of return	customer name	customer date of birth	CD title	CD rating	rental cost per day
1	99	01-Oct	03-Oct	freddie	04/04/1993	doom	12	£3.00
2	98	01-Oct	03-Oct	billy	05/01/1989	doom 2	18	£4.00
3	97	02-Oct	05-Oct	mohammed	06/02/1993	less doom	pg	£2.00
4	96	02-Oct	05-Oct	jamila	07/01/1985	happiness	U	£1.00
5	99	03-Oct	07-Oct	freddie	04/04/1993	scare 1	12	£3.00
6	98	03-Oct	08-Oct	billy	05/01/1989	scare 2	18	£4.00
1	97	04-Oct	07-Oct	mohammed	06/02/1993	doom	12	£3.00
2	96	04-Oct	06-Oct	jamila	07/01/1985	doom 2	18	£4.00
3	99	05-Oct	10-Oct	freddie	04/04/1993	less doom	pg	£2.00
4	98	05-Oct		billy	05/01/1989	happiness	U	£1.00

Example

Repeat the normalisation process for the following relation in 1NF:

Rental activity (CDid, customercode, startdateofrental, returndate, customername, customerdateofbirth, rentalcostperday, CDrating, costperday)

An aspect that has not been introduced through normalisation as yet is that of constraints that might be applied to the data and to the processing. This is done in LDM and assists the developer in moving forward with the system development.

Think Just for interest look at the data in the table for the rental activity exercise and see if you can spot any potential constraints that could be applied.

EVIDENCE ACTIVITY

P1 – P2 – P4 – M1

You have seen the post of junior database analyst with a small software consultancy, Manford doIT4U, that you think you are suitable for. As part of the application process you have been asked to prepare two presentations.

Presentation 1 will be delivered in the morning session, after which a shortlist will be drawn up for applicants to attend the second stage of the interview process during which presentation 2 will be delivered.

Obviously you need to prepare both presentations in preparation for the whole interview process. You should develop PowerPoint slides with notes pages for the panel to collect during the day.

Presentation 1

You should demonstrate your knowledge and understanding of different database types. The interviewing panel wants to know the difference between a flat file database, a relational database and a network database. In order to support your knowledge give an example of each, state situations where each type might be suitable for use. You should also give an overview of the pros and cons of each type of database listed above. **(P1)**

Presentation 2

You should show your knowledge and understanding of analysis and design methodologies. The interview panel wants to know the pros and cons of each of logical data modelling (LDM) and the normalisation approach **(P2)**. You should support your knowledge with an example of how each might be used. You should also give details of the different concepts, constraints, stages and outcomes of LDM **(P4)** and explain why LDM produces an effective model in any situation **(M1)**.

11.2 Understand the tools and documentation required in a logical data modelling methodology

LOGICAL DATA MODELLING

One particular approach has been taken in this text to represent aspects of the modelling process. Details of it will be given throughout the coming section.

Definitions

Entity
A distinguishable concept to be held in the database. It has properties or attributes that belong to it. For example, person.
The entity name ought to be a noun and should be singular not plural to show that each tuple or row in the entity is only ever about one instance.

Attribute
A property of an entity. It is something that describes something about the entity. For example, person-name.
It should be a noun, it should also be singular

Primary key
A unique identifier for an entity. It may be an existing attribute or set of attributes or may be generated automatically. For example, person-number.
It should be a noun and, wherever possible, should be generated from the existing attributes rather than making up a new one.

Tuple
One row of data in an entity.

E-R diagram
A picture of the set of entities in the database model with indication of how sets of data relate to each other. For example, see Figure 11.16. (p.59)

Relationship
A line in the diagram that links two entities together, showing that two data sets rely on each other.

Relationship name
A name given to the relationship, written on the diagram next to the line.
For example, belongs-to
Relationship names should be verbs.

Degree
The number of times one entity might be related to another, only two choices, one or many.

Participation condition
Whether a relationship is required on not between two entities, only two choices, optional or mandatory (may or must take place).

Constraint
An aspect of the proposed database that cannot be directly recorded in the model but is necessary to ensure the validity of the data held in the system.
For example, an attribute can only hold values in a particular set of data – e.g. days of the week.
For example, one date must be later than another date, e.g. current date must be later that date of birth.
For example, an attribute has to come from a range of values, e.g. S0001 to S9999.

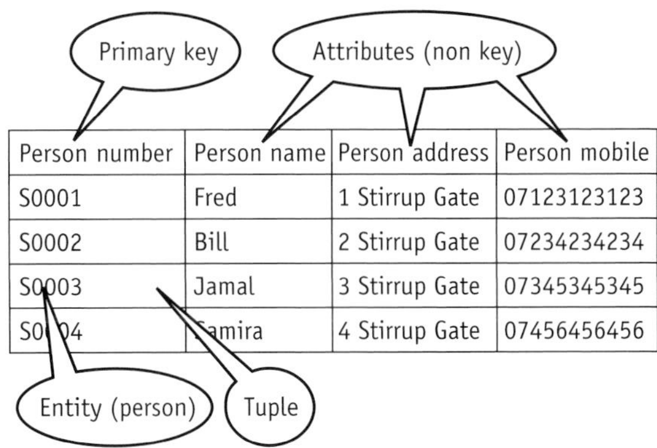

Person number	Person name	Person address	Person mobile
S0001	Fred	1 Stirrup Gate	07123123123
S0002	Bill	2 Stirrup Gate	07234234234
S0003	Jamal	3 Stirrup Gate	07345345345
S0004	Samira	4 Stirrup Gate	07456456456

Figure 11.15 Naming conventions

Diagrammatic representations

Entity Entity name

Rounded corner rectangle with the name of the entity inside

Primary key Person

Underlining the attribute name(s) in the entity definition

Relationship and degree

one to one

one to many

many to many

Participation condition

optional

mandatory

In different stages of the modelling process different terminology is applied to, essentially, the same concept. It is worthwhile noting the differences even though the terms are often interchanged.

The best way to demonstrate how to undertake the modelling process works is by example. Examine the case study for the car sales organisation and pick out all the nouns, decide which are 'things' or entities and which are properties or attributes of the entities.

Research tip

Investigate different diagrammatic representations of E-R diagrams.

Research tip

Investigate different software available for drawing E-R models, e.g. Visio.

Table 11.4 Different naming conventions

Term	Conceptual model	Relational model	Implementation
Structure	Entity	Relation	Table
Occurrence of data	Tuple	Row	Record
Data item	Attribute	Column	Field
Key	Primary key	Primary key	Primary key
Link	Relationship	Foreign key	Foreign key & relationship
Data structure	Not applicable	Domain	Data type

CASE STUDY: CAR SALES

Tesbury's car showrooms has a number of types of showroom, each type is identified by a unique code and a description. The description can take the values 'large forecourt', 'small forecourt' and 'no forecourt'. Each showroom is to be stored with its town location (this can be assumed to be unique), full address and telephone number. Each showroom is of a particular type but one showroom type can apply to many showrooms. Tesbury's also holds details of all the cars in its possession nationally. The details held for a car include the unique registration number, manufacturer, model, date of registration and current price. At any one time a car is only ever held in one showroom that has a forecourt.

Note that in this answer no formation of the relationships takes place except through the diagram. The 'implementation' of the relationships takes place after the structure of the data sets has been completed.

QUESTIONS

1. Decide what the links between each entity would be (relationships).
2. What constraints might exist on the system?

Entity definitions

Based on the ideas for the attributes and the clear identification of potential primary keys in the case study, these two definitions can be presented:

Showroom type (<u>showroom_type_code</u>, showroom_type_description)
Showroom (<u>showroom_location</u>, showroom_address, showroom_telephone_number)
Car (<u>car_registration_number</u>, car_manufacturer, car_model, car_date_of_registration, car_current_price).

The primary key attributes have been underlined to distinguish them from other non-key attributes in the entity definition.

Relationship descriptions

Is_of_a – a showroom is of a given showroom type, one showroom type can apply to many showrooms.
Is_held_at – one car must be held at a given showroom, one showroom may hold many cars (bearing in mind that not all showrooms have a forecourt, not all showrooms can hold cars).

Constraints

Registration date must be earlier than or equal to current date.
Showroom type description can be one of 'large forecourt', 'small forecourt' and 'no forecourt'.
Cars can only be held at showrooms with a forecourt.

E-R diagram

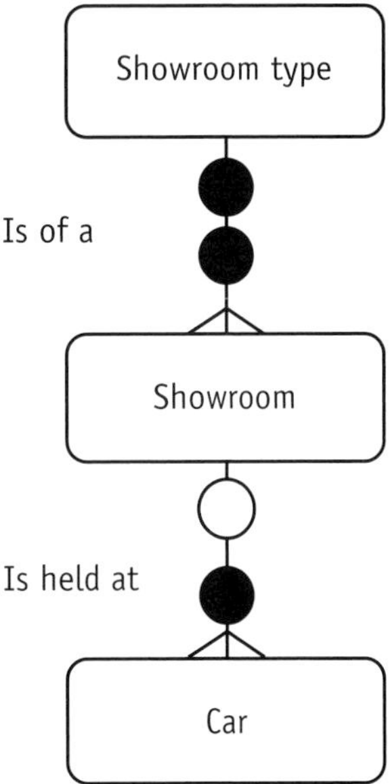

Figure 11.16 Car showroom entity relationship diagram

Now repeat the process for a different example. This example is very similar to the one carried out in the section on normalisation and should arrive at the same answer.

Examine the case study for the hospital and pick out all the nouns, decide which are 'things' or entities and which are properties or attributes of the entities. Decide what the links between each entity would be (relationships) and any constraints that might exist on the system.

CASE STUDY: HOSPITAL

The local community hospital has several wards, each ward is identified by a unique code, the other data to be held includes the ward name and speciality of the ward. Each ward may hold many patients at a time. Patients are admitted to the specialist ward from a start date (when they go in to hospital) to an end date (when they are discharged). Patients are identified by their unique hospital number. Any patient could go into several different wards over a period of time but never two wards at the same time.

Other data held about patients includes their name, address, next of kin and date of birth. A database is required to record the details of the wards, the patients and their stays in hospital.

QUESTIONS

1. Decide what the links between each entity would be (relationships).

2. What constraints might exist on the system?

Note again that, in this answer, no formation of the relationships takes place except through the diagram. It may be apparent that the links are there as the same key fields appear in more than one entity definition; however, the real 'implementation' of the relationships takes place after the structure of the data sets has been completed.

Entity definitions

Based on the ideas for the attributes and the clear identification of potential primary keys in the case study, these two definitions can be presented:

Ward (<u>ward-code</u>, ward-name, ward-speciality)
Patient (<u>patient-hospital-number</u>, patient-name, patient-address, patient-next-of-kin, patient-date-of-birth).

The primary key of stay has been made to include which ward has which patient starting a stay on which date. The key allows the same patient to enter the same ward on different start dates, or the same patient to enter different wards, or different patients to enter the same ward on the same date. It is unique for all situations.

Stay (<u>ward-code, patient-hospital-number, stay-start-date</u>, stay-end-date)

Relationship descriptions

Holds – a ward may hold many patients during their stay, a patient must be held in a ward.
Is-admitted – a patient must be admitted for their stay in a ward, a patient could have many different stays in hospital, any stay must involve a patient.

Constraints

Stay-end-date must be equal to or greater than stay-start-date.
No stays for any patient can overlap so stay-end-date of one stay must precede next stay-start-date for any one patient.

E-R diagram

No detail is known about whether the ward can be with or without patients at any one time so it is made optional. However, any stay in hospital must be about a patient in a ward on a given start date so both sides of stay are mandatory. This fact is also shown in that both ward-code and patient-hospital-number are part of the primary key and therefore must be there!

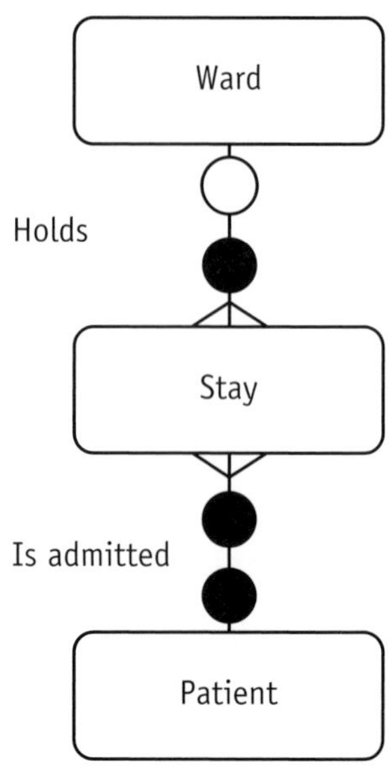

Figure 11.17 Hospital entity relationship diagram

Relation headings

This includes posting the foreign keys or at least highlighting where they are using italics.

Ward (<u>ward-code</u>, ward-name, ward-speciality)
Patient (<u>patient-hospital-number</u>, patient-name, patient-address, patient-next-of-kin, patient-date-of-birth)
Stay (<u>*ward-code, patient-hospital-number*, stay-start-date</u>, stay-end-date)

The normalisation answer was:

Ward (<u>wardno</u>, wardname, wardspecialism)
Patient (<u>patientId</u>, patientname, dob, nok)
Inpatient (<u>wardno, patientId, admissiondate</u>, dischargedate)

So, apart from different attribute names, the two answers are the same. This shows that the three relations produced through the LDM are in 3NF. This shows that LDM is an effective modelling technique as it should always produce a well-normalised model for a database.

OTHER CONSTRAINTS

So far we have looked generally at constraints on the system but there are many forms of constraint that are applied to relational database models.

Definitions

Domain integrity
Only allowing certain data types to be used, keeping values allowed to be entered to a set or range of values.

Entity integrity
Making sure that only one row can be entered with the same values in the primary key (usually handled by the software but may need extra validation in some older software versions).

Referential integrity
Making sure the relationships all work properly, checking that mandatory and optional values are catered for (again most of this is done by the software but some instances will need extra 'support').

User requirements
Usually done through queries and if these do not work then the user will not get the expected results from the system. However, there are circumstances where the user requirements are met through the use of constraints such as restricted values in certain fields, only performing an action on the data if a particular circumstance exists and so on.

Operational
Some software platforms do not have the same functionality as others and 'code' may require developing to overcome these issues.

Some organisations may have particular constraints such as not allowing staff access to parts of the data.

Think Go back to the case studies for the hospital and the car showroom and consider what other constraints might apply on the system.

TECHNICAL DOCUMENTATION

Why use a conventional naming convention?

There are various reasons but the most important are:

- Mnemonic value – so that the developer can remember the name.
- Suggestive value – so that others can read the 'code'.
- 'Consistency' – this is often viewed as an aesthetic idea, yet it also has to do with the information efficiency of the program text. Roughly speaking, it is important to have similar names for similar quantities or variables.

The system that became widely used inside Microsoft came to be known as '**Hungarian notation**' because the prefixes make the variable names look a bit as though they're written in some non-English language and because its 'founder' is originally from Hungary.

As it turns out, the Hungarian naming convention is quite useful – it's one technique among many that helps developers produce better 'code' faster. Since most of the headers and documentation Microsoft has published over the last 15 years have used Hungarian notation names for identifiers, many system developers outside of Microsoft have adopted one variation or another of this scheme for naming their identifiers.

Research tip

Investigate Microsoft naming conventions at http://support.microsoft.com/kb/q110264/
Most of this relates to programming but when developing systems, for example in Access, it is useful to follow these conventions.

When working for an **organisation** it is far more likely that you will be asked to use a naming convention that fits the company naming policies. This could be a range of approaches. The most common involves a mix of Microsoft Hungarian and a standard convention such as prefixing attribute names with the name of the table concerned. An example of this is, using the Tesbury's case study:

Tbl_Showroom_type (<u>showroom_type_code</u>, showroom_type_description)
Tbl_Showroom (<u>showroom_location</u>, showroom_address, showroom_telephone_number)
Tbl_Car (<u>car_registration_number</u>, car_manufacturer, car_model, car_date_of_registration, car_current_price).

Note the use of the underscore to separate parts of the names used - this is because most systems do not recognize the hyphen as a separator.

In database systems there will be many constraints implemented – the convention here is to use a prefix for the constraint name that describes the constraint, e.g. for a primary key constraint use pk_, for a foreign key constraint use fk_.

If, when designing the database, the general constraints have been numbered such as:

C1. Registration date must be earlier than or equal to current date.
C2. Showroom type description can be one of 'large forecourt', 'small forecourt' and 'no forecourt'.
C3. Cars can only be held at showrooms with a forecourt.

then the prefix would be C1_ etc.

C1 would be set up as table constraint when entering data. C2 would be set up as a domain constraint (or a validation rule using Access). C3 would be set up as a table constraint.

Polish or reverse **Polish notation** (RPN) refers to the way in which mathematical expressions are laid out in order to get the computer to perform the calculation in the correct order, thus producing the correct result.

When developing queries, etc. in the database system that involve any arithmetic expressions, it is important to lay them out using RPN to ensure that correct information is gathered and produced.

Research tip

Investigate Polish and RPN at www.computeruser.com/resources/dictionary/definition.html?lookup=5276 or www-stone.ch.cam.ac.uk/documentation/rrf/rpn.html just to make sure that you are conversant with the techniques.
(if these web sites are no longer available use a search engine to find other sites).

If you follow the BODMAS style you were taught in primary school you will do just as well. Forgotten BODMAS?

B **B**rackets first
O **O**rders (i.e. Powers and Square Roots, etc.)
DM **D**ivision and **M**ultiplication (left-to-right)
AS **A**ddition and **S**ubtraction (left-to-right)

A data dictionary is a vital part of the documentation; it is used to pass the final design to the developer showing full details of how tables should be created and what restrictions there are on the data. It can also be used as a basis for the start of the test plan (more of which in Section 11.4. Types of testing (page 68). It should be set up in tabular format with column headings as follows:

Column name	Table name	Domain	Sample values	Validation required	Allowed null	Primary key field	Foreign key field

Column name	Listing all the attributes in the system
Table name	Listing the table in which the attribute 'resides'
Domain (or data type)	Showing the data type that the attribute must take when implemented, e.g. TEXT(5), DATE
Sample values	This is where the beginning of test data can be specified, e.g. 'Billy', 29/12/2007 It can also be used to describe the ranges or sets of values, e.g. 'small forecourt', large forecourt', 'no forecourt' or C001...C999
Validation required	Describes any checks that need be made on the data, e.g. meeting ranges or sets of values, above or below a certain value
Allowed null or not	Answer Y or N – helps when setting up the tables
Primary key field	Answer Y or N
Foreign key field	Answer Y or N and include the name of the table column to which it maps

This is a basic set for a data dictionary. You may care to add additional columns to provide further information if you so wish. It is conventionally sorted in column name within table name order to ease finding the detail in the table. It is the final part of the design documentation.

You have already looked at the **LDM tools** used in the previous section examples. Just as a reminder they are listed here for revision. Your documentation should contain the following:

1. The specification of the user requirements
2. The E-R diagram (the picture of the named database concepts and relationships, including degree and participation conditions)
3. The entity types (entity name, primary key fields underlined, attribute list, foreign key fields in italics)
4. The relationship descriptions (sentences showing what the relationship means including one, many, may, must type words to show degree and participation conditions)
5. The constraint list (all the general constraints on the system).

Then there is the data dictionary as described above which not only summarises the LDM tools but also provides a platform to move forward to implementation.

The test plan (11.4.) should be set up when the design is completed so that the developer of the system knows exactly what areas to test and in which order.

PURPOSE OF DOCUMENTATION

What is the purpose of the documentation? Without it anyone else who has to work the system you have set up will find it very difficult and may have to start all over again. It is much easier to maintain a system that has accurate and compete documentation. If the user requests alterations to the system then it will be easy to see how these can be accommodated. Of course, the documentation will need to be updated if any changes are made but none of the original documents should be discarded.

11.3 Be able to create a logical data model

USER REQUIREMENTS

In the previous sections you have already looked at a minimal set of **user requirements**. This is where the analyst outlines what the organisation does, what **data is stored** and processed and what **information is sought** from the system. This information is both operational and strategic. This means that it helps with the day-to-day running of the organisation and also allows management to see an overall picture and make long-term decisions. The user requirements should also detail what types of **data validation rules** are needed on the data stored. The data validation rules are laid down in the general constraints when the modelling is done. The data to be stored is organised into the entities. The main area that has not yet been truly addressed is that of information to be sought from the system.

The easiest way to explain this is to look at examples. In the Tesbury's example possible queries might be:

- Which showrooms currently have Ford Escorts valued over £2000? – This would be operational information.
- How many showrooms does the company have with no forecourts? – This would be strategic information as the boss may decide to close these as making money could be difficult if cars are not on regular display.

In the hospital example possible queries might be:

- How many patients are currently in the cardiac wards? – This would be operational information as it could help decide if there is space for a new admittance.
- Which wards have admitted the fewest patients over the past year? – This would be strategic information that hospital managers might use to close low functioning wards.

It is important to ascertain from the end user what they want to do with the data that is stored, otherwise the queries and reports cannot be developed accurately.

DOCUMENTATION

The **LDM documentation** remains the same as highlighted in Section 11.2 but it is advisable to add a section on 'information to be sought' just to be able to use with the end user when clarifying the results of the analysis process. This section would list, in words, the queries and reports that are required to make the system be effective for the end user.

Once all the design has been thoroughly completed then the implementation can take place. The **implementation documentation** must include documentation showing how the tables, relationships and constraints have been set up. If using Access then the most obvious evidence for this would be printouts of all the create table statements (probably design view for the tables), the relationship diagram and all the data validation and other rules set on the data (some of this may come from macros behind the data entry screens).

When the data dictionary has been developed it is possible to work out how much **data storage** is needed for each record. Then the possible overall requirements can be calculated for the system as a whole. Although this is not such an important feature, bearing in mind the storage power of today's computers, it is certainly worth being able to tell people how much space is expected to be taken up.

The **data validation required** in the system has already been documented in the data dictionary and in the constraints list. It is unlikely that any further validation will be highlighted provided that the other processes have been carried out thoroughly.

It is important that you practise the whole process so another case study has been provided here. This time you will be expected to set the system up to make sure that all the design that you have undertaken is correct.

CASE STUDY: MANFORD4MASSAGE

Manford4massage is a small holistic therapy group who offer a range of treatments to clients. There is a problem maintaining the booking records for the treatments and sometimes people have turned up for their treatment only to find a double booking or no staff available. Staff only come in when they have got confirmed bookings, so it is important to keep their contact details in case bookings are made for them in their absence. Mark, the owner, also has a need for extra information to help run the business effectively and profitably.

Staff

Name	contact number	gender
Mark	07123123123	M
Sara	07234234234	F
Yomu	07345345345	M
Wanda	07456456456	F

So far no staff with the same name work in the group but this must be allowed for when setting up the system.

Charges to clients
The treatment charges are as follows:

Code	Treatment description	Cost and time
T1	Full body Swedish massage	£50 – lasts 1 hour
T2	Full body Thai massage	£50 – lasts 1 hour
T3	Indian Head massage	£35 – lasts ¾ hour
T4	Reiki	£50 – lasts 1 hour
T5	Combined massage and Reiki	£80 – lasts 2 hours
T6	Half body massage	£25 – lasts ½ hour
T7	Reflexology	£25 – lasts ½ hour

Additional treatments could be added as and when the staff are trained to deliver them.

Client list
This is only a subset of the full list and, of course, new clients come along all the time due to the popularity of the group's treatments:

Name	Mobile Number	Therapist preferred
Bill	07567567567	don't mind
George	07678678678	male
Edna	07789789789	female
Freda	07890890890	don't mind

Edna prefers to have treatments delivered by females so she is currently restricted to Sara and Wanda, George wants a male therapist and Bill and Freda currently have no preference. All clients are asked to specify their preference when they register with the group.

Booking process
Clients ring the shop to arrange an appointment. Appointments do not take place on Sundays. Appointments are scheduled between 0830 and 1900; the longest appointment slot is two hours.

Appointments are made for a therapist to work with a client on a particular day and a given time. It is important that the therapist is of the correct gender to suit the client. It is also important for the therapists to know what treatment the client wants during the appointment. Obviously no member of staff or client can attend two appointments at the same time.

Mark's current requirements from the system:

R1. To be able to print out a daily sheet for each member of staff showing their appointments for the day.
R2. To be able to print out receipts for each client and to track the daily earnings.
R3. To be able to show the annual earnings and gauge whether the prices should be raised.
R4. To be able to track the weekly workload of each member of staff to see whether it would be appropriate to adjust the working hours.

Remember to provide ALL the documentation for each stage of the process from clarifying the analysis, through the LDM to implementation.

1. The specification of the user requirements
2. The E-R diagram (the picture of the named database concepts and relationships, including degree and participation conditions)
3. The entity types (entity name, primary key fields underlined, attribute list, foreign key fields in italics)
4. The relationship descriptions (sentences showing what the relationship means including one, many, may, must type words to show degree and participation conditions)
5. The constraint list (all the general constraints on the system)
6. The information requirements.

EVIDENCE ACTIVITY

P3 – P5 – M2

You work for Manford doIT4U. You need to produce a model to meet the needs of the local employment agency, MannEA.

MannEA deals with companies who need additional employees on a short-term or long-term basis. All the information they store is kept in filing cabinets and roll-a-decks on staff desks. They are not, at this time, looking to record any timesheets and other payroll aspects, although it is expected that this would be an extension to the system at a later date. The initial database must be capable of expansion. Also eventually the organisation would like to set up an online application process.

The organisation currently owns two desktops and one printer for preparing standard letters to companies and workers. They are aware that they will need to purchase a networked system and relevant software so you need not be concerned with their current facilities and equipment.

The MannEA staff have limited expertise with the use of computerised systems so will need a very easy to operate and manage product that does not require the staff to interface with the underlying database directly.

Process

Applicants walk into the offices to discuss their skills and job requirements. The office staff record details of the applicants' name, address, telephone number, next of kin and date of birth. The date of the interview also needs to be recorded. Once these details are recorded and the applicant accepted onto the MannEA books they become workers. Each worker is given a unique code. Each worker is required to identify and prove all their qualifications, showing the year in which the qualification was achieved.

If an applicant does not become a worker then the organisation may later wish to retain their details in order to avoid re-interviewing previously unsuccessful applicants unless the applicants can prove they have additional qualifications. Currently this is not a requirement but the system must be capable of expansion to include this.

In order to match workers to companies MannEA needs to record skills requirements and qualifications obtained by workers. Currently they have no way of doing this and much time is taken up searching through paper records. It would be useful to allocate each qualification a code, a description and title. This would then save time in typing in each qualification for every applicant, especially where some workers have more than one qualification. It would also be useful to record the currency of the qualification possessed by each worker.

The organisation records few details about the companies who employ the workers. Currently all that is retained is the name of the company (assumed to be unique), the name of the main contact in the HR department of the company, the company telephone number and address.

When the company representative contacts MannEA details of the requirements are noted and the records searched to find suitable workers. If a suitable worker cannot be found, no further details are recorded. However, at a later date, it would be useful to record such information so that the organisation can look for workers with appropriate skills and qualifications. Therefore the database created must be capable of including this information through expansion of the system.

What is required to be stored is the assignment of workers to companies – what date they started, when the expected end date of the assignment is and which member of MannEA fixed up the assignment. This will enable the organisation to track the workload of their own staff as well as that of the workers. Weekly reports are also required of the qualifications possessed by the workers to be able to judge the skills required by companies. Weekly reports will also be required concerning the workloads of each worker and each member of staff. Eventually MannEA will use this information to award additional-responsibility-pay based on the number of assignments set up and controlled.

No requirement has been stated as yet to record details of the timesheets submitted by each worker. Therefore the system is not expected to calculate the pay due to workers but the system must be capable of allowing expansion to include this.

As an additional requirement MannEA needs to store a couple of details about their own staff. Each staff member is given a unique staff number. MannEA wishes to know the name of the staff member, whether they are employed on a full- or part-time basis, the date they started work and who their supervisor is. Obviously the founder of the organisation will not have a supervisor but all the others will. Some members of staff may supervise many and others will supervise none. It is presumed that no-one can supervise themselves. Eventually MannEA will use this information to award additional-responsibility-pay based on the number of staff supervised. Currently MannEA just requires the ability to produce a report of the supervisory structure.

1. Review the requirements specification and:
   - Identify and describe the data to be stored
   - Identify and describe the information to be extracted
   - Identify and describe any potential constraints embedded in the system to be incorporated in the processing, stating why these have been included **(P3)**
   - Identify the limitations on the system to be created and what is not being addressed at this stage
   - This will help you understand the overall requirements of the database that you are going to set up. It will assist you in the planning of the model. It will also help you with the documentation that you need to produce throughout the process.
2. Prepare a complete data model **(P5)** for the requirements specification including:
   - An entity relationship diagram including named relationships
   - Entity definitions including primary keys and non-key attributes
   - Relationship descriptions including degrees and participation conditions
3. To include details of all constraints on the system:
   - Explaining their presence **(M2)** and which user requirement is being addressed.
4. Show how all relationships **(P5)** will be implemented by:
   - Including foreign keys in the entity definitions (thus forming relation headings)
   - Developing a data dictionary of the format:

Attribute name	In relation?	Sample data to be used	Validation required on data held	Allowed NULL? Y or N	Key field? PK? FK?

NOTE: Both tasks 2 and 4 must be completed satisfacorily for P5 to be awarded.

11.4 Be able to test a logical data model

TYPES OF TESTING

Testing is one of the most important aspects about the development of a database as with any working application. Testing is done at many stages of the development:

1. The first stage is passing the model back to the end user so that they can review it to make sure all aspects have been understood and interpreted correctly.
2. The second stage is to create a **test strategy** – set the **order and priority** of the tests to be carried out. Conventionally, the entity tests are performed first then domain, then referential, next would come the constraint tests and finally the system functionality (queries). It is important to make sure that the data can be entered accurately before looking at the performance of the system. At the time the tests are being planned it is also necessary to decide what data will be used not only to do the testing but also to populate the tables.
3. The third stage is in the development of a suitable test plan for the model incorporating all the aspects listed below.
4. The final stage is to put the test plan into action, changing the set up of the system if required.

You have already looked at definitions of integrity but it is an important concept so a quick revision is appropriate here:

Domain integrity
Only allowing certain data types to be used, keeping values allowed to be entered to a set or range of values.

The testing for this comes by trying to enter data values in a different domain from that expected; the outcome should be an error. If a range or set of values is placed on the domain then these need testing too.

Entity integrity
Making sure that one only row can be entered with the same values in the primary key.

The testing for this comes by trying to enter a second row with the same data in the primary key attributes. The database software should really check this out for you, but, in order to practise the testing approach, it is important that these tests are carried out.

Relationship integrity
Making sure the relationships all work properly, checking that mandatory and optional values are catered for.

To test this, it is important to check that the foreign keys work appropriately with their matching primary key at the other end of the relationship. Again, the database software should really check this out for you, but, in order to practise the testing approach, it is important that these tests are carried out.

Constraint integrity
Making sure that all the general constraints are correctly set up and work properly.

To test this you should try values that work and ones that do not – these tests are very important and should never be ignored.

TEST STRATEGY

The types of tests that should be performed are based on **normal** data (values that you would expect to work), **extreme** data (values set at the edges of ranges) and **erroneous** (values that you would definitely not expect to work). Examples are shown in the table opposite:

It should be noted here that the priority of the tests is built on the need to

a. Make sure that records can be entered appropriately
b. Make sure that the data formats can be adhered to
c. Make sure that tables link together properly
d. Make sure that operational and general constraints work and restrict data values entered
e. Prove functionality of the system developed.

The ordering of the tests will develop from the priority. When entering data into a database you

Table 11.5 Typical test log requirements

Test type	Entity Done first	Domain Done second	Referential Done third	Constraint Done fourth
Normal Will work	If one primary key value is PPPPP then enter QQQQQ	If the domain is set as text(5) enter any data of text type up to 5 characters	If the primary key is PPPPP then enter a foreign key value of PPPPP	If the value must contain one of the days of the week then enter one of those days
Extreme Might work, might not	If one primary key value is PPPPP then enter PPPPQ	If the domain is set as text(5) enter any data of text type at exactly 5 characters, then try it with 6 characters	If the primary key is PPPPP then enter a foreign key value of PPPPQ	If the range of values is set at 00...99 then try 00, 99, 100
Erroneous Should not work	If one primary key value is PPPPP then enter PPPPP	If the domain is set as text(5) enter any data of text type at exactly 15 characters	If the primary key is PPPPP then enter a foreign key value of QQQQQ	If the value must contain one of the days of the week then enter anything but one of those days

will find that you need to start with the entities at the one end of the relationships and work into the middle of the system where the many ends of the relationships are.

The final set of testing that should be carried out is that of functionality – can the required information be extracted successfully? To do this requires **populating the tables** with sufficient data from which information could be created. The population must always include data that would not answer the queries as well as that that would. It is inappropriate just to prove that tests work but opportunity for failure should be present. If this is not done then the testing is not robust and the system may end up with errors.

TECHNICAL DOCUMENTATION

One of the most popular ways to provide the **technical documentation** of the testing process is in a tabular format. This table is split into two sections:

I. **Test plan** to be carried out
The plan needs to address the following aspects:
1. The order of the test (numbered) to show priority
2. The test to be carried out
3. The test data to be used
4. Justification of the test reason and data chosen
5. The expected result.

II. **Outcomes** of the testing
The test plan should be followed in the order specified and all the results noted in the outcomes section. This should address the following aspects:
1. The actual result that was achieved
2. Whether the test was successful or not
3. What changes were made to the application
4. A re-run of the test if changes were made.

Any test that fails should be retested until the correct result is achieved. If any major changes are made to the application then it might be necessary to redo all the tests.

PURPOSE OF TEST DOCUMENTATION

A well prepared and monitored plan makes it easy to **repeat** the tests. It makes it simple for someone else to revisit the application and make changes, repeating the same tests. It also gives everyone who interacts with the system the opportunity to see what tests have been carried out. A well-prepared test plan is the first step in ensuring the **rigour** and **reliability** of the testing process as it should mean that every test is known in advance and the process is not haphazard.

A plan should show:

Test number (priority) **(P6)**	Test to be carried out	Reason for test (justification) **(M3)**	Test data to be used	Expected result

- The order of the test (numbered) to show priority
- The test to be carried out
- The test data to be used
- Justification of the test reason and data chosen
- The expected result
- The actual result that was achieved
- Whether the test was successful or not
- What changes were made to the application
- A re-run of the test if changes were made.

EVIDENCE ACTIVITY

P6 – P7 – M3 – M4 – D1 – D2

You must prepare an overall test strategy and complete test plan on the model you have created for MannEA. You must include:

- A brief discussion on why ordering and priority of testing is important
- A list of all functional requirements of the system and the queries that will be used to achieve these
- A test plan **(P6)** of the structure, giving full details in each column:
- The reason behind each test **(M3)**.

The following two assignments complete the assessment process for the unit.

- Assignment 3 allows you to put the design and test plan into practice to prove full functionality and gauge whether the model actually meets the user requirements.
- Assignment 4 allows you to evaluate the process rather than the product and discuss how well all the theory has helped with the development.

The model is complete and has been agreed by your line manager. In order to prove the efficacy of your design you need to create a prototype of the final system and review this against the initial user requirements.

1. Implement the model **(P7)** using Access, providing evidence of table creation and population.
2. Follow the test plan prepared as part of the design, providing evidence of tests carried out, results achieved and any changes needed to the design of the system.
3. Review the outcomes in light of the test results evaluating the model that you produced and suggesting areas in which the model could be changed to meet, more effectively, the user requirements. You should also discuss how effective the modelling process was in developing the model **(D2)**.

Your efforts on the model for MannEA have impressed your line manager to the extent that you may be given a change in job role. This new role requires supervising the latest junior to join the team.

Your line manager wants you to write a report outlining various Manford doIT4U policies so that he can be assured that you understand the reasons behind the policies and would be able to supervise someone else appropriately.

The report must cover the following policies:

- Technical documentation
- The modified Hungarian naming convention
- Testing
- Using the data modelling process

The report must justify **(M4)** the need for full technical documentation at all stages, including testing, of the modelling process and the use of the Hungarian convention. It should also evaluate **(D1)** how an efficient data model can be developed to meet the needs of a user.

unit 14

The world is full of automatic control systems, which help to run our lives with minimum human input. From your DVD recorder to your washing machine, most domestic devices are in some way controlled automatically.

This unit will explain the different types of control systems, and give an insight into how they work. The unit also looks at the different devices used to sense the current state of the environment to provide feedback for a control system and how this feedback is used to make decisions.

By the end of this unit you will:

So you want to be a...

Control Unit Circuit Board Designer

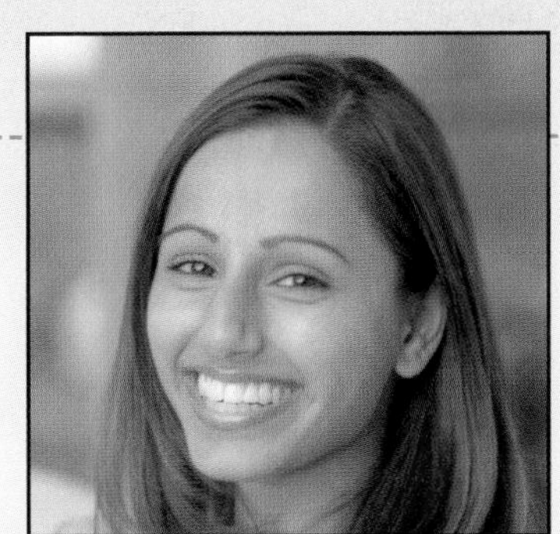

My name Ali Mellor
Age 22
Income $36,000 (Approx £24,000)

What do you do?

I work for a small electronics company who design and build circuit boards for electronic devices. I'm a member of a small team of designers who design the circuits which control the devices. We receive requirements for the device, which include what is to be controlled, and then we design an electronic circuit board to do the job. We build a prototype, or a series of prototypes, based on our device to test it out. Once we're satisfied with the design, we pass it to our production department and they put the circuit board into mass production.

How did you get the job?

I applied for it straight from university. My parents had moved to Phoenix in my second year of university because of my father's job. When I completed my degree, I decided that I'd like to go out and join my parents. They found the company, and I applied. The interview was thorough. I was set a couple of practical design tasks, as well as undertaking a personality assessment test. There was an awful lot of paperwork to complete before I was allowed to work in America, but I'm here now and I really love the lifestyle.

> "I've got so many career choices open to me."

What training did you get?

I guess I received most of my training at university. I studied under some of the biggest names in Robotics and got an honours degree in Robotics and Systems Engineering. The team I work with now are very talented and I've learnt a lot from them. The company sends us on regular seminars to keep our knowledge up to date.

What are the hours like?

Normally I start at 8:30 and work till about 6 in the evening. Sometimes, if we're under pressure, I've had to work as late as midnight. However, we can take days off to get the time back.

How good is the pay?

The pay is very reasonable for someone as young and inexperienced as me! I'm the junior member of the team and, therefore, probably paid the least. I get generous pay rises every year.

What about the future?

I've got many choices of career path. Initially, I'd like to run my own design team, but I may decide to go down the management path. At the moment, however, I'm extremely happy doing what I do.

Grading criteria

The table below shows what you need to do to gain a pass, merit or distinction in this part of the qualification. Make sure you refer back to it when you are completing work so that you can judge whether you are meeting the criteria and what you need to do to fill in gaps in your knowledge or experience.

In this unit there are four evidence activities that give you an opportunity to demonstrate your achievement of the grading criteria:

page 81	P1
page 85	P3, M1
page 93	P2, P5, M2
page 101	P4, P6, M3, D1, D2

To achieve a pass grade the evidence must show that the learner is able to...	To achieve a merit grade the evidence must show that, in addition to the pass criteria, the learner is able to...	To achieve a distinction grade the evidence must show that, in addition to the pass and merit criteria, the learner is able to...
P1 describe how data can be represented in control systems	**M1** compare analogue and digital signals and explain the need for signal conversion	**D1** design a control system for a given user need that uses different types of sensors
P2 describe using examples types of control systems	**M2** explain the principles and uses of proportional control	**D2** critically evaluate the design and performance of a control system.
P3 describe the characteristics of digital and analogue control systems	**M3** propose and explain potential improvements to a control system.	
P4 demonstrate the operation of different sensors and output devices		
P5 explain the stages of control loop operations		
P6 assemble, implement and review a control system for a given purpose.		

14.1 Know how data is represented in control systems

WHAT IS A CONTROL SYSTEM?

Figure 14.1 Traffic lights

Control systems have been around a long time. Over 30 years ago if you were driving home on a route with many traffic lights you would find that as long as you were travelling at a sensible speed the traffic lights would turn green as you approached them. It wasn't magic or luck but simply an early control system. It would sense your vehicle some distance from the lights and as long as no vehicles were sensed on any of the other roads the lights would be instructed to change.

Control systems have moved on since then and now you can even land an aircraft using control systems. Control systems have become much more complex as technology has developed but they still work in fundamentally the same way and the only real difference between landing an aircraft and operating traffic lights is the number of variables which have to be taken into account.

What, then, is a control system? A control system is everything that is needed to undertake a task or a series of tasks.

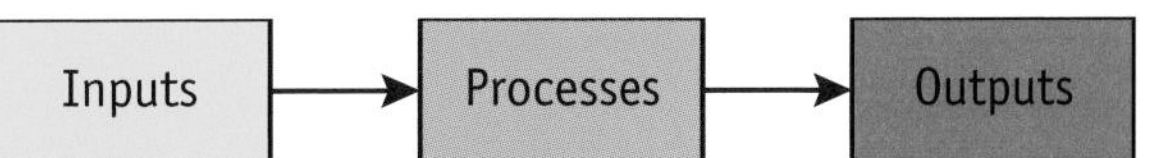

Figure 14.2 A control system

In computer terms a system is considered in terms of

- inputs – what is entered into the system
- processes – the things that happen to the inputs within the system and
- outputs – what the system produces.

Imagine a sausage-making machine. The task the system has to undertake is to make sausages. The inputs are the sausage meat and a long thin skin. The processes are to force the sausage meat into the skin, twist the skin at various lengths to define the end of one sausage and the beginning of the next. The outputs are the completed sausages.

The problem with some systems is that they involve human intervention. Take the sausage making machine for instance. Someone has to get the sausage meat from the storeroom and put it in the machine, someone has to load the skin, someone has to turn on the machine and someone has to cut off the sausages and take them on to the next phase of the operation. Normally human intervention is of a controlling nature in that a human will set the speed, make sure the inputs are input and the outputs are disposed of correctly. In a control system a computer is used to make these decisions and perform these tasks. It could be said therefore that a control system controls the operation of another system, generally to avoid the presence of human intervention.

This unit is about automating tasks so that they can be completed without the need for a person to be present. In the traffic light example, the sequence could be controlled by someone sitting at the crossroads operating a set of switches. This would be a very boring job and an awfully expensive way of operating traffic lights.

CASE STUDY: EXERCISE TREADMILL

Many familiar control systems occur in everyday life. In a health club or gym a common item of equipment is a treadmill. The treadmill is based on the hamster wheel – it is designed to keep you stationary no matter how much effort you put in to walking or running. Initially a treadmill was simply a rubber belt wrapped around two pulleys. When you took a step forward this would move the belt backwards in reaction which would turn the pulleys thereby keeping you in exactly the same position you were before you took the step. Nowadays the belt is powered by electric motors meaning that rather than you providing the power to move the treadmill the treadmill keeps moving and you have to keep running to avoid falling off.

The whole treadmill is a complex control system with elements of all the types discussed. The secret of the control is all contained in a control panel worthy of a light aircraft.

You are usually allowed to set the speed of the belt and the incline of the platform. You can initially set a speed that you wish walk or run but after starting if you feel you are going too fast or too slow you can use the buttons on the control panel to speed up or slow down. This is a simple command system.

On some of the more expensive models you are more likely to set a speed in kilometres per hour. There will be an electric motor to power the band and probably a sensor on one of the pulleys to test how quickly it is turning, which as long as you know the diameter, is going to tell you the current speed of the belt. The current speed will be compared to the set speed and if it is lower the motor will be speeded up but if it is faster the motor will be slowed down. This is a conditional system as it is comparing with an input value and also a sensing system as the speed of the rotation of the pulleys is sensed.

The treadmill is also potentially a programmable system as many different workouts can be chosen based on a few inputs. On some machines, if you choose a particular cardio workout you will be asked a few parameters such as your weight and age. These are used to work out a target pulse rate for you. You enter the speed you wish to go and the workout will start. You can either place your hands on some sensors or wear a wrist band; both of these devices sense your pulse rate. If your pulse rate is lower than the target pulse rate it will slowly make the workout harder by raising the incline of the bed, the equivalent of making the hill you are running up steeper. Once you have reached the target heart rate the bed will be raised and lowered in an effort to keep your pulse rate at a constant level. This particular workout has elements of all the types of control system discussed.

When you are asked to implement a system, the temptation is to start building your device and system, and design it as you go along. This can lead to inefficiencies. To start the design process it is advisable to look at the system as a series of processes. Each of these processes has inputs and outputs.

Think Read the case study again and list the processes you think may be required for what is described, then for each process try to decide what the inputs and outputs are.

CODING

Digital computer systems (including control systems) work mainly by recognising the difference between two states. These states might be

- the presence or absence of an electric current,
- the presence or absence of a magnetic charge, or even
- the detection or non-detection of light.

The system will assign a value of zero to one of these states and a value of one to the other state. So in the computer's world there are only two symbols: zero and one. Anything that is stored in a computer, including numbers, letters, colours and sounds, is assigned a code that is made up of a series of zeros and ones. The computer recognises these codes and uses them appropriately. How does the computer recognise whether a particular code is a number, letter, colour, sound or even a program instruction? After all, in some cases the number 65 is represented by the same code as the letter 'A' (1000001). The answer is that it doesn't. Computers do exactly what they are told to do, so if they are asked to do a numerical operation on the representation of a colour then that is what they will do.

Binary

Control systems can only tell the difference between two states, 0 and 1, and consequently they work in a number base which only has two symbols. They work in a number system with a base of 2, the **binary system**. Data, in whatever form, are stored in binary. See Unit 9 for more on the binary system.

> **Key words**
>
> **Binary system** – a number system which has only two digits, 0 and 1. It is particularly useful for computers which work by being able to tell the difference between two states.

Hexadecimal

The **hexadecimal** system has a base of 16; it is often called hex for short. See Unit 9 for more on the hexadecimal system.

Binary is difficult and unwieldy for humans to deal with. Large numbers are even larger in binary. Doing quick conversions from binary into decimal is not possible. The fact that the base value of hex (16) is a power of the base value of binary (2), i.e. $16 = 2^4$, makes conversion between the two systems very easy.

> **Key word**
>
> **Hexadecimal (or hex)** – is a numbering system which has 16 digits. 16 is a power of 2 so it is easy to convert binary numbers to hex and hex numbers to binary. As 16 symbols are needed to represent digits the numbers 10 to 15 are represented by the letters A to F.

So when technicians talk to each other about the actual stored values in a system, they use hex. Suppose a particular location in a computer's memory contains 1001110110011010. To convert from binary to hex, split the number into groups of 4.

1001	1101	1001	1010

Then simply take each 4-digit binary number, convert it to decimal and substitute in the hex symbol.

Binary	1001	1101	1001	1010
Decimal	9	13	9	10
Hex	9	D	9	A

> ***Think*** Convert these numbers from binary to hex.
>
> 1. 1111111111111111
> 2. 1011011110100001
> 3. 0011001001000101
> 4. 0001001000110100
>
> Convert these numbers from hex to binary.
>
> 5. F1A1
> 6. 2222
> 7. 58F9
> 8. ABDE

Binary coded decimal

Pure binary is not the only way of storing numbers; another way is called **binary coded decimal** (BCD). See Unit 9 for more on BCD.

Key words

Binary coded decimal – is a way of representing decimal numbers using 4 bits to hold the binary representation of the digits 0–9.

Groups of four bits are used to represent decimal digits.

BCD	Decimal
0000	0
0001	1
0010	2
0011	3
0100	4
0101	5
0110	6
0111	7
1000	8
1001	9

Hence
319 would be represented by 001100011001
4386 would be represented by 0100001110000110

The circuits needed to manipulate numbers stored in BCD are much more complex than those used for arithmetic operations on pure binary numbers but the advantage is that the system is actually manipulating decimal numbers which makes it easy for it to format the numbers for output.

Think How would these decimal numbers be represented in a computer using BCD?

1. 748
2. 22
3. 41
4. 38,972

What decimal numbers do these BCD patterns represent?

5. 000101011000
6. 0101011110010110
7. 10011001
8. 10010100000101100110

ASCII

In the early days of computers the different manufacturers all tended to use different codes to represent letters. This made it very difficult to move information from one manufacturer's computer to another. The American National Standards Institute created a common code that everybody could use: **ASCII** (pronounced 'askie') or to use its full name, American Standard Code for Information Interchange. ASCII officially uses 7 bits to represent letters but most computers store them as 8 bits largely because of the way it is designed. The eighth bit is often used as a parity bit to check that data has been transferred without error, but this is beyond the scope of this unit. It's easiest to think of ASCII data as being held in groups of 8 bits, the left-most bit being always zero. See Unit 9 for more about ASCII.

Key word

ASCII (American Standard Code for Information Interchange) – a standard way of representing letters by using 7-bit binary codes.

LOGICAL OPERATORS

Common arithmetic operators, like plus, minus, multiply and divide, work for any number base but the binary number system provides some further operators, called logical operators. A meaning can be assigned to the two binary states, such as yes and no, or true and false. Traditionally 0 is assigned to false and 1 to true.

The main logical operators are AND, OR and NOT. They are used a lot in real life. For example you cannot take your driving test unless you have a current provisional license AND you have passed the theory test. You can go through the gates at a concert if you have a valid ticket OR your hand has been stamped with a special stamp. If you are under 18 you can NOT be served alcohol.

Truth tables like this are used to illustrate logical operators.

A	B	Result
1	1	?
1	0	?
0	1	?
0	0	?

Most logical operations require a combination of two conditions which have two states, usually true and false. If there only two conditions (A and B) and each can only be true or false (1 or 0) then there are four possible combinations:

- A is true and B is true,
- A is true and B is false,
- A is false and B is true, and
- A is false and B is false.

This is depicted in the truth table. The result column depends on the operator.

AND

A	B	Result
1	1	1
1	0	0
0	1	0
0	0	0

The table shows the result of the logical operator A AND B. It shows that the result is only true if both A and B are true, otherwise it is false. Using the example of the driving test, if condition A is the possession of a current provisional driving license and condition B is having passed the theory test, the result would be the ability to take a driving test. As the truth table shows, the test can only be taken if both conditions are true. If either or both are false the test cannot be taken.

OR

A	B	Result
1	1	1
1	0	1
0	1	1
0	0	0

The truth table shows that the OR operator produces a true result if either or both of the conditions are true and is only false if both conditions are false. Using the concert example, the result is entering the concert which can be done by showing a valid ticket or having a re-entry stamp. You can, of course, enter if you have both a ticket and a stamp.

NOT

The NOT operator only requires one condition and simply negates this. This leads to an unusual truth table.

A	Result
1	0
0	1

Using our example, if the condition is that you are under 18 then you cannot be served alcohol. On the other hand, if the condition is false (you are 18 or over) then you can be served alcohol.

Other operators

The exclusive or (XOR) operator is like the OR operator only this time the result is false if both conditions are true.

A	B	Result
1	1	0
1	0	1
0	1	1
0	0	0

NAND is a combination of the NOT and the AND operators. It negates the results of a normal AND

A	B	Result
1	1	0
1	0	1
0	1	1
0	0	1

NOR is a combination of NOT and OR.

A	B	Result
1	1	0
1	0	0
0	1	0
0	0	1

XNOR is a combination of NOT and XOR.

A	B	Result
1	1	1
1	0	0
0	1	0
0	0	1

Logical operators are very useful when programming control systems. Using various logic operations it is possible to tell if switches are on or off or motors are going forward or backward.

NUMBERS

The two ways of storing numbers discussed above only store positive whole numbers (integers). What about fractions, decimals and negative numbers? Control systems need to use these for such quantities as weights and temperatures. Ways of storing binary equivalents of these values are needed.

In the decimal number system the units column represents 10^0 and the values to the left represent increasing powers of 10. Logic states therefore that any values to the right (the other side of the decimal point) have decreasing powers of 10. So to the right of the decimal point numbers would be multiplied by the values 10^{-1}, 10^{-2}, 10^{-3} etc. 10^{-1} is equivalent to $1/10^1$, 10^{-2} is equivalent to $1/10^2$ or 1/100 etc. The table summarises this.

10^3	10^2	10^1	10^0	•	10^{-1}	10^{-2}	10^{-3}
1000	100	10	1	•	0.1	0.01	0.001

This also works for binary numbers. The point should probably be called a binary point but it is not often referred to as such. 2^{-1} is equivalent to 1/2 or 0.5, 2^{-2} is equivalent to $1/2^2$ or 1/4 or 0.25. The table shows the values.

2^3	2^2	2^1	2^0	•	2^{-1}	2^{-2}	10^{-3}
8	4	2	1	•	0.5	0.25	0.125

Fixed point

The decimal point doesn't physically have to be stored as long as there is a way of finding out its position.

Recall that the smallest storage value in a computer is a bit. In early machines these were grouped into groups of 8 bits called a byte. This was largely due to restrictions within the computers, architecture and although these restrictions have been lifted the traditional byte has remained and consequently the storage of numbers has always been in multiples of 8 bits.

If all numbers are stored in 16 bits then using the **fixed point** method of storage this area can be defined so that a certain number of bits are to the left of the decimal point and the rest are to the right of the point. Let's assume that there are 8 bits to the left of the point and 8 bits to the right.

Key words

Fixed point – is a way of storing numbers in a computer system where the decimal point is assumed to be in a specific position.

Let's take the number 177.421875 and try to convert it into binary. The table shows all the values needed.

Power	Value
2^7	128
2^6	64
2^5	32
2^4	16
2^3	8
2^2	4
2^1	2
2^0	1
2^{-1}	0.5
2^{-2}	0.25
2^{-3}	0.125
2^{-4}	0.0625
2^{-5}	0.03125
2^{-6}	0.015625
2^{-7}	0.0078125
2^{-8}	0.00390625

177 = 128 + 32 + 16 + 1

0.421875 = 0.25 + 0.125 + 0.03125 + 0.015625

So the number held in binary would be

1 0 1 1 0 0 0 1 0 1 1 0 1 1 0 0

One of the problems of this method is that there is a limit to the size of the number. The biggest number using this method is 255.99609375. This number can be made bigger by changing the place of the decimal point. If there were four digits to the right and the rest to the left of the decimal point then the biggest number is 4095.9375. This is a bit better but the only decimal values that can be represented are the ones in this table.

0.0625
0.125
0.1875
0.25
0.3125
0.375
0.4375
0.5
0.5625
0.625
0.6875
0.75
0.8125
0.875
0.9375

This leads to less accuracy or precision. The position of the decimal point is actually a trade-off between the size of numbers and the numbers' precision.

Floating point

Floating point allows us to store a much larger range of numbers than fixed point but once again there is a trade-off with the precision of the number. Obviously using more bits would increase the precision of the number. See Unit 9 for more on floating point numbers.

Key words

Floating point – is a way of representing real numbers by holding a fixed point number in a mantissa and multiplying it by a power of the base held in an exponent.

EVIDENCE ACTIVITY

P1

You have been employed by EJA Control Systems to produce information and training material for various aspects of controlling systems using IT. You will be required to undertake various tasks in producing the material, and will be expected to work in a variety of formats.

The first material you are to produce is a set of posters that describe how data can be represented in control systems. You must describe coding data, logical operators and integer, fixed point and floating point numbers.

14.2 Understand the requirements of control systems

TYPES

There are many different types of control systems but they all control something. They are becoming more common every day and people tend to use them without thinking or recognising what they are. Most control systems are combinations of the various types.

Command systems

Let's start with one of the simplest types. In a command control system the user issues a command which affects some aspect of the system or device they are trying to control. The most obvious example of this is the TV remote. The user points it at the television and by pressing buttons controls the television, e.g. changes channels. All control systems have an element of a command system in them; the device issues a command which is undertaken by the device it is controlling.

> **Research tip**
>
> *Your home is littered with command systems. Choose about five and, using books or the Internet, research how they work.*

Programmable systems

In a programmable system, different parameters are input to make it perform different operations. Programmable systems are fairly common in the domestic environment, for example the automatic washing machine. Different programs are provided depending on the type of material the clothes are made of or whether they are white or coloured. Dials and buttons on the front of the machine are set to request the exact washing program required.

Sensing systems

A sensing system uses an electronic device to sense some aspect of the environment. A central heating system does this by using a device (called a thermistor) to read the current temperature. It will then turn on the boiler or turn it off depending on what the temperature is.

Conditional systems

A conditional system will do different things depending on a parameter. How the parameter is set depends on the system itself. For example this will happen in the previous example where the boiler is turned off or on depending on the temperature.

It is often difficult to decide which category a particular control system should be put in. This is because most systems have elements of all of the types mentioned. As suggested above, the central heating system is a sensing and a conditional system. A lot of central heating systems have different programs depending on the time of year and of course they will have an override switch to turn the boiler on anyway.

DIGITAL

The differences in requirements between a home or office computer and a control system often lead to considerable differences in the type of device required. A home or office computer is a multipurpose system that is likely to undertake a wide variety of tasks. A control system may only need to perform one or a few simple tasks and can be, therefore, much less sophisticated technically in terms of speed, memory and so on.

As a generalisation, one needs to treat this with care, for instance we may regard the controlling systems of a space rocket or fly-by-wire aircraft as control systems – they are, after all, controlling systems using IT. Whilst these are outside the general content of this unit, it should be noted that these systems are much more sophisticated than the average home or office computer, and the generalisation of simpler systems for control breaks down when addressing these more sophisticated systems. It is important to note, however, that the underlying theory is still true (for example, the loop control systems referred to later in this chapter) for those more sophisticated systems, which may often be regarded as large groupings of basic systems.

Speed

A program is a series of statements which tells a control system what to do. Before the processor can execute the program instructions it has to translate them into the language of the processor, which is a much lower level language called machine code. Each instruction can be translated (compiled or assembled) into up to 30 machine code instructions. The programs are stored in the system's memory and each instruction is fetched from memory and executed when it is needed, using a process called the fetch/execute cycle.

The fetch/execute cycle works on the system clock and effectively each machine code instruction takes two pulses of the clock. The statement that a processor works at 1.6 gigahertz is saying how quickly the clock works and therefore how quickly the processor works. 1.6 gigahertz means the clock pulses 1,600,000,000 times per second which means it can perform 800,000,000 machine code instructions per second. Obviously the faster the clock, the quicker the processor. When choosing a processor for a control system, however, other things need to be taken into account. Large powerful processors generate a lot of heat which is dispersed by fans which take up space and make a noise. The controller may need to be small and quiet. As a control system has only one function and speed isn't always of the essence, the latest, fastest, most sophisticated processor is not usually necessary.

Memory

The memory of a control system has to contain the program and data it requires to run the program plus software to run the various input and output devices. The system must therefore have enough memory for this purpose. Memory is usually specified in bytes. As stated above 1 byte = 8 bits. 1 gigabyte of memory, therefore, is 1,000,000,000 groups of 8 bits.

The memory requirements of controllers depend on their size and the sophistication of the job they will do.

Input/output ports

Control systems collect and distribute instructions and information to a number of different devices. Each of these devices has to be connected to the processor so that information can be swapped. There are many different connection types and the system must have enough places to connect all the devices required, to it. These connection areas are called ports.

A selection of output devices is described later in this section. The number of devices that are used to collect data defines the required number of input ports, and the number of devices to which information is output gives the number of output ports needed. It is always useful to include a small number of additional ports for things like expansion and breakdown.

ANALOGUE

Analogue to digital (ADC)

Unfortunately analogue signals are normally in a continuous form but, as mentioned above, the processors of control systems work digitally using binary zeros and ones. Some form of conversion is needed.

Analogue devices use one property of a material or event to measure a different property of the material or event. A non-computer example is the simple mercury thermometer, which uses a linear measurement (length of the mercury column) to represent temperature. It is said that one property (in this case length) is analogous (the word means related or proportional) to another property (in this case temperature). This is why these devices are known as analogue devices.

Where this analogous property is an electrical property (voltage, frequency, current, etc.) then it is possible to harness this for continuous monitoring, and ultimately control, of a particular device.

Let's take the example of checking temperature over a period of time. Temperature is measured on a continuous scale. The actual temperature could be any value, such as 28.5°C, 28.526°C or even

28.4773927648826648459°C, depending on how accurately it is measured. Time is also a continuous variable.

A control system requires finite values. It cannot cope with infinitesimal changes and has to be given a value it can cope with. Effectively this is the job of an **analogue to digital converter** (ADC) and it uses pulse-code modulation (PCM) to do this.

PCM is a procedure that samples an analogue signal, normally at a rate of 8,000 samples per second, and converts those sample values to a series of digital values. The complexities of PCM do not form a part of this unit, but learners should be aware of the term and the existence of the process.

The output of a temperature sensor over a period of time will look something like Figure 14.3. This continuous output cannot be fed directly into a processor but has to be converted into series of numeric values. The signals are sampled at regular periods and the value read and transferred to the control system.

Suppose the temperature was sampled every hour (red values), the values taken at that point and transferred into the system. The system will recreate the actual values based on a uniform progression between the points measured (red line). Obviously, the shorter the time between the samples, the nearer to the real signal the produced signal will be. (The green and blue lines are sampled at 30 minutes and 15 minutes respectively.)

It is normal for an ADC to use serial communications with a processor. Where an ADC receives input from several devices, the signals will pass through a multiplexer prior to entry.

Key words

An **analogue to digital converter** – a device, normally an electronic integrated circuit, that converts a continuous analogue signal to discrete digital numbers.

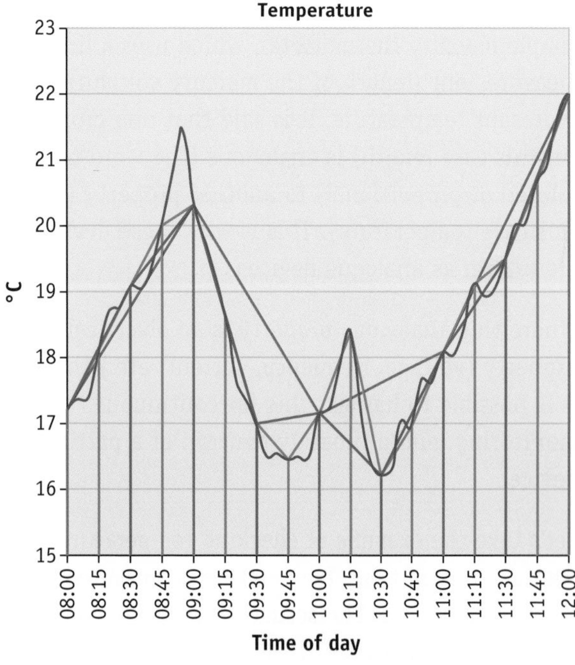

Figure 14.3 Output of a temperature sensor

Signal conditioning

ADC devices have a limited sensitivity, in other words they may not be able to work with some signals. For example our input device may input a signal measured in millivolts or even smaller signals. There may also be other reasons why the signal produced by our input device may not be within the recommended operating range of the ADC device. If this is the case the signal has to be converted to a signal that is within the device's operating range. This is called **signal conditioning**. The most common form of signal conditioning is amplification.

As Figure 14.4 shows, the difference in voltage between adjacent sample points is much greater in the amplified signal. This makes it easier for the ADC device to differentiate between them.

Key words

Signal conditioning – translating the signal output by one device suitable for input into another device.

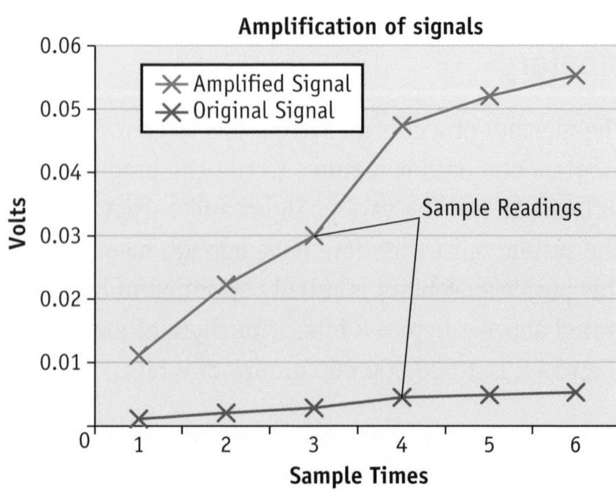

Figure 14.4 Amplification of signals

Noise filtering

The biggest problem when processing electronic signals is the concept of noise. Noise is caused by interference to the signal. Noise can be picked up from many sources. It can be caused because of fluctuations in temperature, interference from magnetic fields or even from the connections between the devices. These unwanted elements of a signal can lead to the ADC device misreading the value. Most signals are in a known frequency range and filters are used to remove unwanted frequencies, thereby smoothing the signal.

Key words

Noise filtering – is the removal of unwanted interference from an electronic signal.

Level shifting

Analogue input devices will produce signals within a specific voltage range and ADC devices are designed to work in a specific voltage range. Unfortunately even with amplification these ranges are not always the same. The voltage of the signal, therefore, has to be raised or lowered to fit the optimum operating range of the ADC device.

Matching to sensors

Connecting sensors to a computer is not as easy as it seems. By their very nature sensors will produce a finite output. This is not usually of a form which can be directly input into a computer. The signal may go through many stages before it matches a required range.

Digital to analogue converter(DAC)

A similar process has to occur if the output device requires an analogue signal such as the rotation speed of a motor. The system will produce a series of values representing the speed at various intervals producing actual speeds, such as shown in Figure 14.5.

Key words

Digital to analogue converter (DAC) – a device which converts a continuous finite step digital signal to a continuous analogue system.

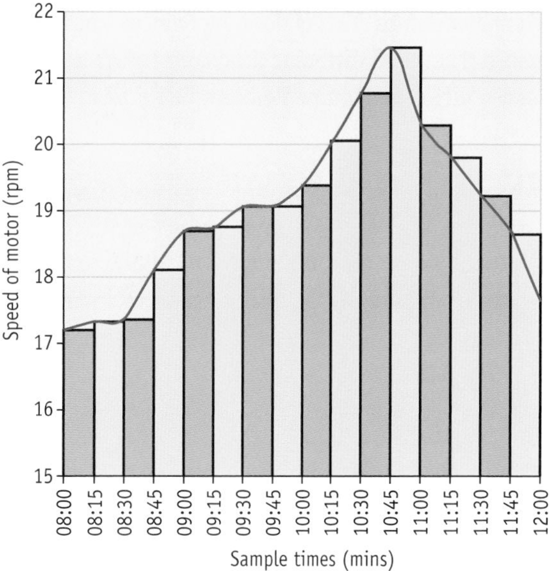

Figure 14.5 Motor speed

EVIDENCE ACTIVITY

P3 – M1

EJA Control Systems have now asked you to prepare information and training materials to explain analogue and digital signals.

You need to prepare a slide presentation and handouts in two parts:

1. To describe the characteristics of digital and analogue control systems. **(P3)**
2. To compare analogue and digital signals and explain the need for signal conversion. **(M1)**

SENSORS

Most control systems need, in some way, to get information from the environment. A traffic light system needs to sense if a car is coming, a central heating system needs to sense the current temperature and a treadmill needs to sense the user's current heart rate. This is done by devices known as sensors. There are different kinds of sensors designed to sense different things. Here are just a few.

Key word

A sensor is a device which senses some aspect of its environment and converts it to an electronic signal.

Temperature

A temperature sensor will sense the temperature of the local area. It is in effect an electronic thermometer. There are a few different types but generally they work because the electrical characteristics of various materials vary with temperature.

- As its name suggests, in a **resistance thermometer** the resistance varies with temperature. Currently resistance thermometers are made out of platinum produced to have a change of resistance of 0.385 ohms per degree centigrade. This value is known as the European Fundamental Interval. It is also required to have a resistance of 100 ohms at 0°C. This is defined in British Standards Institute standard BS EN 60751:1996. A small current is passed through the platinum so that the resistance can be calculated.

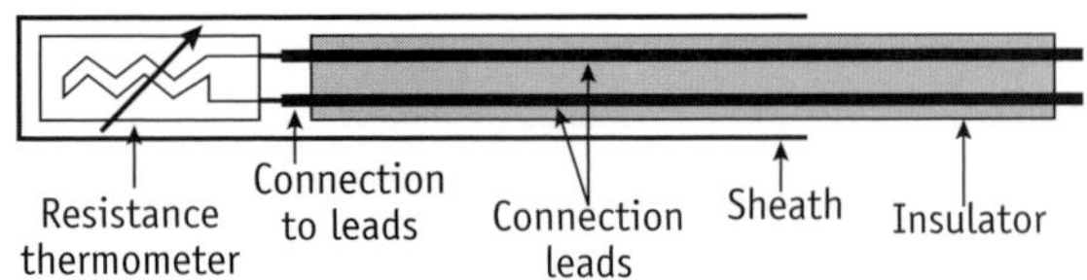

Figure 14.6 A resistance thermometer

- In a **thermocouple**, the voltage changes with the temperature. This is known as the thermo-electric or Seebeck effect after its discoverer, Thomas Seebeck. Unlike the resistance thermometer the relationship between temperature and voltage is not linear but is determined by a mathematical process called polynomial interpolation. There are lots of different types of thermocouples which are usually defined by the conductors used for the positive and negative electrodes.

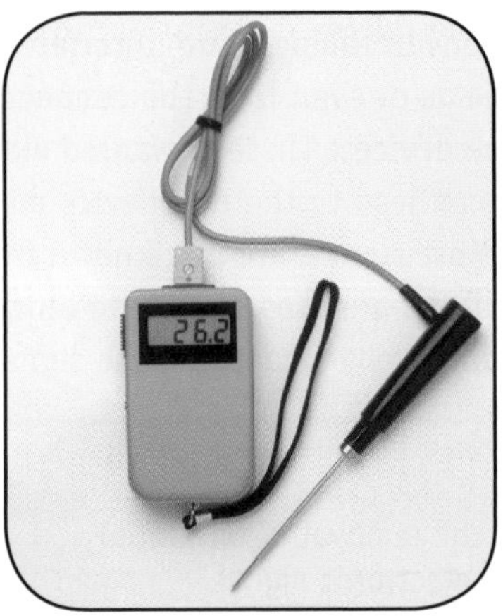

Figure 14.7 A thermocouple

Light

A light sensor is designed to measure the intensity or brightness of the light in its immediate area. The most common type is the light dependent resistor (LDR) or photoresistor.

In an LDR the resistance varies with the amount of light shining on it. It consists of a layer of light sensitive material, probably a semi-conductor such as cadmium sulphide, with connectors at each end. LDRs are quite common and have been in use in electronic circuits for many years.

Figure 14.8 An LDR

Linear position

There are many ways of measuring linear position electronically. One of the most common is the string potentiometer (sometimes known as a string pot).

Inside a string pot a cable is wound accurately (by machine) around a constant diameter cylinder. When it is required to measure the movement of an object, the end of the cable is attached to it. As the object moves the cylinder is turned, producing an electrical signal proportional to the extension of the cable. A spring is also attached to the cylinder to wind the cable up if the object moves nearer to the housing of the string pot in a similar way to a builder's measure.

Figure 14.9 A string potentiometer

Rotation speed/shaft position

Rotation speed sensors are often integrated into electric motors on the basis that the speed of the shaft the motor is driving will be the same as that of the motor itself unless gearing is used. Many modern sensors use what is known as the Hall effect to sense either rotation speed or shaft position. Basically the Hall effect is about the potential difference created at opposite ends of an electrical conductor in which an electric current is generated by a magnetic field perpendicular to the current. The magnetic field could be created by a rotating magnet shaped like a toothed wheel. Each time a tooth passes the sensor the current is generated. Obviously if the number of teeth is known then both the number of rotations per minute and the position of the shaft can be calculated.

Figure 14.10 A rotation speed sensor

Switch

A switch is a two-state device usually used to turn something on or off. In control systems switches appear as both input and output devices. The input devices tend to be more mechanical than electrical and generally depend on an electric contact being open or closed. One of the most common uses in control systems is to check whether a door or a cover is closed. In its simplest form a switch can be two bare wires which are brought into contact when a cover is closed but when it is open the wires are not in contact, thereby breaking an electric circuit. More sophisticated devices exist but the principles are the same.

Selection of sensors can be a difficult task. Amongst several other possible parameters, many of the following must be taken into account:

- property or event which sensor must detect
- accuracy
- environmental conditions in which sensor is to be installed (e.g. heat, toxicity, corrosiveness, etc.)
- size and space for installation
- energy consumption
- ease of use
- ease of maintenance
- mean time between services
- cost
- interfacing with existing equipment.

OUTPUT DEVICES

The outputs of a control system are usually instructions to change the way the device is controlling functions. This could be anything from switching a light on to making a motor go faster. A control system can do many different things. Here are just a few examples.

Relays

As stated above, a switch is a two-state electronic device which is commonly used to switch other devices on and off. As the signal to turn an output device on and off will come from the control processor it is likely to be electronic so the output switch is likely to be more electronic in operation than the input equivalent.

An electronic switch is sometimes known as a relay. It requires a separate electronic circuit to operate the switch which provides on/off conditions for another circuit. The switch is operated by an electromagnet which, when power is provided, closes one or a number of circuits by attracting a moving armature which closes the circuit. When the current to the electromagnet is removed a spring returns the armature to its original position thereby opening the circuit. As shown in Figure 14.11 it is possible to operate two mutually exclusive circuits using a relay as the open state in one can correspond to the closed state in another.

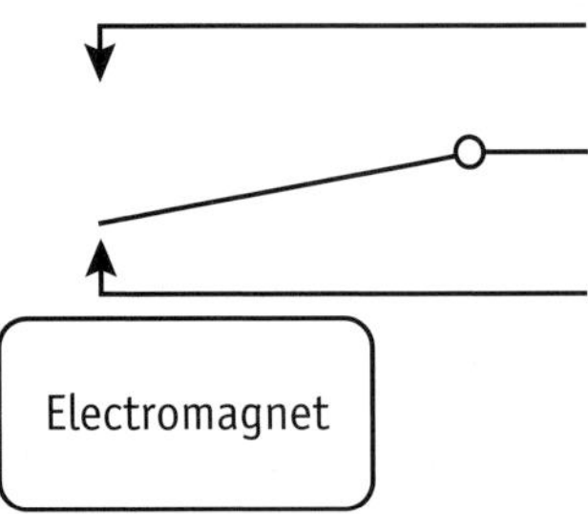

Figure 14.11 Diagram of a relay

With the rapid advances in electronics, there are now solid state switching circuits that perform similar work to that of the electro-mechanical relays described in this section.

Electric motors

An electric motor is based on the principle that a force is generated on a current-carrying wire when a magnetic field is applied. The direction of the force is perpendicular to both the magnetic field and the current. Other types of electric motors exist but the most common types are rotary. These have a static or fixed cylindrical outer casing and an inner rotating shaft (in some motors the shaft is fixed and the casing rotates but the other way round is more usual). Coils of wire conductors are arranged in such a way as to produce a torque on the rotating shaft thereby turning it. One of the properties of an electric motor is that the bigger the current applied the faster it goes.

Figure 14.12 Sectional diagram of an electric motor

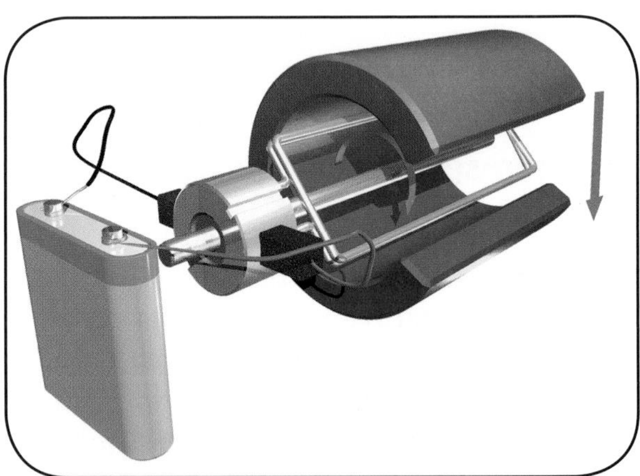

Figure 14.13 Cut away diagram of an electric motor

Lamps

A large number of different types of lamp can be used in control systems. Normal bulbs similar to those used in houses can be used; they work because a current is passed through a filament (thin wire) causing it to heat up and glow. The problem with these is the heat produced. An alternative is the light emitting diode (LED).

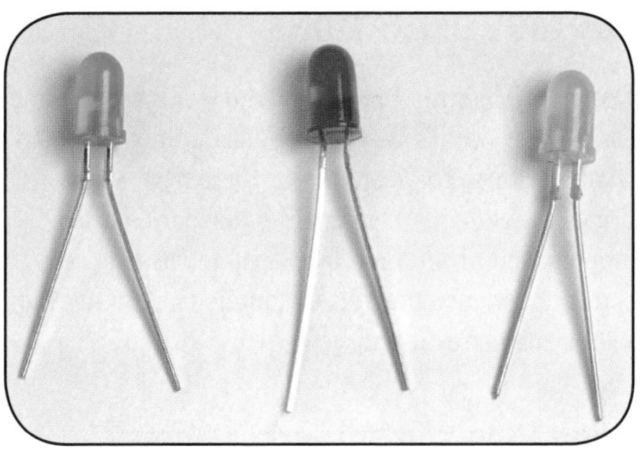

Figure 14.14 LEDs

This device emits light when a current is passed through it; the colour of the light depends on the composition of the material used.

Solenoids

A solenoid is a wire wrapped around a metallic core which produces a magnetic field when an electric current is passed through it. In control systems solenoids can be used for many things, such as electromagnets, relay switches or to convert electric energy into motion as described above for the electric motor.

LCD displays

Liquid crystal displays (LCDs) first appeared in calculators but now are the basis of flat screen monitors. A liquid crystal is a substance that shows properties of both a solid and a liquid. The molecules in a solid remain in the same orientation relative to each other whereas the molecules in a liquid can move relative to each other. Liquid crystals are somewhere in between; their molecules can remain in the same orientation but also move relative to each other. Liquid crystals can be in several different forms known as phases. What makes LCD screens possible is a phase called the nemantic phase where all the rod-like molecules are aligned. A particular form of this phase is naturally twisted and untwisted as an electric current is applied. This untwisting allows increasing amounts of light through which shines on fluorescent pixels.

Figure 14.15 A flat screen monitor

Interfacing to controller

As has been mentioned previously, one of the problems in this field of study is that the devices have to talk to each other, and that frequently they do not speak the same language. This involves two ideas:

- Protocols, which are conventions that control how two devices can talk to each other. They may be regarded as a set of rules that both devices follow, allowing data to pass between them. For example, TCP (Transmission Control Protocol) is one with which Internet users will be familiar.
- Interfaces, that are the boundaries between one device and another, mainly used to refer to the physical boundary (but not always). For example, the USB (Universal Serial Bus) is a common interface between devices that you will almost certainly have used.

Where output is fed to a device via a general purpose computer, then the interfacing and protocols are usually taken care of.

Where a simpler control processor is directing output to one or more devices, then care has to be taken to ensure that the controller and the output devices are compatible.

14.3 Understand control loop operation

SENSOR SIGNAL CONDITIONING

Sampling of analogue signals

The sampling of analogue signals in an analogue to digital converter was mentioned above. Figure 14.3 shows that the shorter the sampling intervals the nearer to the original signal the digital signal is. As the interval tends to zero the signal received tends to the original signal. Time intervals of modern processors can be measured in nanoseconds (10^{-9} seconds) which makes the signal very close to the original.

Digital filtering and digital filters

In simple terms, a digital filter performs mathematical operations on a digital signal such as that produced by sampling. The main aim of the digital filter is to delete unwanted bits of the converted signal. These unwanted bits of signal are known as noise and the purpose of a digital filter is therefore to reduce or even eliminate noise. The major source of noise in a digital filter is the conversion from analogue to digital signals where unavoidable errors are introduced because of the finite representation of the signal as a digital value. This type of unavoidable error is called a quantisation error. Many digital filters are based on the Fast Fourier Transform (FFT), a complex mathematical algorithm which can extract the frequency spectrum from a signal and allow it to be manipulated.

Figure 14.16 Digital filter circuit

CONTROL OPERATIONS

There are basically two types of control system and the easiest way to describe the difference between them is to use the example of the motor which drives a treadmill. This could be either a closed loop system or an open loop system. In simple terms the bigger the voltage applied to an electric motor the faster it will go.

Open loop control

An open loop control system does not measure the effect of instructions. An open loop control system can be implemented where the results of an action can be accurately predicted by a mathematical formula based on a model of the system. In the example of the treadmill motor, it is possible to work out a formula which will convert the rotational speed required to a voltage. Having calculated this voltage it can be applied and the voltage should produce the required rotational speed. The system makes no attempt to check it.

Closed loop control

In a closed loop control system, a sensor is used to detect the results of an instruction. The next instruction is then generated depending on the effect of the first instruction. A common closed loop control system is a central heating system. The user sets the required temperature; a temperature sensor senses the current temperature and if it is below the target the system will turn the boiler on. Once the temperature is raised to above the target temperature, the sensor tells the system which turns the boiler off. These systems are used when the effects of an instruction cannot be accurately predicted. In the treadmill example, a rotation speed sensor could be placed on the motor to sense its speed. If a certain speed is required then the system will incrementally increase or decrease the voltage until the sensor is detecting the correct rotational speed.

Feedback

The difference between open loop control and closed loop control is known as **feedback**. The controller is presented with the input from the sensor and the initial reference, compares the values and decides upon the output. The difference between the reference and the feedback value is known as the error.

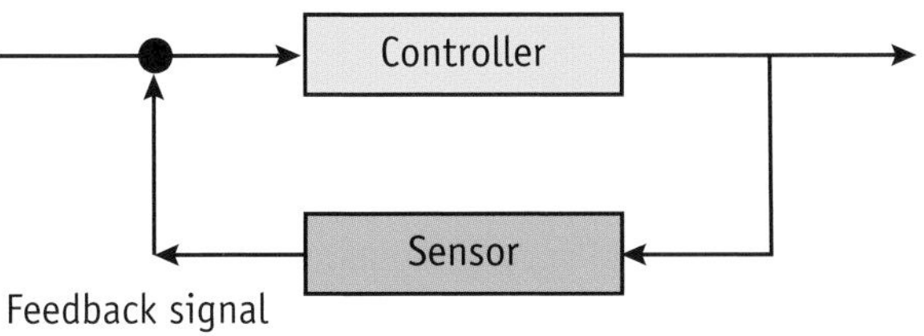

Figure 14.17 Feedback

Key word

Feedback – input about the environment from a sensor which forms part of the decision making in the controller of a closed loop system

Loop stability

Stability in a control system means that if the input is bounded over any period of time then the output must also be bounded. This is known as BIBO (bounded input/bounded output) stability. For a system to be stable the input must be of a known magnitude. In other words there must be a maximum value that it cannot exceed. It must be within set boundaries. The system is stable if, in this case, there is a known maximum boundary. This stops the output from 'blowing up', i.e. becoming infinitely large.

Proportional-integral-derivative control (PID)

Adding small intervals until the control system reaches its target is an inefficient way of doing things. Think about the motor powering the treadmill – if the required speed needs a 10 volt voltage and an increment of 1 volt is added each time it would take 10 loops of the program to achieve the objective. A target of 10.5 volts would never be reached as once 10 volts was reached it would keep adding 1 volt then removing it again. PID controllers attempt to adjust the input based on a comparison of the magnitude of the difference between the target value and the current value of the output.

To calculate its response to a particular situation a PID controller uses parameters, which are adjusted by an algorithm at each cycle of the system's operation.

Each parameter value is based on what is known as the error. The error is basically the difference between the target value and the current value of the output. The parameters are:

- the 'proportional' – the required reaction (the suggested adjustment to the input) based on the current error
- the 'integral' – the required reaction based on adding up all the recent errors
- the 'derivative' – the reaction based on the rate of change of the error.

The new input value is determined by adding these together, each multiplied by a different factor. The 'proportional' governs the size of changes while the 'integral' and 'derivative' are responsible for fine tuning near the target.

Proportional control

Proportional control is a little simpler as the reaction is based simply on the 'proportional' value.

That is to say that the control effort is proportional to the error, that is the critical definition of a proportional control system.

Where the error is defined as:

$$\text{Error} = \text{input} - \text{measured output}$$

Where the measured output is simply the output of the sensor.

And: $\text{Control Effort} = K_p * \text{Error}$

Where K_p is a constant representing the gain of the proportional controller. In other words, confirming the Control Effort is proportional to the Error.

The size of the adjustment to the input depends entirely on the current error. The controller would use a formula or algorithm to decide what adjustment is made in response to a particular error.

Think

A treadmill motor could be controlled on the basis of the formula:

$$A = \frac{2E}{300}$$

where A is the adjustment to the voltage and E is the current error.

Initially a user set the motor to run at 1200 revolutions per minute and set the voltage to 8 volts. He now wishes to increase the speed to 1500 revolutions per minute. What is the additional voltage to be applied?

OUTPUT

Using pulse-width modulators (PWM) to control DC motors

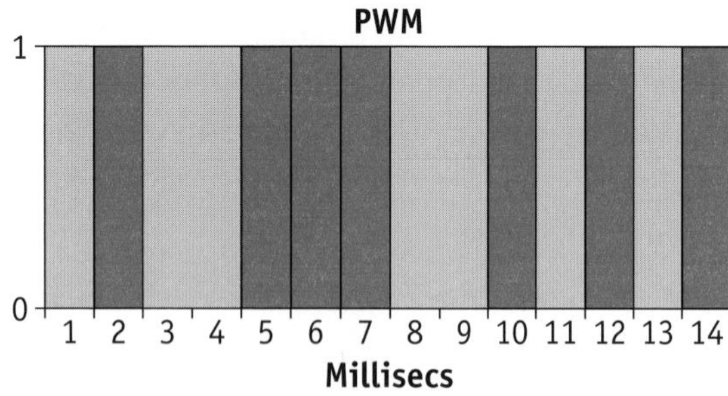

Figure 14.18 PWM

There are many output devices, some of which work on an on–off basis. The control system of a central heating system will sense the temperature. If it is below a set temperature the system will switch the boiler on. This will heat up the radiators in the house which will cause the temperature to rise. When the temperature rises beyond a set limit the boiler is switched off. This is a fairly simple operation. The problem occurs when the device being operated has more than two states, for instance an electric motor may go faster or slower. The most common way of controlling a DC motor is with a pulse-width modulator (PWM). PWM is way of converting an analogue signal into a digital one.

Think Look back at PCM on page 84. Compare PWM and PCM.

PWM output is a square wave which represents a variable on–off ratio. The on–off ratio can vary from 100% which would mean the motor working at full speed to 0% which would mean the motor not working at all. If the on–off ratio was 50% the motor would go at half speed. The PWM will supply power to the motor in the on part of its cycle and no power during the off part. PWM is often used for light dimmer switches.

Operator displays

Displays in control systems can range from the very simple to the very complex. Complex screens are not always necessary to interface with the operator as little has to be displayed. It is possible to attach a normal computer screen but as the amount information to be output is usually limited it can be contained in a matrix of LEDs where some are lit and others remain unlit, forming a letter or number.

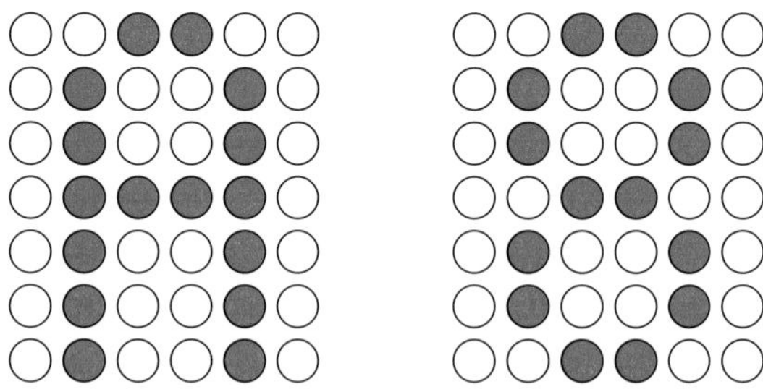

Figure 14.19 How 'A' and 'B' are shown on an LED display

Think One of the most common applications of this type of display is to show the scores at a football match. Using squared paper as a grid, make a display that says

England 5

Germany 1

Think Read the case study again and decide what input and output devices you may need.

EVIDENCE ACTIVITY

P2 – P5 – M2

The next materials you are being asked to prepare for EJA Control Systems are a small series of three information leaflets.

These leaflets should be directed at people who have no detailed knowledge of control systems. They should be in A5 (folded A4) format and should include diagrams, photographs or other illustrations to make the text more accessible and add to the reader's understanding of the text. The series titles have been left for you to decide, but the leaflets should contain the following details:

Leaflet 1 – A description of types of control systems.
Include examples to help with the description. **(P2)**

Leaflet 2 – An explanation of the stages of control loop operation. **(P5)**

Leaflet 3 – An explanation of the principles and uses of proportional control. **(M2)**

SIMULATION

Use of simulation packages to simulate control systems

It is unlikely that you will be using real devices to build your system. Most colleges and schools use simulation packages. These consist of a central multi-purpose controller and a number of different sensors. They also usually have some form of Lego-type building kits to build models of your controlled devices.

Kits are available from Lego and Economatics; both kits are robust and fun to use. There are also some simulation programs which simulate the devices using on-screen displays. These packages are also fun to use but there is something about building a working physical device that gives a sense of achievement.

Converting the control model to hardware/software

When designing a control system in real life, the use of simulation packages such as those discussed above are a valid way of ensuring that the program logic is correct. Be aware, however, that all the parts used in the model are designed to connect together. They also usually have their own programming language. Essentially this means that the signals produced by the input sensors are in the form that the control box wants. If normal components are used for a control system, the operating ranges must be checked prior to assembly. Signal conditioning of various types may be needed.

14.4 Be able to implement, test and document a control system

The BTEC syllabus requires that you build, test and document a control system. The one you implement depends on what equipment you have. There are a number of different manufacturers of simulated control equipment and the language you use to program them varies depending on which brand your school or college purchases. This section will take you through creating the control system for the treadmill described in the case study.

CONTROL SYSTEM IMPLEMENTATION

Assemble a control system

Assembling a control system is something that needs a lot of thought. The assembler has to go through a number of stages before the system is assembled. When you open a flat pack of furniture the first thing you should do is check that you have all the equipment you require. It is very frustrating if you get the furniture half built and then find there is a piece missing. The first thing you should do, therefore, when you are building a control system is to make sure you have got everything. It is a good idea to make a checklist of what is needed.

Remember that all systems are built up from inputs, processes and outputs. Look back at Figure 14.2 to remind you.

You can make your list by looking at what your inputs are and deciding what device is going to provide that input. Then find out whether the signal produced from that device is of a form that can be input to the controller or if you need to provide an interface in the form of ADCs or signal conditioners. Go through a similar process with the outputs. Your list should now be complete.

Implement control procedures

The programming language you use to implement your control system will depend on the equipment you use. See Unit 12 for more about programming.

Documentation

There are generally two types of documentation to go with a control system.

- 'How to use' instructions. You will need instructions that are clear to the user of the system. Bear in mind that these users may not be computer literate or well versed in control theory. The instructions should be aimed at that sort of audience. Pictures and diagrams are always a better option than text.
- System documentation. In real life system documentation enables another competent professional to take over the maintenance of your system if necessary. Program listings and descriptions of how things work are a must. It is a good idea to comment your programs. If a program is complex it can be difficult to establish what a particular piece of coding is for. Good comments are worth their weight in gold.

REVIEW

Test plan

To test your product you will need to produce a test plan. A good plan will test every function of the system to ensure it works. Most test plans are designed in the form of a table. Each test should be given a number so that evidence supporting the test finding can be cross-referenced. A description of the test should also be supplied. Values for the inputs should be stated for each test and an expected output should be detailed. The 'actual outcome' column is not completed until after the test has been performed.

Test number	Description	Input data/ values	Expected outcome	Actual outcome

Functional testing

Each function of the system should be tested individually. It is not enough just to test the functions themselves; you need to know that the system will reject invalid data. If your system is designed to take a maximum input value you need to know that it will reject a larger one. Control system testing should be based on

- valid data
- invalid data and
- extreme data (the largest or smallest possible valid data).

Test results

Once the test has been run the results should be documented. It is not enough to simply put OK in the 'actual outcome' column. Each test should have a comment about what happened and some cross-referenced evidence of the result. If an unexpected outcome occurs you should document why it happened, what was done to correct it and then re-test.

Research tip

Using the Internet, trade catalogues, magazines and any other source of information, research different types of sensors and output devices. Make a record of a variety of different types in a table that you can refer to when you do your practical work.

CASE STUDY: IMPLEMENTATION

Processes

You are going to concentrate on five programs for the fitness treadmill.

- Set initial speed – The initial speed of the treadmill's motor is set to an input value.
- Adjust speed manually – While the treadmill is running, it can be made to go faster or slower, probably by pressing buttons.
- Set initial incline – The initial incline of the treadmill is set by inputting a value. This could be in degrees but is usually simply in levels where a certain level corresponds to a set angle.
- Adjust incline manually – The incline can be increased or decreased while the treadmill is running.
- Adjust incline automatically – The process will set a target heart rate. Initial values are set for the initial speed and incline and nothing happens until the user's heart rate reaches the target heart rate. From that point on if the heart rate falls below the target value then the incline is increased but if the heart rate goes above the target heart rate then the incline is decreased. The aim is to keep the heart rate constant at the target rate. This is the most complex process and it may be necessary later to break it down into sub-processes.

Having decided on your processes, now look at what inputs and outputs are needed.

Set initial speed

The initial speed must be input into the system. This will be in kilometres per hour and to make it easy the smallest increment is normally about 0.1 of a kilometre per hour.

The motor which powers the treadmill does not actually know how fast it is going. It can be told to go faster or slower but it cannot be told to go at 10.1 kilometres per hour. The system needs to know what speed the motor is going so it will have to sense this. Another input is the current speed of the belt. These are the inputs and outputs.

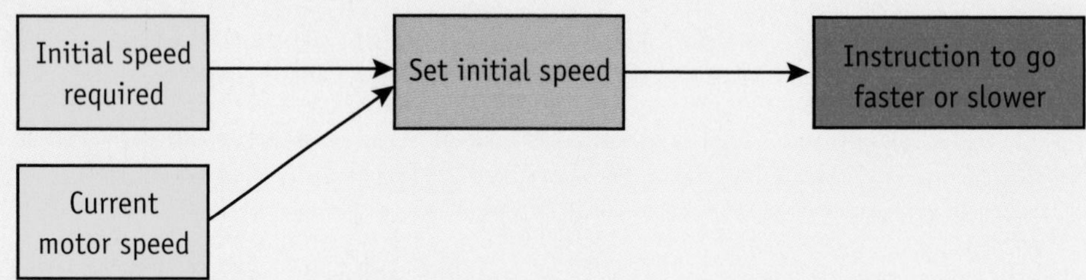

Figure 14.20 Inputs and outputs for set initial speed

Adjust speed manually

Adjusting the speed manually on a treadmill usually involves two buttons: one that raises the required speed by one increment (0.1 km/h) and another that reduces the speed by one increment. Generally these are marked with an up arrow and a down arrow respectively. The output is an instruction to increase the speed or an instruction to decrease it so again the current speed of the motor needs to be sensed.

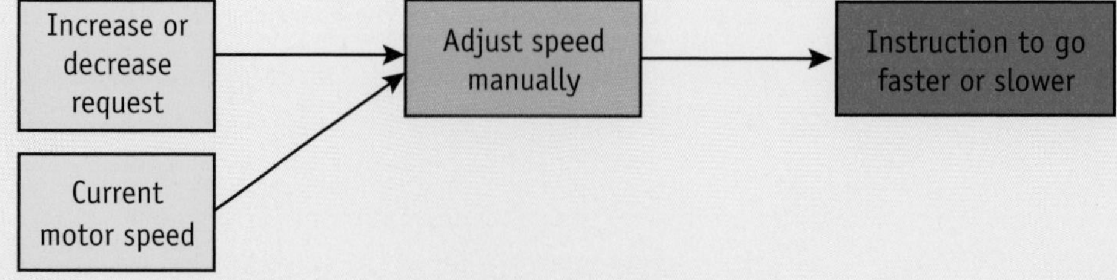

Figure 14.21 Inputs and outputs for adjust speed manually

CASE STUDY: IMPLEMENTATION – continued

Set initial incline

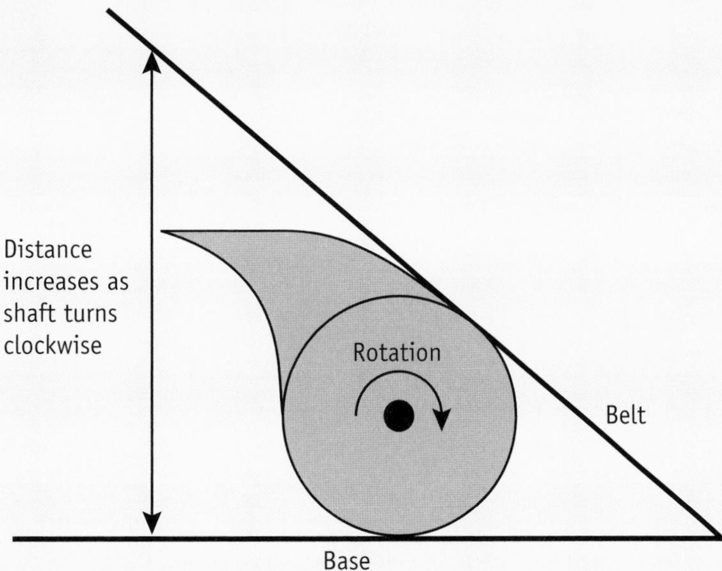

Figure 14.22 Adjusting the incline

The biggest problem here is to move the belt in relation to the base of the treadmill. This could be done by using hydraulic shafts but this would be expensive. The alternative is to use the arrangement shown in Figure 14.22. A roller shaped like a circle with increasing radius is placed between the base of the machine and the belt. As the roller is turned the belt is forced further away from the base and as it is anchored at one end this will increase the incline. As it is usual to give levels of incline and not degrees, the angles corresponding to the various levels must be defined. The maximum angle must also be decided.

Now the inputs and outputs can be decided. Again the initial level required must be input and this must be converted either to an angle or more probably to the perpendicular distance between the base and belt at a particular point along the base. The current angle or distance is also needed so that the system can work out whether to send instructions to rotate the shaft clockwise or anticlockwise.

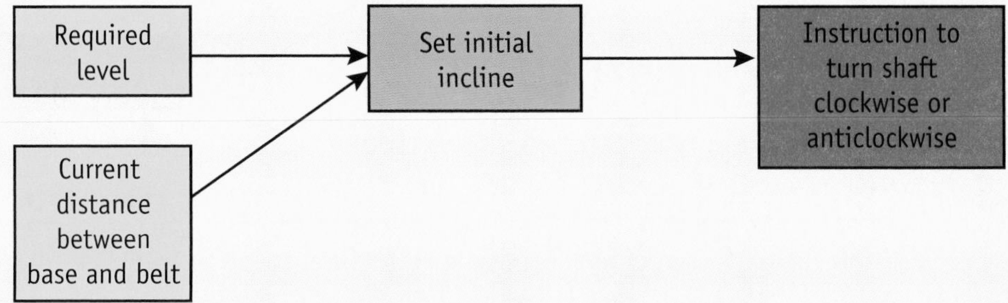

Figure 14.23 Inputs and outputs for set initial incline

Adjust incline manually

This is similar to adjusting the speed manually. Two buttons will raise or lower the target level by 1, the program will change this into a distance and the shaft will be rotated clockwise or anticlockwise depending on whether the distance is less than or more than the target.

CASE STUDY: IMPLEMENTATION – continued

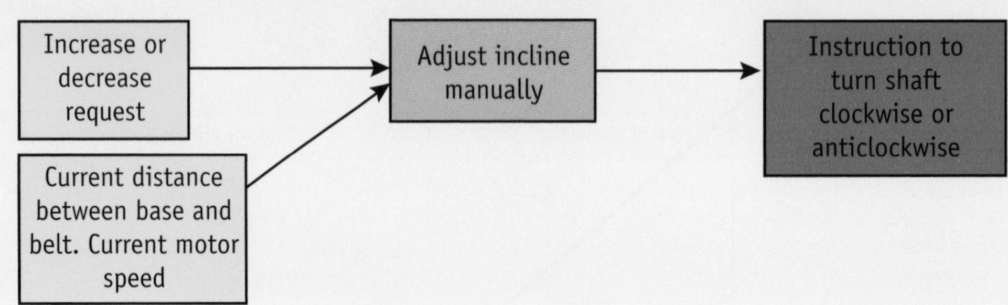

Figure 14.24 Inputs and outputs for adjust incline manually

Adjust incline automatically

This is the most complex of the processes. To set this program you normally have to press a button which starts the program entry session. You will then be asked to input your age and your weight in kilograms. The program then calculates a target pulse rate. You are also asked to set an initial speed and incline. If you show no signs of reaching your target pulse rate, i.e. if your pulse is constant at a level below your target rate, then you are asked to increase the speed. If your pulse rate is above the target level and the incline is level, then you are asked to decrease the speed. Otherwise, once you get to the target pulse rate the incline is adjusted to keep the pulse rate steady. There are six subprocesses.

1. Calculate target pulse rate
2. Set initial speed
3. Set initial incline
4. Gain target heart rate
5. Adjust speed manually
6. Adjust incline based on heart rate.

Calculate target pulse rate

The age and weight must be input in turn so instructions must be output. The target pulse rate is also output once it has been calculated.

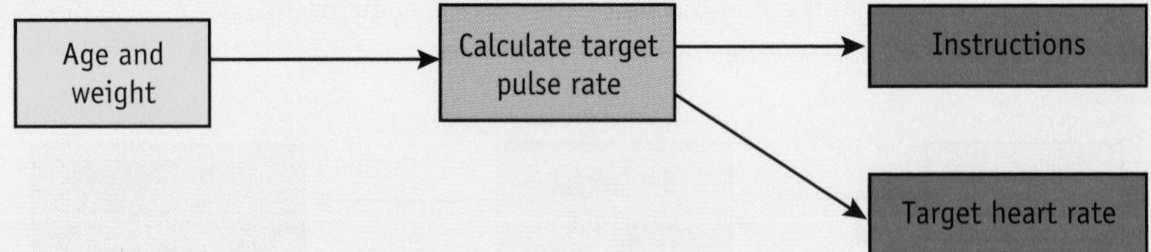

Figure 14.25 Inputs and outputs for calculate target pulse rate

Set initial speed

This process is discussed above. The program must ask for the initial speed to be input.

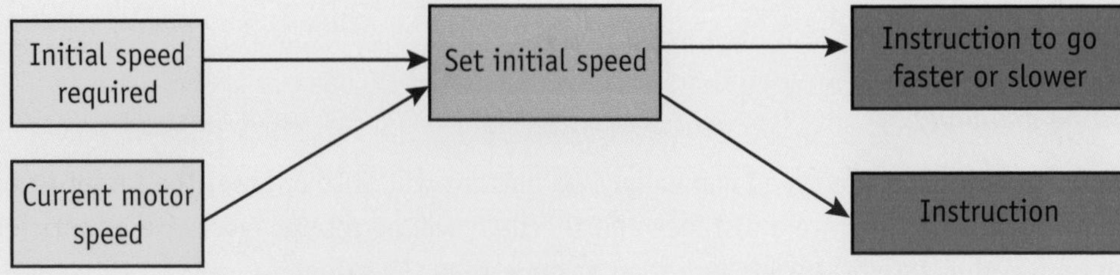

Figure 14.26 Inputs and outputs for set initial speed

CASE STUDY: IMPLEMENTATION – continued

Set initial incline

This process is also discussed above. Again the program must ask for the initial level to be input.

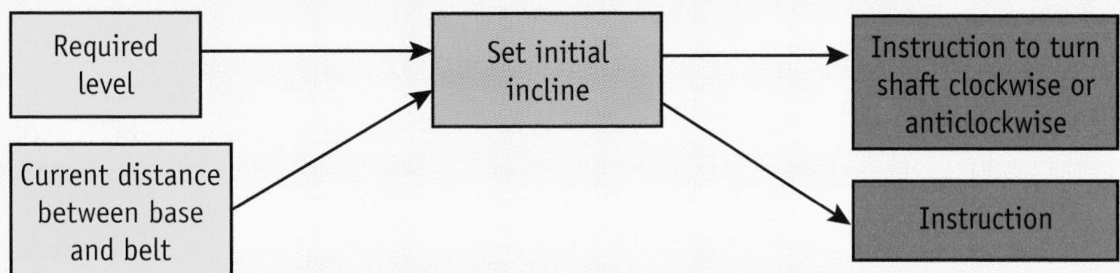

Figure 14.27 Inputs and outputs for set initial incline

Gain target heart rate

This is an interim state where the speed and the incline should be enough to enable the target heart rate to be achieved. To check whether the target heart rate has been reached, the current heart rate must be input. The system should keep track of it and ensure that it is climbing towards the target heart rate. If it appears to be static, a request to increase the speed of the treadmill should be output.

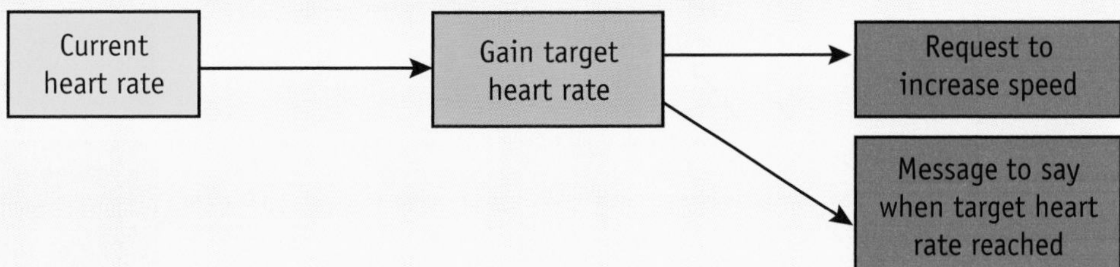

Figure 14.28 Inputs and outputs for gain target heart rate

Adjust speed manually

This process is discussed above.

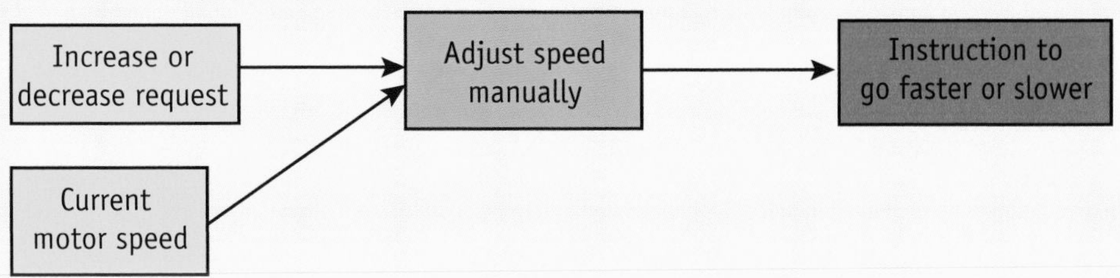

Figure 14.29 Inputs and outputs for adjust speed manually

Adjust incline based on heart rate

The input is the current heart rate and this is compared against the target heart rate. If the current heart rate is below the target then the incline is raised and if it is above the target then the incline is lowered.

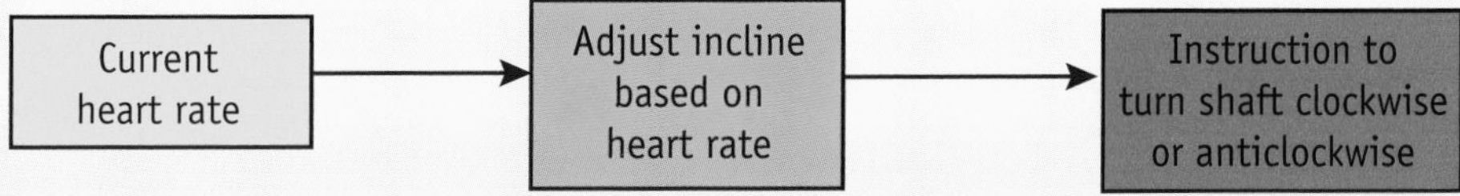

Figure 14.30 Inputs and outputs for adjust incline based on heart rate

CASE STUDY: IMPLEMENTATION – continued

The whole process

Some of the inputs and outputs are duplicated in some of the subprocesses. The current heart rate is read in both the 'gain target heart rate' subprocess and the 'adjust incline automatically' subprocess. Obviously the heart rate only needs to be read once so in the overall picture these are combined.

The overall system diagram will look something like Figure 14.31.

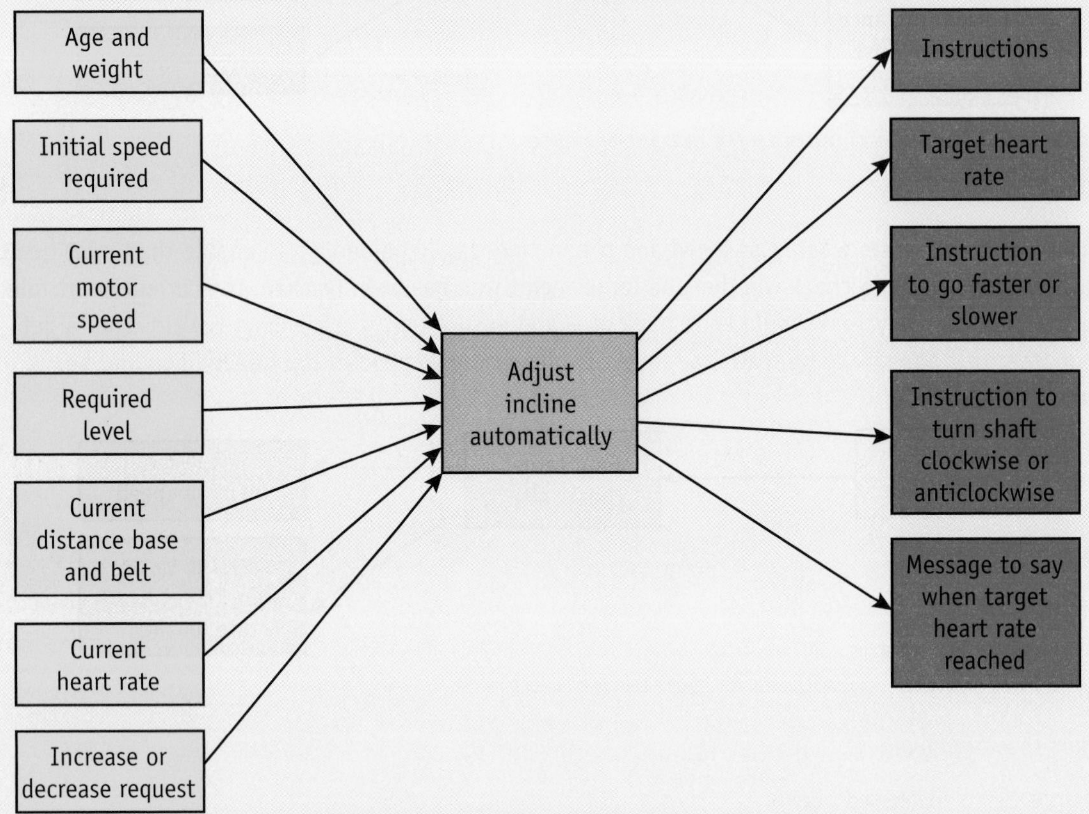

Figure 14.31 Inputs and outputs for the whole process

Hardware

Now you have a clear idea of what is needed you can choose your hardware.

You need a processor which will undertake all these functions. Before you can choose a processor you need to know how many input and output ports you need.

Input devices

An input device is needed to input the various values the system requires.

Age
Weight
Initial speed
Required incline level
Increase speed
Decrease speed
Increase incline level
Decrease incline level

CASE STUDY: IMPLEMENTATION – continued

Usually a treadmill has a control console consisting of a number of pressure switches. These generally relate to the numbers 0–9 and other processes like increase and decrease speed and incline level. Other pressure pads allow you to enter different programs or to cancel and delete previous information. If you are using one of the kits suggested in the specification a keyboard input is provided for use when inputting these values.

Other inputs needed are:

- the values of the current speed of the motor powering the belt – this can be detected by a rotation speed sensor
- the current distance between the base and the belt (in order to calculate the incline) – this can be detected by a linear position sensor, or a rotation sensor on the motor which drives the cylinder which lifts the belt;
- the user's current pulse rate – pulse sensors are common and cheap; they are a form of pressure sensor which produces an electronic pulse at each beat of the pulse.

Output devices

A display is needed for the instructions. As shown in Figure 14.32, real treadmills use a form of matrix display. You can use your computer monitor. Two electric motors are also needed: one to power the belt and one to power the cylinder to adjust the inclination.

Figure 14.32 The control console of a treadmill

EVIDENCE ACTIVITY

P4 – P6 – M3 – D1 – D2

EJA Control Systems have given you a statement of a user need for a control system from a client. This client requires a system that needs at least two different types of sensor for it to be fully operational, but within which individual functions may use only one type of sensor.

You are asked to produce a DVD containing demonstrations, presentation slides and other information referring to the user needs of this client's system.

You will need to:

- Produce full designs for a control system for the user, that include different types of sensors. This material will be scanned and added to the DVD. **(D1)**
- Prepare a presentation during which you demonstrate the operation of at least two different sensors and at least two different output devices. It would be useful if the sensors and output devices relate to the system you have designed for the client, but they do not have to. You will be filmed presenting your demonstration and this will be added to the DVD. **(P4)**
- Assemble and implement a control system which meets at least one of the purposes required by the client in the control system you have designed. You will be filmed while you undertake this task and the film added to the DVD. On completion, you will review what you

have produced, either by presentation to the camera for addition to the DVD, or by producing a short review leaflet that will be scanned and added to the DVD. **(P6)**

- Present a critical evaluation of the design and performance of the control system that you have produced. You will include the good points about the design and performance, any less-good points, comments on how well it meets the user need, any specific points where it does not meet that need, and any other issues related to design and performance. **(D2)**
- Within this evaluation you must present proposals for, and explanations of, potential improvements to the control system. This presentation will also be added to the DVD. **(M3)**

If a DVD (or equivalent) cannot be produced then more traditional written materials plus relevant witness statements will suffice. The demonstrations will depend on what sensors, output devices, etc. are available at the time.

Principles of Software Design and Development

Organisations can now fulfil many of their software needs by obtaining off-the-shelf software, such as CAD/CAM, video production software, spreadsheets, web tools and many more. There will always be instances, however, when off-the-shelf software cannot fulfil the exact business need of the organisation and a custom solution will be required. This need might be met by customising generic software using a scripting language or by building an application from scratch in a full-strength programming language. Which approach is taken will depend on a match between the choice of the languages available and the business needs of the organisation.

This unit will introduce you to the different types of language available and the differences between them, in order that you will be able to choose the correct language to use in different circumstances. You will learn to program in one of these languages and show your newly acquired skills in a series of mini applications. You will also learn to use a variety of design and development tools to prepare for the design and implementation of a larger program to fulfil specific business requirements. You will then demonstrate through real professional programming practices such as review, testing and correct documentation that your program fulfils these specific needs.

By the end of this unit you will:

So you want to be a...

Software Developer

My name Jane Bandul
Age 25
Income £27,000

What do you do?

I am in a team that develops and maintains code for a large chemical engineering company.

What responsibilities do you have?

I work as part of a development team to develop and maintain products for the chemists and the ICT support and infrastructure team. I have recently been given responsibility for leading a project team that is creating a new statistical analysis program using Visual Basic and SQL. This involves working through a specification, designing the product, dividing the work between three coders and then reviewing the work as it progresses and reporting back to my manager on progress.

> "We have contractors working here earning up to £1,200 per week"

How did you get into the job?

I have a BTEC National Diploma for IT Practitioners, followed by a Foundation degree I took at my local college. I then looked for a job in programming.

How did you find your current job?

I found my job on one of the many websites to which I had submitted my CV. They sent me details of this opportunity and I was interviewed locally.

What training did you get?

Every year I am allowed two weeks off-site training with a training budget of £3,000. I agree the courses with my line manager when I complete my appraisal each year.

What are the hours like?

My normal hours are 9 to 5. If we are under pressure to correct an error in a critical program or release a new product then the team often works over.

What skills do you need?

You have to be able to look at requirements in an analytical manner in order to understand quickly what needs to be achieved. You must be able to program in at least two of C/C+ , Java and Visual Basic and have some knowledge of SQL and relational databases. You need to be capable of making high level design decisions, be a team player and have leadership skills.

How good is the pay?

People in my team who have been working longer than me earn up to £35,000 and the manager a good deal more. We also have contractors working here earning up to £1,200 per week.

What about the future?

I hope to become a team leader within a couple of years and in the future I may become a self-employed contractor.

Grading criteria

The table below shows what you need to do to gain a pass, merit or distinction in this part of the qualification. Make sure you refer back to it when you are completing work so that you can judge whether you are meeting the criteria and what you need to do to fill in gaps in your knowledge or experience.

In this unit there are four evidence activities that give you an opportunity to demonstrate your achievement of the grading criteria:

page 119 P1, P2, P3, P4, M1, D1

page 131 P5, M2

page 136 P6, M3, D2

To achieve a pass grade the evidence must show that the learner is able to...	To achieve a merit grade the evidence must show that, in addition to the pass criteria, the learner is able to...	To achieve a distinction grade the evidence must show that, in addition to the pass and merit criteria, the learner is able to...
P1 describe, using examples, why different types of programming languages have been developed	**M1** compare and contrast two different types of program languages	**D1** justify the language used for two different circumstances
P2 describe, with examples, the benefits of having a variety of data types available to the programmer	**M2** justify the choice of data types used in a programmed solution	**D2** evaluate a programmed solution and suggest potential further extensions.
P3 write and test the functionality of a number of internally documented programs that demonstrate the features available in a given language	**M3** adapt and improve a programmed solution based on formal testing and review.	
P4 describe the features of a programming language		
P5 design and create a working programmed solution based on a defined set of requirements		
P6 document, test and review a programmed solution.		

18.1 Know the nature and features of programming languages

TYPES OF LANGUAGE

Computers are controlled by electronic signals, which can essentially be in one of two states, most easily thought of as on or off. These two states are controlled at the machine level by binary code, a combination of 1s and 0s that can be used to represent numbers, text, graphics, sound and, crucially, instructions to the processor. All computer languages ultimately are used to control these instructions and manage the data on the machine. Modern processors are so fast and memory so plentiful that it has been possible to develop languages with vastly different styles for different purposes.

Procedural languages

Procedural languages cover a massive range from early attempts at structured languages such as Algol to modern object-oriented languages such as C++ and Java, from strict languages such as Pascal and Modula II to languages such as C and more modern variants of BASIC. They are all characterised by the use of self-contained sub programs to structure the whole application.

Procedural languages allow the programmer to break down a program into smaller sub-programs and then each sub-program potentially into smaller parts until each part is more easily coded. A program may be decomposed into modules or units; a module can be created from procedures, which may in turn be composed of functions and sub-routines.

This type of language has at least three major benefits:

- Programs can be designed more simply by decomposing problems into smaller parts.
- Code is made much simpler to understand if it is in small, self-contained chunks.
- Many of the smaller problems being solved are generic and these can be reused in different modules and in different applications.

Object-oriented languages

Object-oriented programming languages also break down problems into smaller units and foster re-use, but use an object model rather than a process model to implement this. The idea is that the real world is made up of objects that have certain properties and behaviours (often called methods).

A programmer creating an alien invader game could define an alien class. This would have properties such as colour, size, value, x, y, and behaviours such as position(x,y), move(), hide(), explode(), changeColour(col), getValue(), etc.

Once a class has been defined, alien objects can be created and manipulated very simply. Assuming the alien object is named blob, blob.position(10,10) would position him near the top left of the screen, blob.move() would move him along and down the screen, blob.changeColour(green) would cause him to change colour to green, and blob.explode() would cause him to explode into pieces. All the programmer now has to do is tie these behaviours to appropriate events.

A particular variant of these languages are object-event languages, usually created in a visual environment. These types of language (e.g. Real Basic or Visual Basic) allow the user to create objects such as textboxes and command buttons by dragging a visual representation of the object onto a form. The objects have a series of predefined events that can happen to them, such as a click on a button, loading of a form, or changing of the text in a textbox. The programmer has to write the code to define the behaviour when the event occurs on that object. The properties of the object can be defined in code or directly in a properties table.

Visual languages

Visual languages attempt to make it possible to create an application using visual tools rather than written code. Full visual languages make it possible to create an application using a mouse to drag and drop objects onto a stage or background, and then clicking to set values and states. They are usually less general purpose than the procedural and object-oriented languages described above.

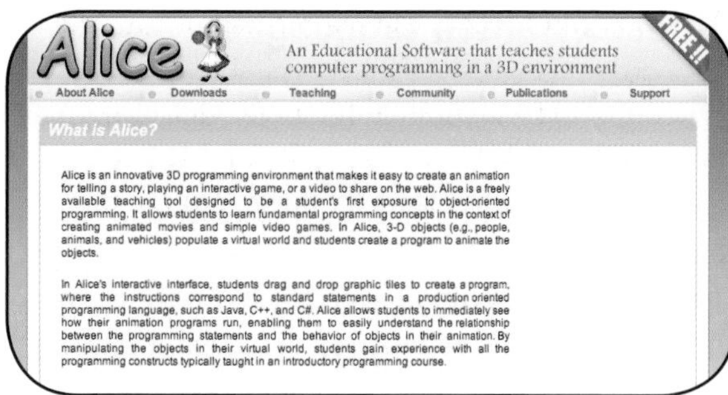

Figure 18.1 Alice visual programming language

Alice (www.alice.org) enables the creation of 3D animated worlds, with the main aim of introducing solid programming concepts through creative play. Automator has been developed by Apple to automate tasks on its computers. Klik and Play (www.clickteam.com/eng/tgf2.php) has been developed to allow users to create games through drag and drop, and clicking on visual icons. Microsoft's Visual Programming Language (msdn2.microsoft.com/en-us/library/bb483088.aspx) is targeted at a robotics environment. In practice there are visual languages for a great many specialist areas.

Other languages

There are a whole host of other types of languages, but the most commonly used are those for mark up and for scripting as these are used extensively in all web programming. The most common mark up languages are html, xml and their offspring xhtml. They are known as mark up languages because text is marked up, usually with tags, e.g. <title> </title> to instruct the translator what to do with that text. Html, or hypertext mark up language is used for defining web pages. Simple tags such as <title> tell the browser application to display the following text in the title bar. <img src="dog.jpg" alt="doug" /> instructs the browser to fetch an image named dog.jpg and display it in the current position.

Xml is a formal language for structuring data hierarchically. Tags are used just as in html to structure the data. However, any name can be given to a tag and any tag opened must also be closed. Tags can be nested within each other to create hierarchical structures. xhtml is a formal version of html, in which it is a syntax error to open a tag and not close it again.

Scripting languages have become extremely important for developing both small customisations of existing applications and more recently for building full blown applications. Scripting languages come in a variety of forms. Some allow the programmer to manipulate objects in existing applications or across groups of applications. One such language is Visual Basic for Applications (VBA) which enables programming across a number of Office, Project and Drawing applications using a Basic-like syntax. Similarly, Actionscript, which now has many full object-oriented features, allows the programmer to manipulate objects in the Flash multimedia environment using a C/C++ style syntax.

Another form of scripting is of web objects and html. Client-side scripting languages such as VBScript and JavaScript allow a programmer to add more dynamic behaviour to a web page using Basic and C style syntax respectively. Server side scripting languages such as PHP and ASP enable full database-driven web applications to be built.

Think How many programming languages can you think of? Why are there so many?

Example

Below is a fragment of the iTunes library stored in xml.

```
<dict>
      <key>Track ID</key><integer>66</integer>
      <key>Name</key><string>Symphony No. 9 (Scherzo)</string>
      <key>Artist</key><string>Ludwig van Beethoven </string>
      <key>Genre</key><string>Class cal</string>
      <key>Kind</key><string>AAC audio file</string>
</dict>
```

Simple overviews and uses

Programming languages have been developed with different purposes in mind. Early languages such as COBOL (Common Business Oriented Language), BASIC (Beginners All-purpose Symbolic Instruction Code) and Fortran (Formula Transition) were developed for relatively slow computers with very different uses in mind. COBOL was for managing structured files for data processing on massive computers. BASIC was created to be as English-like as possible to help everyone access computers. To a large extent it succeeded in this, as it was the basis of operation of most early personal computers and introduced a whole generation to programming. Fortran was created to help scientists with fast processing of scientific data such as formulae.

The next generation of languages included the very influential Pascal and C. Pascal was created to allow programmers to develop programs following the top down design ideas prevalent at the time with as little compromise as possible. This was then to be the basis of many languages including Modula II, Delphi (Object Pascal) and ADA, which allowed for real time programming. Pascal and its variants were to become the main development vehicle for small, medium and even large projects with a formal design structure. The first Apple Macintosh operating system was documented and specified using a Pascal interface.

C, on the other hand, was designed to be a tight, efficient language that could be translated very simply into machine code. It allowed direct access to memory and a terse, concise syntax totally unlike Pascal. C was synonymous with the Unix operating system and thus a generation of university computing students learnt to program using it. It was to become the main development language for these people as they progressed to employment and enterprise, and became for a while the pre-eminent programming language, especially for developing operating systems and applications.

The development of C++ enabled some of the safety and formality of object-oriented programming using the familiar C syntax. This was to become the main development language for small and major projects of almost any nature.

Then the web became the main force in ICT. The main strength of C++, that it was able to do anything in almost any style of programming, was seen as a weakness when it came to running programs over the web. It was too easy for programmers to develop components that would write to users' computers with or without their knowledge. In addition, whilst C++ can be written in object-oriented form, a programmer could just as easily ignore objects altogether and create an application as inherently unsafe as any created in C. Java sought to deal with these issues. It is a mainstream development language using C/C++ style syntax, tailored for the new web-dominated world, offering strict security and safety. JavaScript was similarly developed to script behaviours for web pages using C style syntax with a degree of security built in.

BASIC was simultaneously re-developed using a visual development environment with the aim of realising the original vision of BASIC. The new versions allowed almost anyone to develop programs. At the same time it brought a good deal of the structure of Pascal. From a base of enthusiasts these new versions of Basic became full-strength development languages, especially when used in combination with C++ for creating any functionality Basic could not. Microsoft's version, Visual Basic, spawned variants in VBS and ASP for scripting on the web and VBA (Visual Basic for Applications) for manipulating desktop applications. Other scripting languages for applications have also gained some popularity including Lingo and the most successful of these Actionscript, which uses C++ style syntax to manipulate multimedia shows in Flash.

In addition to all of these, a number of toolkits were developed that allowed programmers to build applications using drag and drop, and click and point. A few of these have been developed into visual programming languages. Entirely visual versions of BASIC were produced, but the greatest success for this type of language has been for more specialist development purposes such as creating games, creating 3D worlds, or controlling robots.

CASE STUDY: BREWING JAVA

James Gosling, an expert in C++ and object-oriented programming, developed Java in the early 1990s. He and his team wanted to create a language that would offer a security model appropriate to its environment and the safety of correct object-oriented features. Sun, manufacturers of some of the most powerful workstations available, pushed it as the development language of choice and have gone on to see it through standardisation and into the open source community.

QUESTIONS

1. What makes Java a great deal more object-oriented than C++?
2. What makes pure object-oriented programmers say Java is not OO?
3. What specifically were Gosling's main aims in developing Java?
4. What systems can Java be used on?
5. What applications is Java best suited to creating and why?

REASONS FOR CHOICE OF LANGUAGE

Organisational policy

An organisation will often have policies that state which development environments and languages can be used. This might be dictated by organisational style or by simple expediency. Some major organisations will wish to maintain very strict design standards and follow this through into their choice of language. Other organisations might have a policy of choosing the exact language for the job. Others might favour in-house languages even when there is a better one available.

Suitability in terms of available features and tools

Different languages and their associated development environments have different strengths and weaknesses as a result of their different combinations of features and tools. Visual and Real Basic have, for example, excellent user interface features and tools. Java is ideal for creating applets for the web, where its security features are invaluable. PHP has ideal features for managing databases over the web. None of these languages, however, has the pure speed and efficiency of a well-written C program, and thus are not as suitable when speed is the essential feature. In addition to the features and tools of the language itself, it is possible to obtain libraries of pre-written components that can be used with particular programming environments. These might provide toolkits for accessing spreadsheets or databases, new user interface tools, or even a full scripting language for an application. A programming team will therefore consider the strengths of a language and its development environment alongside the availability of external libraries.

Availability of trained staff

A major determinant of the choice of language is of course the human resources. If a programming team is made up entirely of C++ programmers, then the chances are that C++ will seem the natural choice. Organisations have to be careful to ensure that they do not become too dependent on doing things the way they have always done, and thus most programmers will continue to attend training both in their main language and in additional development environments.

Reliability

A crucial feature of programming languages is, of course, reliability. If the code created is not stable or any bugs discovered are hard to fix, then the reputation of the programmers will suffer and maintenance costs will rise. The most important factor in the reliability of a program in the long term is usually how well it has been designed and how well the design has been followed in the implementation. This means that programming in languages such as C is inherently more risky than programming in visual or object-oriented languages. In practice, a well-established programming organisation will create and test many components and sub-programs that they can use and re-use and in this way boost the reliability. Thus the ability to create solid, reusable code will often be the major determining factor in choosing a language.

Development and maintenance costs

In the end, the benefits of creating a program must outweigh the costs, and programmers will inevitably attempt to achieve the lowest costs possible when developing an application. These costs will include the cost of the hardware, the development environment, the language and the libraries. The largest cost by far, however, will almost certainly be the programmers' time. Some projects will only be possible when certain languages are chosen. It may be possible to create a small application using VBA with Excel in 12 hours, whilst programming it in C++ could take 60 hours. The C++ solution might be preferred, all other things being equal, but if the budget will not stretch that far, the VBA solution may still be chosen. Maintenance costs will also need to be taken into account when opting for a solution. A small website advertising disability aids for local users could be developed using complex scripts or simple html. If it is to be maintained regularly, then the simple html solution may be preferable so that the owner can do it himself, rather than having to employ expensive web programmers for each change.

Expandability

Example

A final important factor to be taken into account is that of expandability or scale. A program was written to track the training of would-be taxi drivers. It worked extremely well for a period of time, but then slowed dramatically when it recorded just over 65,500 driver-training events. At this time the whole program had to be re-engineered in a completely different language because the initial choice of language was not suitable for this scale of operation. It is essential that the initial scale of the problem and any future scale are taken into account when deciding on a language to solve the problem.

FEATURES

There are a number of features that are common to all the most used programming languages, although these might have a slightly different syntax in each. In practice, most modern languages are based loosely on C style syntax or Basic/Pascal style syntax.

Variables

A variable is essentially a data item, representing somewhere data can be stored in its many forms in a program.

Proper use of variables underlies all good programming practice. The data should normally be given meaningful names rather than shorthand symbols, but equally the name should not be over long and cumbersome. It is possible to have data names that are very long and descriptive such as the_quantity_in_stock, but these are long-winded in use and thus it is preferable to use short, descriptive names such stockLevel. Ideally programmers will use a naming convention for all names. As a substitute for spaces, e.g. capitalise each successive word stockLevel, or use an underscore where a gap would be: stock_level. Some programmers incorporate the data type in the name as in intStockLevel. The exact naming convention does not matter as much as being consistent. If you are consistent with your data names, you will use the same names naturally and be able to refer to them fluently throughout the development process.

Understanding scope of variables is another crucial area, touched on above, in creating the most efficient programs.

	Duration	Visibilty
Global variables	Lifetime of program	Whole program
Local variables	Life of procedure/ function	Procedure/ function
Static variables	Lifetime of program	Procedure/ function
Module variables	Lifetime of module/program	Global to module

Figure 18.2 Scope of variables

In order to make components as reusable as possible, it is essential that there is a mechanism for restricting the visibility of variables to the place they are created. Variables created in a function or procedure should only be visible in that function or procedure. For example, the function factorial(x) uses variables total and i (and x, in fact, though this strictly is a parameter). If anyone who wanted to use this function had to remember that the variables i and total were already in use, this would make programming very hard. Where they copy and paste the function into a project, as in VBA, this is difficult enough. If the project was created in C, and a compiled object file contained the actual code, all the programmer would see is a prototype definition in the header file: long factorial(x):

Example

Below is an example of VBA factorial function.

```
Function factorial(x)
'computes X! ( 5!=5*4*3*2*1=120) for
numbers between 2 and 12
Dim total As Long
Dim i As Integer
total = 1
For i = 1 To x
    total = total * i
Next i
factorial = total
End Function
```

The more sophisticated the programming language, the more control a programmer will have over visibility and duration of variables. Early languages had entirely global variables. The most sophisticated now enable a programmer to tune variables exactly to a module, a procedure, a function or even a single statement. Static variables are often available as well. These allow local visibility with global lifetime, which allows for behaviour such as checking how often a routine has been used, and thus, for example, how many objects have been created, without having to resort to global variables.

Loops

Loops are a fundamental control structure for programs. Most conventional programming languages will allow at least three main types of loop to be implemented. The first of these is the fixed loop, which loops for a set number of times, as is shown in the factorial function. The second, shown in the read file routine, checks, before the loop starts, whether to loop or not. This is essential for operations such as reading files or other input streams, where the stream might be empty and thus performing any operations on it would be nonsensical. The third type is a loop that performs a check after looping at least once. This is used in many validations, for example.

Example

Below is a VBA read file subroutine using pre-check loop.

```
Sub readfile()
Dim filename As String
Dim strMessage As String
  filename = "message.txt"
  Open filename For Input As #1
  Do While Not EOF(1)
     Input #1, strMessage
     MsgBox (strMessage)
  Loop
  Close (1)
End Sub
```

Example

Below is an example of C routine using post-check loop.

```
/* getyn.c
   a re-usable code module   gets only a yY or nN keypress
   returns TRUE on y or Y and FALSE on n or N
*/

int getyn(void)
{
char ch;
  do {
    ch=upper(getch());
  }
  while(ch!='Y'  && ch!='N');
  return (ch=='Y');
}
```

	Fixed	Pre-check	Post-check
Number of loops	Fixed	0..∞	1..∞
Main uses	Where the program knows how many iterations are required before it starts to loop	Where the process may or may not be run	Where the process is run at least once

C style	`for(j=0;j<10;j++){`
	process();
	
	}
		`while(ch!="x"){`
		process();
		
		}
			do{
			process();
			
			`}while(ch!="x")`

Basic style	`For j=1 to 10` process() Next j	`Do while ch<>"x"` process() Loop	Do **process()** Loop Until ch = "x"

Figure 18.3 Table of loops

Conditional statements

Another fundamental construct of all conventional programming languages is the ability to branch to different code depending on some condition or conditions being met. Virtually all languages use the if statement to do this.

Example

Below is the if statement in VBA

```
Sub passorfail()
 Dim intMark As Integer
 Dim strMessage As String
 intMark = InputBox("Enter mark (0..100)")
 If intMark >= 40 Then
    strMessage = "You have passed"
 Else
    strMessage = "You have not passed yet"
 End If
 MsgBox (strMessage)
End Sub
```

As is shown in the passorfail() routine, the if statement has a check part just like the loop statements. The check evaluates to either True or False. If the check is True, the if part of the statement is executed. If the check is false, any else statement is executed. In practice almost any expression can be used in the check provided it yields a True or False result for the check to evaluate. Thus it is possible to include a function whose result is a Boolean (True or False) value, or a logical expression as described below whose result is always a Boolean value. The else part of the statement does not have to be present, but from a design point of view it should be, even where the operation is to do nothing, as this shows that you have considered all possible paths. It is also possible to nest if statements inside each other, thus dealing with more complex conditions such as if the person is married and female or single and male.

Case statements

A variation on the simple conditional is the case statement. This allows the programmer to deal with a number of conditions in a single, simpler statement as is shown in the days of the week routine that would have required a large number of if statements to render. C style languages such as JavaScript need to use a break statement after every case statement to implement the classic case design, as without it execution simply proceeds through all cases from the one that has been switched to.

Example

Below is an example of Case statement in JavaScript.

```
<html>
<head>
<title>switch with dates</title>
</head>

<body>
<script type="text/javascript">
var d = new Date()
var theday=d.getDay()
switch (theday){
   case 1:
      document.write("monday")
      break
   case 2:
      document.write("tuesday")
      break
   case 3:
      document.write("wednesday")
      break
   case 4:
      document.write("thursday")
      break
   case 5:
      document.write("friday")
      break
   case 6:
      document.write("saturday")
      break
   case 0:
      document.write("super sunday")
      break
   default:
      document.write("day not known")
}
</script>

</body>
</html>
```

Example

Below is an example of Visual Basic style case statement.

```
Sub season()
Dim intMonth
intMonth = InputBox("Enter month")
Select Case (intMonth)
    Case 1 To 3: MsgBox ("Spring")
    Case 4 To 6: MsgBox ("Summer")
    Case 7 To 9: MsgBox ("Autumn")
    Case 10 To 12: MsgBox ("Winter")
    Case Else: MsgBox ("Huh?")
End Select
End Sub
```

Arithmetic, relational and logical operators

There are a number of types of operators, usually shown as arithmetic operators, relational and logical operators. Languages vary a little in the operators they make available.

Operator	Meaning	Example	Result
+	Add	int a = 5+9;	a=14
–	Minus	int a = 9–5;	a=4
/	Integer Divide	int a = 9/4;	a=2
	Divide	float a = 9.0/4.0;	a=2.25;
%	Modulus	int a = 9%4;	a=1
*	Multiply	int a = 9*4;	a=36

Figure 18.4 Arithmetic operators in C style languages.

Operator	Meaning	Example	Result
==	Is equal to	a==b	is TRUE if a equals b
!=	Is not equal to	a!=b	is TRUE if a does not equal b
>	Is greater than	a>b	is TRUE if a greater than b
<	Is less than	a<b	is TRUE if a less than b
>=	Is greater than or equal to	a>=b	a greater than or equal to b
<=	Is less than or equal to	a<=b	a less than or equal to b

Figure 18.5 Relational operators in C style languages.

Operator	Meaning	Example	Result
<<	Shift bits left	<<a	shifts all bits left
>>	Shifts bits right	>>a	shifts bits right
&	And	a & b	a AND B
|	Or	a | b	a OR B
^	Xor	a^b	a XOR B
~	Not	~a	NOT a

Figure 18.6 Bitwise operators in C style languages.

Operator	Meaning	Example	Result
&&	logical and	(a && b)	True If both a and b are true else false
||	logical or	(a || b)	True If either a or b are true else false
~	Not	~a	True If a Is false

Figure 18.7 Logical operators in C style languages.

Assignment statements

One of the most fundamental statements in a programming language is the assignment shown in Figure 18.7. This is the method used to give a variable or object a value, or reset a value for the variable or object. The value on the right hand side of the assignment operator is assigned to, or copied to, the variable on the left. If there is a complex expression on the right, it is evaluated first and then the result is copied to the variable.

Both C and Pascal distinguish assignment from equality, whereas BASIC uses the context to determine what is intended. In C it is vital that that the assignment operator (=) is not used where the equality operator (==) is intended.

The expression while (ch="y") looks innocent but actually means assign "y" to ch. When it is evaluated it yields true and the loop will never terminate.

It should also be noted that in the standard C language, but not usually other C style languages, strMan="mark" does not copy the string "mark" into the variable strMan but rather copies the address where the string is stored, with potentially dangerous results if it is subsequently reset.

Input and output statements

All conventional languages have to provide ways of inputting data into and outputting data from a program. This is perhaps the area where there is largest variation in methods and syntax.

DATA TYPES

All data in the processor is ultimately binary numbers. The programming language has to instruct the processor how to represent the data in order that the user can work with whole numbers, characters, strings of characters, floating point numbers, images, sound, etc. A language does this through the type system. Data in programs therefore comes in different basic types. A type tells the language how much storage to allocate to the data, how to input it, how to output it and how to deal with operations on the data. The amount of types available and how strictly these types are enforced vary with the language. Object-oriented languages allow programmers to invent their own classes, thus effectively extending the types available to whatever is necessary. These are, of course, created on a foundation of the basic types.

Text

Text is a basic type in all modern conventional languages. Text can be a single character, often known as a char, or a sequence of characters that is most often known as a string. Characters comprise the letters of the alphabet, the 10 digits of the decimal system, punctuation and special characters such as ~ # | ^. A legacy of older ICT systems is that the normal character set also includes some control characters such as tab, line feed, carriage return and others. It is important to note that each individual character has an associated numeric value. Lower case letters,

Pascal style	Basic style	C style
intNum:=5;	intNum=5	intNum=5;
strMan:="mark";	strMan="mark"	strMan="mark";
TxtUser.value :="steve2".	txtUser.value ="steve2".	txtUser.value ="steve2";

Figure 18.8 Assigning in different types of language

naturally, have different numeric values than their upper case equivalents otherwise they could not be represented separately. Strings of characters are treated very differently in different languages. It is important that a programmer understands how strings are treated in the language they are intending to use.

Integer

An integer is a whole number. In the real world an integer comes from the set of numbers from $-\infty$ to $+\infty$. Thus 100, 500, −900, 50,000, 9999999999999, and −999999999999999 are all valid integers. This is not true in programming, and serious errors can arise if there is a misunderstanding of this. What range an integer has in any language will depend on two factors: how much storage is allocated to the integer type and whether signed (positive and negative) integers are allowed. The most common integer type is signed and is allocated 2 bytes. This means that the highest number that can be represented is $2^{15} - 1$, i.e. 32767 and the lowest is -2^{15}, i.e. −32768. Unsigned integers have a range 0–65535 ($2^{16} - 1$). Most languages also use a long type which has 4 bytes. The signed version of this has a range of approximately +−2billion, i.e. −2,147,483,648 to 2,147,483,647.

Byte

A byte data type (char in c) is a special variant of an integer that uses 1 byte of storage. This has a range of 2^8, i.e. 0 to 255.

Floating point

Floating point numbers, also known as real numbers, are used to represent fractional or decimal numbers (e.g. 1.33, $\frac{1}{2}$, −7998765.22, 3.14159, 0.000000004). They can be manipulated just like decimal numbers but are stored in a compact form as a sign (+−), exponent (power) and a mantissa (fraction), a bit like standard form in maths or the scientific notation for numbers in spreadsheets (where 125678.99 is stored as 1.25678990E+05).

Typically a 4 byte floating point number will have 1 sign bit, 8 bits to represent powers and 23 bits to represent the fraction. This allows very large and very small numbers to be represented (a real number between 3.4E−38 and 3.4E+38 is standard). The format effectively separates the range of numbers from the precision (or the number of digits that can be represented totally accurately). As only 4 bytes are being used to store such a large range these are inevitably only approximations of the number being represented. A special algorithm is used to deal with rounding errors in a known and predictable manner.

Early floating point systems were unique to each computer system but now most developers have standardised on the IEEE standard. This allows for 3 variants: the single precision which has 32 bits, the double precision (which allows for fewer rounding errors) which has 64 bits and the extended which has 80 bits.

Date

Dates are fundamental to many applications, but there is not a standardised method for storing or manipulating dates and/or times. Date and time can be stored in many ways on a computer. Microsoft uses more than one method for storing dates in their different products. One method is to store the date as a double precision floating point number representing the days difference from 31 December 1899. The integer part of the number is the number of days from that date and the decimal part represents the number of seconds since midnight. This representation is accompanied by routines that convert the number to dd/mm/yyyy hh:mm and other related formats. There are internet date time formats which are now becoming more established on the internet (e.g. ISO8601 and RFC822) and hopefully in time programming libraries will adopt a standard.

Boolean

A Boolean data type is one that can have two possible values, TRUE or FALSE. Boolean values are fundamental to programming as every conditional and all loop checks use a Boolean test. In theory only 1 bit of a byte is required to store a Boolean, though most often Booleans will be stored as 1 or 2 byte integers. In Visual Basic, for example, the integer −1 is true and 0 is false. In C 0 is false and every other value is true.

Other

The variety of types available depends on the language. C has many variations on the integer including short (2 byte integer), char (1 byte integer) and long (4 byte integer). Some Basics also have a currency type (e.g. 8 byte integer) that can hold large amounts of money very accurately.

Benefits of appropriate choice of data type

The advantages of having a variety of data types that are strictly enforced (a process called strong data typing) are that they provide a form of automatic validation. Use of strong typing will mean that the translator can recognise meaningless code, such as when the programmer has attempted to do something silly like attempting to divide text, or add a floating-point number to a character. In some environments types can also provide input validation, generating automatic error messages when a user attempts to enter the wrong type of data for a variable or data item. Weak typing can lead to some unintentional behaviour. In C assigning strings directly rather than using the strcpy() function can lead to unknown errors. It is also very easy in C to read in data as one type and cast it to another, often by simply reformatting the output. This makes C really powerful but also very dangerous. Pascal-like languages and more object-oriented languages, on the other hand, restrict type casting to specific, safe circumstances.

Visual Basic can be programmed with or without strong typing (and even includes a variant type to allow for very weak typing). Without strong typing the errors shown in Figure 18.9 can happen very easily. If each of a,b,c are declared as integers this will not happen. For this reason it is advised normally to use the statement "option explicit" with all Visual Basic code.

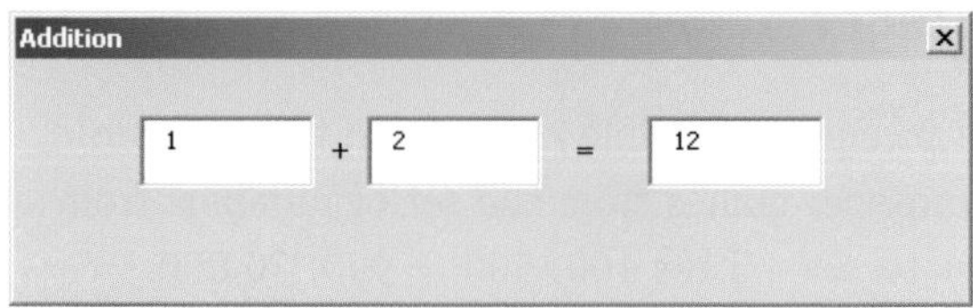

The text "1" is added to the text "2"

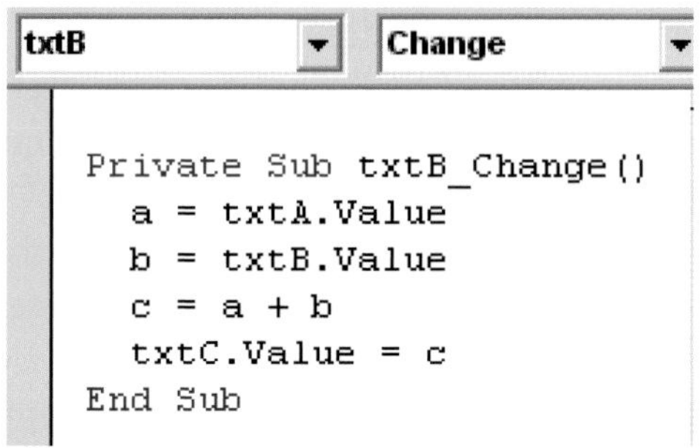

No types have been declared.

Figure 18.9 Unintentional use of string addition.

Another benefit of choosing an appropriate data type is that it makes it possible for a programmer or compiler to control memory storage more tightly and efficiently. If a small number is being used, a byte data type will only consume 1 byte. If the programmer wants a large number but does not need absolute precision then a single precision floating point can be chosen.

EVIDENCE ACTIVITY

P1 – P2 – P3 – P4 – M1– D1

Copy the table shown in Figure 18.11 into your favourite text editor. For the programming language you are studying complete the table. Where there are variants (e.g. char, string, long, short, single, double, etc.) add and/or substitute these types below for those shown in the table in the appropriate rows. NB It is essential that these six main types do appear in the table in some form. In the comment/benefit column it is essential that you describe the data type in your own words as well as stating the main usage or benefit of that type. At the foot of the table you must include a paragraph stating why it is a benefit to programmers in this language to have this variety of data types available **(P2)**.

CustomStore Solutions, a multimedia programming house, develops custom programming solutions for a variety of clients from blue chip companies to small businesses. They work with in-house programmers and software contractors in a variety of languages, priding themselves on utilising the most efficient and effective method to solve a particular problem. They have, for example, used VBA in Office applications to customise existing applications quickly to a client's needs. They have used C++ to develop an in-house automated warehousing application for a large supermarket client. They have used Java to provide web applications for an extranet for a luxury car franchise and then used JavaScript and Flash Actionscript to provide a good deal of the front end for the application.

They are holding an open day for college students aimed at recruiting new trainees for a career in programming and wish you to develop a presentation aimed at these students, describing in detail why different types of programming languages have been developed.

You should create a presentation describing why different types of programming languages have been developed. You should provide examples of four different types (procedural, object-oriented, visual and script and mark-up languages), and of how they are used and why.

You should provide detailed speaker's notes to back up your evidence. **(P1)**

A common question posed by visitors to the open day is: What is the difference between Java and JavaScript? Your manager has asked you to research this and create a presentation explaining the difference between object-oriented programming languages such as Java, and scripting languages such as JavaScript. The presentation is to be created in some depth and should

Type	Example	Space occupied	Comment/benefits
Text			
Byte			
Integer			
Floating point			
Date			
Boolean			
Other			

Figure 18.10 Table of variable types.

include examples and a table showing the main differences. **(M1)**

Your manager wishes to provide case studies to make the day more real for the visitors. She wants you to write up two recently won contracts, 'E-teas' and 'Dart_F1 Engineering' for whom CustomStore are creating solutions in two totally different ways. She wants you to describe the types of job and explain with examples why the particular solution (language) was chosen in each case. **(D1)**

1. E-Teas is a café within reach of a regional chain of garden centres for whom CustomStore developed a web store a couple of years ago. Their concept is to have a touchscreen micro PC on the table. The range of food and drinks is displayed on the screen. The customer can select their order onto a virtual tray by touching pictures of the items they want. When ready they can check out. They can pay by card immediately or if they wish to pay by cash, a message is sent over the network and a cashier comes to finalise the payment. The final order is delivered to the kitchen by network and then is prepared to send to the customer. A web-based solution has been chosen for this application. A mySql database will hold the items and pictures and xhtml and JavaScript used for the user interface.
2. GroundFly Engineering are a racing team who wish to break into Formula 1. They wanted a modelling application to predict how their cars will perform depending on how different variables are set. These include tyre type and pressure, suspension settings, wing heights, brake and performance settings, air temperatures, track conditions and more. The inputs to the model can be fed manually or from sensors on the cars and track. The outputs required are full multimedia including numeric tables, graphical displays and an animated car which can be driven around simulated versions of all the race tracks that GroundFly visit. C++ was chosen as the development vehicle for this application.

Use your chosen programming language to create the following short programs.

Study the tasks to be undertaken, and note which programming features should be employed in each task to achieve an efficient solution. Design, implement and test the solution ensuring that each 'programming feature' listed in the text is employed at least once. You should comment your programs sufficiently fully so it is obvious what each section of code is attempting to achieve. **(P3)**

The programs may be written with basic or sophisticated user interface features depending on the language chosen for implementation. A solution in a visual language would be expected, for example, to use elements such as buttons and text fields, whereas a solution in a text-based language would be expected to use simple text prompts.

For each program below write supplementary notes describing the programming features you have used and the reasons you used them in this context. **(P4)**

Task 1: Times table calculator
Output a multiplication grid that is based on the following:

×	1	2	3	4	5	6	7	8	9	10	11	12
1	1	2	3	4	5	6	7	8	9	10	11	12
2	2	4	6	8	10	12	14	16	18	20	22	24
3	3	6	9	12	15	18	21	24	27	30	33	36
4	4	8	12	16	20	24	28	32	36	40	44	48
5	5	10	15	20	25	30	35	40	45	50	55	60
6	6	12	18	24	30	36	42	48	54	60	66	72
7	7	14	21	28	35	42	49	56	63	70	77	84
8	8	16	24	32	40	48	56	64	72	80	88	96
9	9	18	27	36	45	54	63	72	81	90	99	108
10	10	20	30	40	50	60	70	80	90	100	110	120
11	11	22	33	44	55	66	77	88	99	110	121	132
12	12	24	36	48	60	72	84	96	108	120	132	144

Figure 18.11 Times table

prompt the user for the maximum number (which must be between 6 and 25)
output the table.

Task 2: Complex interest calculator
Prompt the user to enter the amount they have to invest and an interest rate. Show them how much the capital will have grown to at the end of every year until they choose to exit the program.

Task 3: Logical number guessing game
Prompt the user to guess a number the computer has chosen between 1 and 1000. If the user guesses too high put up the message 'too high'.

If it is too low put up the message 'too low'. If it is exactly correct, output the message 'Well done, you guessed the number in ' and output the number of goes it took.

Task 4: Secret text

Part one:
Prompt the user to write some text that they wish to keep secret.
Encrypt the text by xoring every character with 128.
Write the file using a filename provided by the user.

Part two:
Prompt the user for a filename containing encrypted text.
Open the file and read the text, converting it back to plain text by xoring it with 128.

Task 5: Change calculator
Prompt the user to enter an amount in £s and pence. Display the number of £10, £5, £2, £1, 50p, 20p, 10p, 5p, 2p and 1p notes and coins are required to give the minimum number in the change (hint: use the MOD operator extensively).

Task 6: Student statistics
Prompt the user for 20 student scores, each comprising a student name and a mark between 0 and 100. Validate the data entry. The grades achieved are based on the following table:
0–39 U, 40–49 E, 50–59 D, 60–69 C, 70–79 B, 80–100 A

Display how many and what percentage of the 20 students achieved each grade, the students with the minimum and maximum score, and the average mark achieved shown as mean, median and mode.

18.2 Be able to use software design and development tools

SOFTWARE DEVELOPMENT LIFE CYCLE

Define scope	Analyse	Design	Implement	Test	Document	Maintain
→	→	→	→	→	→	→

Figure 18.12 System development lifecycle.

For a project to be successful it is important that it starts from a sound determination of the **scope** of the problem. This will spell out what problem the project has to solve, what the exact objectives are, what resources will be required, any areas of risk, possible constraints, the timescale and crucially the key success criteria for the project, i.e. what must be achieved for the project to be considered a success. These will usually be spelled out as SMART (specific, measurable, achievable, realistic and time constrained) criteria that can be tested at the end of the project to decide whether it has been completed successfully.

The next phase will be to **analyse** the users' requirements. The main aim of this is to produce a functional specification that can be used to create the design. This makes very specific what is required of the system.

The next phase is the **design**. The design is in many ways the most crucial part of the whole project. If any issues and problems are dealt with at design stage, rather than during later stages, the whole project will progress a good deal more smoothly and quickly. This stage converts the users' needs into a form suitable for implementation.

When the design is complete, **implementation** will begin. If the design is complete, this will be a straightforward phase with the programmer simply translating the designs into the chosen implementation language.

Reviewing and **testing** then attempts to ensure that the implementation followed the specification and design and works as intended. All but the very smallest implementations will have flaws and it is the job of the tests to find them before the project goes live.

Once the implementation is working it can be **documented**. This will usually involve technical documentation that includes the designs, sources of data, the tests, fully commented code, and annotated screenshots of the application in action. There will also be a user manual that documents the purpose, the target audience, a walk-through of the main functionality and lists any error messages.

The final phase is the **maintenance** of the project, which attempts to pick up any problems and deals with any extensions to the project. A good project will have a degree of future proofing built in, but inevitably there will be opportunities for further development. These will start another cycle of the system.

DESIGN TOOLS

Data flow diagrams

A data flow diagram is an excellent tool for describing a complete system. It can give a complete visual representation of a complex set of processes, entities, data stores and data flows that is useful to a designer and yet still comprehensible to the client. The power of the diagram is in simplifying the complexity, rather than detailing every aspect of the system. Furthermore no order of processing can be inferred from any ordering apparent in an information flow diagram, though often the logic is such that only one sequence may be possible. Conditional and repetitive operations can be included but are not detailed as such.

Processes within a data flow diagram can themselves be expanded individually either to form lower level data flow diagrams or form the basis of process specifications. These may take the form of a flowchart, a decision table, a structure chart or a similar diagram showing in detail how the process will work.

Creating better diagrams:

- Every diagram should have a title.
- Arrange the diagram so that all external entities (for I/O) are on the left, the processes are in the middle and any data stores are on the right.
- Use an active verb and an object name for each process (e.g., Take Order, Analyse Orders).
- If there is more than one possible output from a process, show each one (e.g., order confirmation, order refusal, request for further information).
- Name data flows using a simple noun (e.g., stock number); never use a verb (get stock number).
- Data flows to an external entity are outputs, from an entity are inputs.
- Data flows to a data store are used to write or update storage; flows from a data store are read only.
- Name all entities and data stores with singular nouns (e.g. Customer, not Customers).
- Avoid crossing flow lines (use bridges/line hops if absolutely necessary).

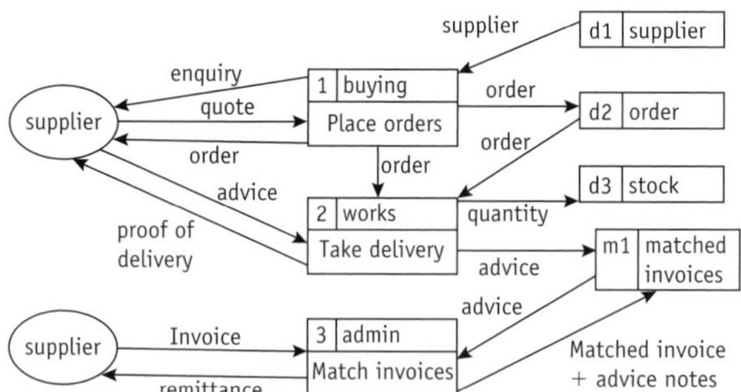

Figure 18.13 A simple order processing data flow diagram.

Entity relationship models

Entity relationship models are an excellent diagrammatic method for understanding and explaining the relationship between the various data items that have to be stored within a program. In the data flow diagram shown in Figure 18.13, the order, supplier and stock data stores are related to each other. Orders for stock items are ordered from suppliers. In addition to this, orders can contain many lines, each showing one stock item bought. An ERM attempts to capture all of this detail in a diagram to allow for efficient storage and processing of the data.

Concept	Definition	Example
Model	A representation of a system or application in the real world.	An order processing system
Entity	A real world object or concept to be modelled.	An order (orders)
Attribute	An individual property of an entity. NB it must not be a group of data (such as a list of stock items sold). Each attribute must be for a single item of data.	date_of_order
Relationship	How one entity is related to another.	One order can contain many order lines
Primary key	A unique identifier for an entity.	Order number in order
Foreign key	The property that relates an entity to a primary key in another entity.	Supplier number in the order entity

Figure 18.14 ERM glossary.

ENTITY	ATTRIBUTE	RELATIONSHIP
ENTITY NAME	ENTITY NAME *Primary KEY* Attribute 1 Attribute 2 Attribute 3 Foreign Key*	
Entities are drawn as rounded rectangles	Attributes are a list of the field names. Primary keys are underlined. Foreign keys are marked with an asterix	Relationships are shown by a line with a crow's foot to show a many end of a relationship and a simple line to show a one end of a relationship. A dotted line shows an optional relationship, and a solid line shows a mandatory relationship. Each end should be named to show each relationship is two way.

Figure 18.15 Basic entity modelling tools.

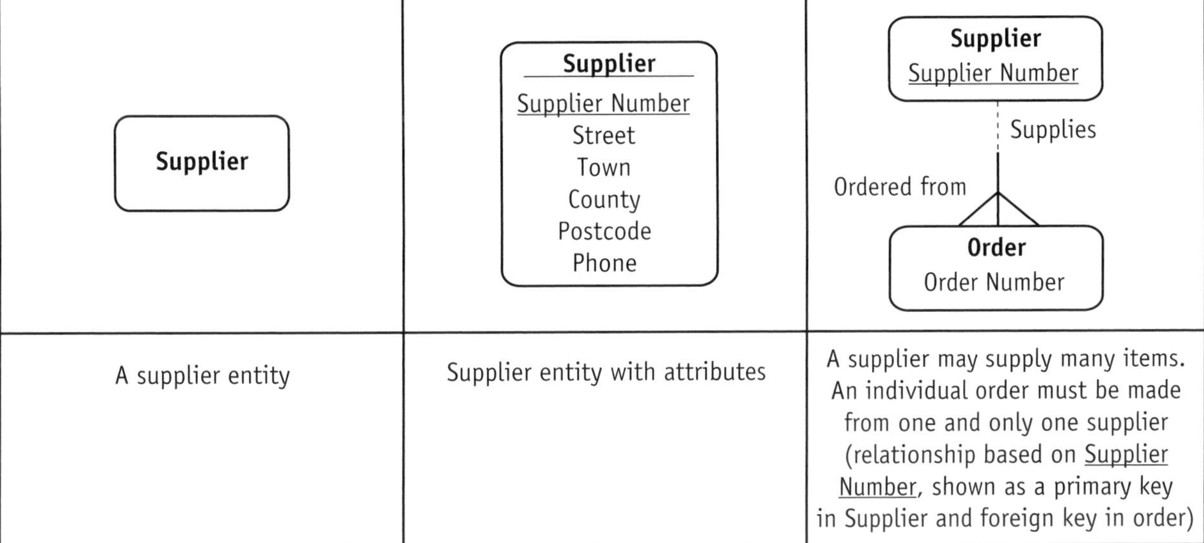

Supplier
Supplier
Supplier Number
Street
Town
County
Postcode
Phone
Supplier
Supplier Number
Supplies
Ordered from
Order
Order Number
A supplier entity
Supplier entity with attributes
A supplier may supply many items. An individual order must be made from one and only one supplier (relationship based on Supplier Number, shown as a primary key in Supplier and foreign key in order)

Figure 18.16 An example of entities, attributes and relationships

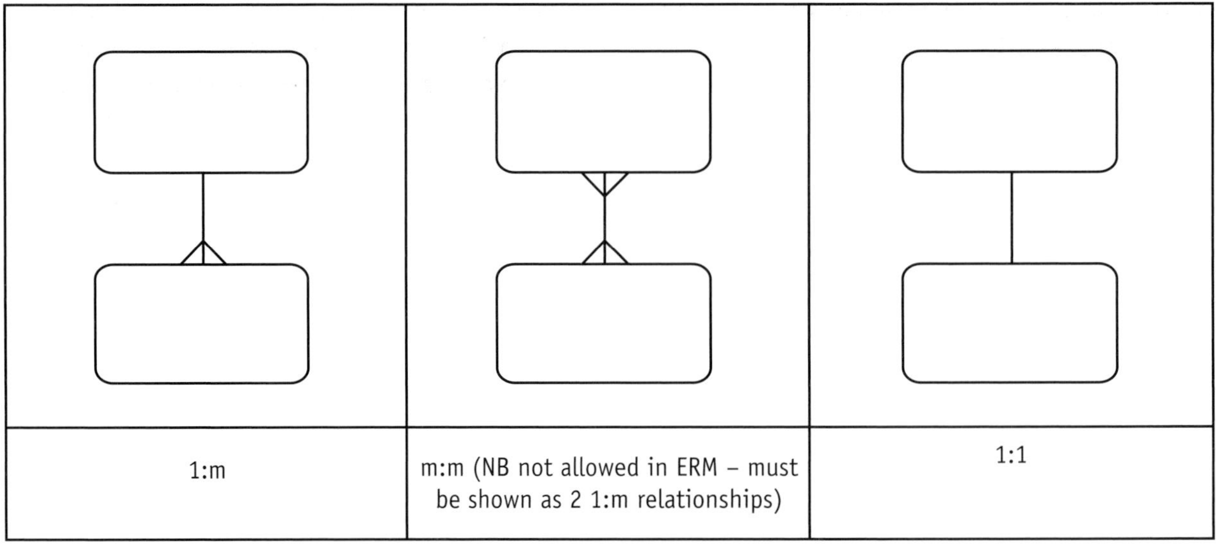

Figure 18.17 Cardinality of relationships

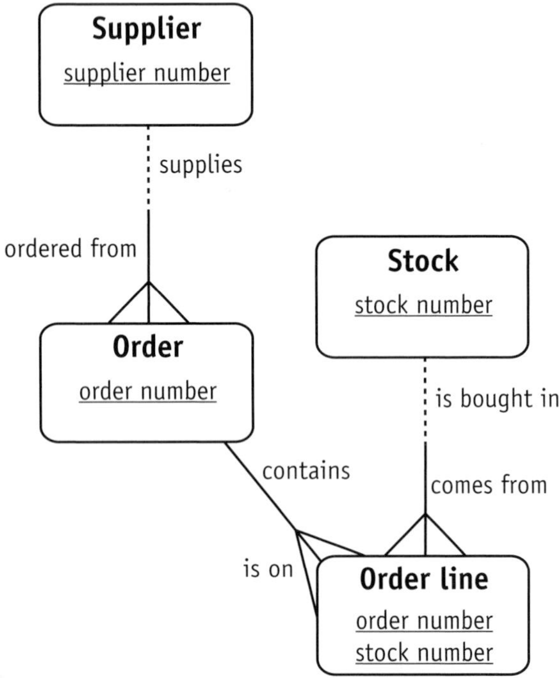

Figure 18.18 The ERM for the order processing system.

The diagram of an order processing system shown in Figure 18.18 illustrates all the features of a sensible entity model. It illustrates how data is related to each other and how it can be stored efficiently in any form of relational database. This is important as many applications, even those created with object-oriented tools, will use such a database for organising and storing the data required.

Structure diagrams

There are a number of different forms of structure diagram available as design tools. For procedural programs diagrams such as Jackson Structured Diagrams (JSDs and JSPs) can provide an overview of the data and processes within a system. When creating totally object-oriented solutions, it is also possible to utilise structure diagrams for giving an overview of the system and the actors within it. A web-based solution will often be designed using a hierarchical structure diagram showing how to move from one page to another. The simplest form of structure diagram will show how the various modules of an application interact or communicate in an overview fashion.

SOFTWARE STRUCTURES

Iteration

Data and processes within an application will repeat. It is important to spot instances of iteration as this will make the code more efficient. If, for example, the user is asked to enter a series of numbers which are validated to be between 1 and 10, then clearly it will normally be simpler and better to write the code to prompt the user, get the number and validate it once and then repeat this as many times as is necessary, than to rewrite the same or even similar code ten times. As has been seen, nearly all conventional programming languages have a number of options for iterative code, and the programmer must make an appropriate choice.

Decisions

Decisions will have to be programmed into all major applications. The critical part for a programmer is ensuring that all possible decision paths have been taken into account. A decision may take the simple form of: if some condition is true then do process a else do process b. However, in most applications they will become more complex than this. Decision tables are good tools to help design for decisions and case statements, and nested if statements are available to a programmer to implement these.

Modules

Modules are self-contained sections of code, potentially containing data and processes. They are an extremely useful structuring device as they allow problems to be broken down into smaller components and then programs to be built back up from these smaller components. They may be employed simply to manage complexity in a single project, or may be used to build reusable components. They are particularly useful in creating data collections, such as tables, linked lists, sets, etc., that can be re-used in many applications once built. They are also useful for grouping together and building up libraries of reusable procedures and functions that can be called again and again from other modules and applications. Long established programming houses or departments will have built up a number of these libraries to make their coding faster and more efficient.

Functions

Functions are self-contained routines that return a value. Functions such as sum() which returns the total of the values in a range of cells, or now() which returns today's date and time are familiar to anyone who has used a spreadsheet.

Example

An example of a function:

```
Function inRange(x As Integer, minVal As Integer, maxVal As Integer) As Boolean
If x >= minVal And x <= maxVal Then
    inRange = True
Else
    inRange = False
End If
End Function
```

Example

An example of a mock up of the top level routine for the order system.

```
Sub ordersystem()
Do
    choice = InputBox("a: Make order  b:Take delivery  c: Receive payment x:exit")
    Select Case choice
        Case "a": Call makeorder
        Case "b": Call makedelivery
        Case "c": Call receivepayment
     End Select
Loop Until choice = "x"
End Sub
```

Most languages allow programmers to write their own functions. They are a superb means of adding structure to applications. There may be many occasions when it is necessary to check a value is within a range. The function inRange() shown can be used on every occasion it is necessary to validate a number as being in a range. This saves time and effort, but also potentially makes programming safer. As each function is created it can be tested exhaustively and then when it is reused in an application only integration testing will be required.

Procedures

Procedures, or sub-routines, or sub-procedures are similar to functions but they do not return a value. They are still immensely valuable in dividing a program into smaller chunks that should be immediately more comprehensible and readable. There are usually many opportunities for reuse of procedures. Because procedures are named sections of code, they are also pretty well self-documenting.

In addition to this the use of parameters in a procedure enables the procedure to be reused in many more situations. If you write a procedure that draws a box on the screen called drawRect(), this can be useful. If you create a procedure called drawRect(x,y,length, width) that allows the size and position to be drawn, then it is even more useful as it can be reused any time a box needs to be drawn. drawRect(x,y,length,width, col, bordercol) may be even more useful. A good programmer will therefore look for opportunities to create reusable procedures, as this will at once simplify the work and make the work done more reusable.

Classes and objects

Classes, as has been seen, are used in object-oriented and object event programming languages. They allow a programmer to structure a program around objects rather than processes. Properly designed classes allow even more re-use than functions, procedures and modules.

18.3 Be able to design and create a program

REQUIREMENTS SPECIFICATION

The design for a program starts with a sound and full understanding of the user requirements. The more clearly these are specified, the more straightforward it will be to create the design, and to agree when the program is working to an acceptable standard. It is much easier to fix any misunderstandings and deal with any problems when specifying the requirements than when conducting sign-off tests. Furthermore it is important that there is a firm documented agreement between client and developer over what constitutes a finished application. The requirements specify this. It is in both parties' interests that these are as clear as possible to avoid any dispute at the final stage.

> ***Think*** McConnell stated that 'a ...defect that costs $1,000 to fix during requirements can cost $25,000 to fix during functional tests'
>
> (McConnell Code Complete Microsoft Press 1-55615-484-4 p26)
>
> Why do you think this is?

Inputs

When analysing the system there are a number of questions about input that have to be considered:

- What is the current system?
- What is the source of the data?
- What data is to be entered into the program for each process or event?
- What volume of data needs to be entered?
- How often is data entered?
- What devices and media are preferred for entering data?

The answers to these questions will guide development. It is important to know how large the input requirements are, and what types of input have to be dealt with and how often, as this will determine what type of input can be considered. If tens of thousands of numbers have to be entered each day, as, for example, with public utilities meter readings, then manual input at the keyboard really is not viable.

Outputs

Similar questions can be posed about outputs for similar reasons:

- What is the current system?
- What reports or other outputs are needed for the system?
- What form should the reports take?
- How frequently should these be created?
- What volume of information is to be output?
- What devices and media are preferred for outputting data?

Processing

Processing converts input data into useful output information. The processing that is critical to the business need should be specified at this stage. Thus any sorting of data, any searches and any calculations that are required should be stated as requirements. For example, any statistical data that has to be calculated, or discounts that should be applied or similar calculations should be shown at this stage.

User interface

The client will also usually but not always specify details of the user interface that are required. It is certainly important to know what the input and output devices are to be. If an application is to be created for a mobile phone, it will be very different from that required for a large touch screen kiosk. A very important feature of most modern applications is that they have built in accessibility for all possible users, including those with poor sight, colour blindness and more. On occasion the user interface needs will be very specialist. They may, for example, require speech input, or spoken output. As always the more detail that can be specified at this stage, the simpler the design will be and the more likely it is that the completed project will be considered a success.

Think What are the main user interface features of your chosen programming language? How can you make applications created with it accessible for most people?

Constraints

In addition to the specific requirements there will always be constraints to the design and development that must be taken into account. In developing some larger systems and in other circumstances the developer may be given a blank canvas to work on, and be able to specify the hardware platform and the operating system to be used. In most cases, however, the client will want a new program to be able to work on the existing computer systems. If the client has stand-alone Apple Mac Pro computers, then it is likely that the new application will have to be able to run on these, not on the Windows Vista on an Intel dual core platform that a developer might prefer to target. A similar consideration also applies to the client's staff and their training needs, which must be taken into account when planning for a new system. A further limiting factor is the timescale involved. If the user needs a new system in one week's time, this will limit what can be achieved.

DESIGN

The next phase of development is to design the program. There are many techniques that can be used for this depending on the language of implementation and any preferences for design methodology in the project. It will cover processes and data, with the exact design methodology depending to some extent on what implementation method is chosen. Ideally a design would be independent of the implementation language but in practice this is not entirely realistic. At some stage in the design process the language will be chosen and the final parts of the design will be tailored to that language. A procedural language with a relational database solution will include entity relationship models, and data flow diagrams with process specifications, whereas a full object-oriented solution will probably require class diagrams and use case diagrams. All designs will include test plans to ensure that at least the key success criteria have been achieved.

A number of techniques will probably be combined to achieve a full design for a program. For the overall application, structure diagrams or DFDs may be used. The data may be designed using Entity Relationship Modelling and/or data dictionaries. It is also usual to design the screens, or forms and reports for an application. The design of modules, functions and procedures may be completed using structured English or pseudocode, flowcharts, and decision tables. If a totally object-oriented approach is taken, then class and instance diagrams may be designed instead.

TECHNICAL DOCUMENTATION

The technical documentation is a record of the design and development of the project, primarily for the developers themselves, but also important as documentation of the process for the client. It aids in understanding the application and enables future maintenance to be undertaken much more simply.

Requirements specification

The fundamental basis of the documentation is the requirements specification created before the design began. This is used to confirm that the application works in the way required. It is also used as the basis of signing off the project as complete.

Form design

It is often very useful to design the forms, screens and reports for an application as this allows the user and developer to confirm the direction of the project. These may be designed on paper, or more usually these days by mocking up a non-functional prototype in an appropriate application (e.g. a visual development environment, a spreadsheet, a drawing or web design application).

Flowchart

A flowchart is ideal for documenting the flow of data through a process or module from start to end. When properly constructed, it will enable a detailed analysis of a process, allowing the developer to consider every step, decision and loop. It also shows up duplications, omissions and bottlenecks in the flow and allows the designer to simplify the process in a visual manner. Once completed, the simplicity of a well-drawn flowchart allows the designer to confirm understanding of the logic of a process with the client and provide a simple, visual document of a process.

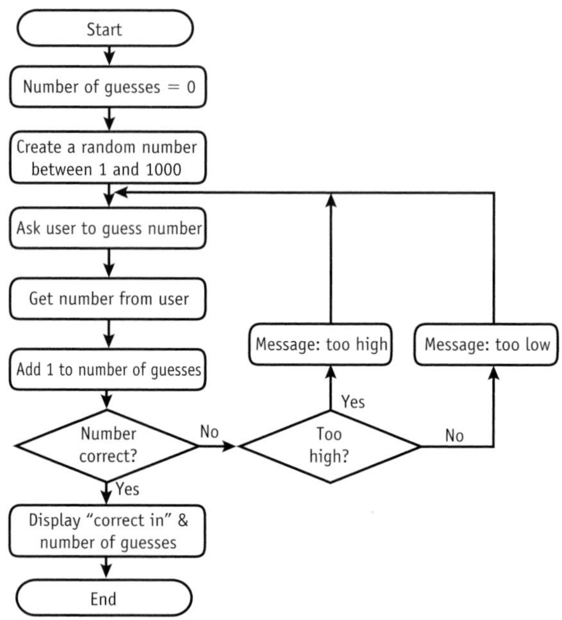

Figure 18.19 Flowchart for binary guessing game (see programming task 3).

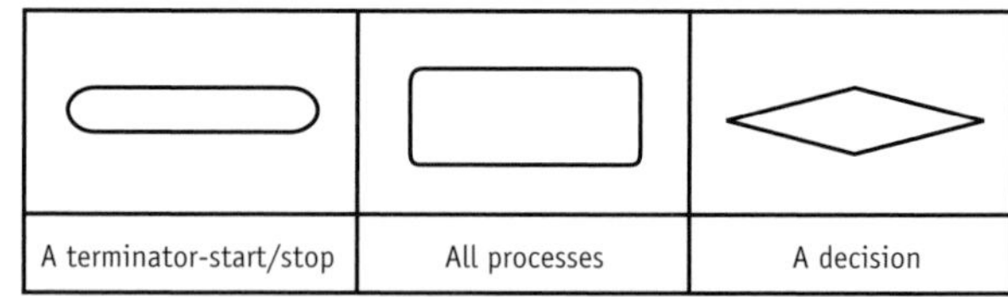

Figure 18.20 The three essential flowchart symbols.

There are a number of standard flowchart symbols that can be used, but successful flowcharts can be written using only terminators, process boxes and decision boxes. Use of other symbols can enhance the diagram but only if all parties that are to use it understand all the symbols. All charts should of course have a title. It is best to arrange them with a consistent line of flow (top to bottom or left to right) and avoid crossing lines wherever possible. Each decision box should have two outputs (and certainly never just one), and a question should always be used for each decision.

Research tip

Open Microsoft Word and investigate the flowchart autoshapes obtained using the drawing toolbar.
Draw flowcharts for programming tasks 1 and 2.

Pseudocode and structured English

Structured English and pseudocode are highly related techniques. Structured English attempts to write an algorithm in English but structured to use the main program constructs of sequences of instructions, conditional statements and iteration. It is often used when designing a single process from a data flow diagram, and thus tends to be, but does not have to be, fairly high level. Pseudocode does the same job but is usually written as a design for a final program, procedure or function and thus tends to be more low level. It may include some syntax from the intended programming language, though theoretically it will be language independent. Both methods allow the designer to consider different designs by building them quickly and reviewing them to see if they will work. It should be noted that the designer does not have to have the whole problem worked out in order to write this type of code, nor does any exact syntax matter, as it does with program code. In the alien invader example, the designer does not have to worry about what the SHOWDEAD or WINNER routines do, nor indeed how to check if the invader is visible. These problems can be deferred until later. On the other hand, the flow of the logic in checking if a missile has hit one of a large collection of aliens is documented very simply and clearly, and is in a form that will be relatively simple to code at a later date.

Think Create pseudocode for programming tasks 5 and 6.

Data dictionaries

Another vital data modelling tool is the data dictionary. This will describe the data in each entity and within each module of the program. Although the simplest dictionaries will merely list the data names, the most useful will also define the types that will be used, along with any maximum length for text, any formats that are to be applied and indeed any validations that are to be applied. A well-defined data dictionary will make the work of the programmer a great deal easier, as many of the decisions about data types will have been made at the design stage.

Example

Example pseudocode that checks if a missile has hit an alien invader progressing down the screen.

```
For each invader
 if the invader is visible then
   if the missile is at the same x position then
      if the missile is in invader from left to left+width then
        Make missile invisible
        Increment number of aliens hit and show using SHOWDEAD
        If all hit then
              USE WINNER routine
        End if
   End if
 End if
Next
```

1	2	3	4	5	6
Name	**Type**	**Length**	**Format**	**Other validation**	**Comments**
StockNumber	String	4	AA00		Primary key
Description	String	25			
Unit	String	4			
Quantity	Integer			>=0 and <=1000	
Cost	Currency			>=£0 and <=£10000	

Figure 18.21 A typical data dictionary layout

Decision tables

Decision tables are very useful language-independent tools for ensuring that every possible path is considered for a set of conditions, documenting the outcome of each. To construct a decision table involves a number of straightforward steps:

1. Identify the decisions and frame them as questions with a True/False or Yes/No answer.
2. Calculate the number of possible combinations this leads to $2^{\text{Number of decisions}}$.
3. Identify all the possible outcomes/actions that the decisions can lead to.
4. Create a decision table with all decisions and outcomes listed in the leftmost column and all the combinations along the top row.
5. Fill in the combinations of columns with the appropriate YN combinations. A simple but effective method for doing this is to lay out the tables as in Figure 18.22. The top row will be $\frac{1}{2}$ N and the $\frac{1}{2}$ Y (8 options will give 4n4y). The next row down will divide this pattern by 2 (2n2y2n2y). The next row will divide this by 2 (nynynyny).
6. Identify the appropriate action/outcome for each decision combination.
7. Review the table and then present it to the user for confirmation.

Example

Create a decision table for a stock ordering system: If the stock level < minimum stock for an item, the reorder amount should be ordered, unless less than the re-order amount has been sold in the last 3 months, in which case put this item onto a report. If the amount sold in the last 3 months is less than the minimum stock, then don't order any at all.

There are 3 questions: quantity <minimum; sales<reorder; sales<min
This means there are 2^3 combinations of decisions
The table will therefore have a label column plus 8 more
There are 3 possible actions: order the reorder amount; put the item on report; order none
There will therefore be 3 actions rows.
This leads to the decision table in figure 18.22.

DECISIONS	1	2	3	4	5	6	7	8
Quantity<min	n	n	n	n	y	y	y	y
Sales<reorder	n	n	y	y	n	n	y	y
Sales<min	n	y	n	y	n	y	n	y
ACTIONS								
Order reorder amount					x			
Put on report							x	
Order none	x	x	x	x		x		x

Figure 18.22: Decision table for stock order problem

Example

Create a decision table for cash and non-cash sales in an organisation that has the following policy:

- Cash is always accepted.
- Cheques under £100 are accepted with a valid cheque card, otherwise they need supervisor acceptance.
- Credit cards under £100 are accepted after checking on printed blacklist report; otherwise they require an authorisation number from the banking service.

Think What is the relationship between binary numbers and the combinations of decisions?

EVIDENCE ACTIVITY

P5 – M2

Special Tea Rooms: Case Study

CustomStore Solutions have been asked to provide a solution for the Special Tea Rooms ordering and analysis system, a scenario and initial requirements for which are shown below. You have been allocated the project to create it. Decide how you will design and implement the system. Sketch out a plan showing how long you intend to take on each phase of the project's lifecycle.

Create a definition of scope document with the headings:

- Purpose
- Audience
- Functional requirements
- System (hardware and software) requirements
- Key success criteria.

NB the functional requirements may be more specific than those written in the scenario, to take into account the development language chosen (to include user interface elements, speed requirements, accessibility, etc.), and any volume of data you feel are appropriate given the scenario. You will use the key success criteria to decide whether the program is deemed a success or not.

Create and document a full design for the Special Tea Rooms application to include process and data diagrams, appropriate process specifications, a data dictionary, screen designs and test plans. These must demonstrate in full how the specified requirements will be met. **(P5)**.

Create a document for your manager that should include a justification of your use of data types for each data item in the dictionary. **(M2)**.

Special Tea Rooms want to have a more automated ordering system for their tables. They currently have 1 'waiter' on for each session serving a total of 15 tables. They take an order from a table, confirm it, take the payment (cash only), give a receipt, and then hand the order to the kitchen. Another waiter then delivers the goods to the table when prepared. This system works very well and they do not wish to change the way it works, but they feel that they could benefit from using a handheld PC to take orders and print out the receipts and the kitchen order.

Currently all the orders are analysed by hand to see who the star employee is. Clearly the proposed system would allow all of this to be automated.

Foods are all categorised and coded as shown in Figure 18.23:

Category	Code	Menu number	Example
Drinks	D	1-15	1 Breakfast tea
Bakery	B	16-31	16 Homemade cookie
Soups	S	32-47	32 Tomato soup
Hot plate	H	48-63	48 Scrambled egg on toast
Rolls and sandwiches	R	64-95	64 Cheese and onion roll
Specials	P	96-99	96 Special

NB not all the numbers are used – there is a total of about 40 items on the menu at any one time.

Figure 18.23 Food and drink categories.

Partial functional requirements

Overview: the tasks the application must perform

- Log on/off each waiter and the manager
- Take orders at table
- Print out receipts
- Print out kitchen order
- Calculate the star waiter
- Calculate summary statistics
- Analyse orders by category/day/waiter/table

Outputs: information the system must supply
Receipt:

Table number, date and time

Food code, Description, Quantity, Price, Item total

Bill total, Amount tendered, Change given.

Kitchen order:

Waiter, Table, Date and time

Food code, Description, Price, Category, Category name

Analysis:

For each waiter, and summarised, for each period:

- The number of orders taken
- The number of people served
- Total order value
- Average value per order
- Average value per customer
- Totals sold in each category

The employee who has sold most in the period.

Inputs: data to be input into the system

Waiter log on

Waiter number, password, date and time

Order

Table number, number at table

Food code, quantity

Payment

Tip given

Change tendered

Analysis

Manager number and password

Processing

Waiter log on

Check that waiter ID and password are valid

Calculate day

Order

Check food code is valid

Find the appropriate food record using the code

Warn if quantity entered exceeds number of guests at table

Calculate item total as quantity * cost

Calculate total bill

Payment

Calculate total including tip if given

Calculate change to be tendered

Printing

Print receipt

Print kitchen order

Storage

As each order is confirmed it is stored

When the analysis is performed the storage is read

NB The method of storage is to be agreed, and whilst a csv, an mdb or sql file are envisaged, other solutions may be designed if they fulfil the specification in all other ways.

Analysis

Check that manager ID and password are valid

Calculate

For each waiter, and summarised, for each period:

- The number of orders taken
- The number of people served
- Total order value
- Average value per order
- Average value per customer
- Totals sold in each of the 6 categories

The employee who has sold the most in the period.

Required security

The waiter ID and password must be correct in order that only authorised employees can generate orders for the kitchen.
The manager ID and password must be correct in order that only management can access and run analysis information.

Special Tea Rooms: Implementation

Implement a working application in your chosen development language using your designs for this project.
You should provide a working program, complete listings of the program, along with any associated data, and annotated screen shots of the working program.

18.4 Be able to document, test, debug and review a programmed solution

TESTING AND DEBUGGING:

Testing is an absolutely critical part of developing an application. It is said by the best developers that a program that has not been tested is worthless, because no-one knows whether it will work at all, or when it will fail. Testing large applications to ensure they are correct, on the other hand, can seem to be an endless task. There are, fortunately, some strategies that help manage the task.

Test strategy

Test plans will usually be created at design stage. When ready, the programmer can then run the tests in the plan to ensure that they give the expected results. The main strategy for designing good tests is to build a good set of sample data to use rather than simply use random data to test with. For example, if a wage in an organisation can be in the range £5.00 per hour to £30.00 per hour inclusive, then designing a good set of test data will save a good deal of time and ensure accurate data input. A common mistake is to test many numbers in the range of £5 to £30, but this only proves that valid data is accepted. Six numbers

Debugging	Checking for errors whilst writing a program. Debugging finds errors that stop a program working.
Testing	Checking for errors in code that is being executed.
Test plan	A table specifying a set of tests that will be performed on a function, procedure, module or application.
Test log	A table recording the results of testing – often the same as a test plan but with two extra columns for the results.
Test data	Data used for a test. It comes in three varieties: normal data, abnormal data and boundary data.
Normal data	Data within the normal range that should be accepted.
Abnormal data	Data outside the valid range that should be rejected.
Boundary	Data on the boundary of the valid and invalid ranges – in practice the place where most problems occur.
Functional or Black box testing	A program or sub-program is tested by checking that the correct outputs are given for each input to check that it works to specification.
Logical or White box testing	A program or sub-program is tested by checking all paths through it to ensure that the logic of the application is correct.
Performance testing	A program or sub-program is tested to ensure it performs adequately in terms of speed with the required volume of data.
Requirements testing	A program or sub-program is tested to ensure that the application does what it was required to.
Top down testing	The application as a whole is checked to ensure it works. If it does not, then each module is checked. If one of these does not, then each part of the module is checked.
Bottom up testing	Each part of a module is checked independently to ensure it works; when it does, then it is integrated with the system and checked again. When all parts have been added to all modules, then the application as a whole is checked.

Figure 18.24 Glossary of testing terms.

properly thought out, like those in Figure 18.25, will provide sufficient evidence that the input is working correctly. By testing once for normal data, once for abnormal data and testing at the boundary between the two, it is possible in most cases to see the entire range of the behaviour. This test data will show that valid data is accepted and invalid data rejected and test that the correct behaviour occurs at the boundary between the two.

£4.99	£5.00	£15.00	£30.00	£30.01	£100.00

Figure 18.25 Test data set

Once a good set of test data has been designed for all input, processing and output, then the tester simply has to work through the test plan. The results will be logged. Where the expected and actual results do not match, the reason for this will be investigated and any errors corrected. At this stage a re-test has to be performed.

> ***Think*** Create a test data set for validating a stockLevel variable which contains the quantity actually held in stock of an item in a supermarket warehouse.

Test plan structure

Different organisations use slightly different test plans and logs, but they all must record the test data used, the expected output and they must log the actual output. The expected and actual output should be what the user actually witnesses, not 'OK', or 'correct' or a similar general statement.

Application: Payroll **Module:** getPayData			**Tester Name:** **Date:**			
Test number	Variable/ control	Purpose/ Test class	Actual input data/file/event	Expected output	Actual output	Comments/corrective action
1	wage	Valid	15.00	15.00		
2	wage	Invalid	100.00	Err 3		
3	wage	Lower boundary	5.00	5.00		
4	wage	Lower boundary	4.99	Err 3		
5	wage	Upper boundary	30.00	30.00		
6	wage	Upper boundary	30.01	Err 3		

Figure 18.26 A typical test plan

Application: Payroll **Module:** getPayData			**Tester Name:** S. Pilau **Date:** 12/2/08			
Test number	Variable/ control	Purpose/ Test class	Actual input data/file/event	Expected output	Actual output	Comments/corrective action
1	wage	Valid	15.00	15.00	15.00	
2	wage	Invalid	100.00	Err 3	Err 3	
3	wage	Lower boundary	5.00	5.00	Err 3	Condition reset to >= rather than > (see log dated 13/2/08 test 1)
4	wage	Lower boundary	4.99	Err 3	Err 3	
5	wage	Upper boundary	30.00	30.00	30.00	
6	wage	Upper boundary	30.01	Err 3	Err 13	The wrong error string used. (see log dated 13/2/08 test 2)

Figure 18.27 A typical test log

Error messages

As can be seen in Figures 18.26 and 18.27 it is a useful practice to design in the required error messages from the start. This means that a consistent style of reporting errors can be developed and a table of possible error messages can be built up to include in the user manual. In practice the programmer is able to build a table of error message strings in the application and simply reference the required string every time an error occurs.

Specialist software tools

Testing for software errors is essentially testing the fallibility of humans in creating solutions. A systematic approach to finding errors is therefore essential. A number of testing tools have been developed in order to automate and systematise testing. There are a number of variants of these that allow a developer to specify tests to be performed or act as a form of macro recorder, capturing user actions and replaying them on the application. Some automation tools will attempt to build a set of test cases automatically. All of these products take some skill to use reliably. Once mastered, they will, however, perform a massive volume of tests in a very short time and at minimal extra cost.

Think Software is usually beta tested (tested by people who represent end users rather than developers) before it is finally released. Why is this considered such an important step?

USER DOCUMENTATION

Once the application has been completed, documentation must be completed for the user. This will usually have at least three major parts. Firstly, the system requirements will be spelled out in some detail. If the application requires a fast processor, a graphics card and DirectX installed, this must be stated, otherwise the user may spend a good deal of time trying to set the application up, only to end up being frustrated.

Secondly, instructions on how to install the application on the user's system must be provided. The developer may choose to provide an installation tool, but even then the user will have to be told where to locate this tool and how to start it, and perhaps how to run through all of its operation.

Finally, a user guide must be provided. This will usually start by defining the purpose and the target audience for the product. It should then provide a walk-through of the main functionality of the product. A full user guide will also include a reference to all menus and functions. Finally, it will include a table of the possible error messages, what they mean and any action that should be taken.

Many users will attempt to use the program without reading the full user guide. Whilst this is not desirable behaviour, the developer should take it into account and most will therefore provide a quick start guide. This will cover starting the application and just a short guide to the main functions.

The documentation for applications has traditionally been bound manuals. It is becoming common practice, however, to provide the user documentation in Adobe pdf files. These are simple to produce directly from the authoring tool, and do not require printing, collating or binding.

Getting help

An application should always provide the user with a means of getting help. There are a number of approaches to this. One of the simplest to implement and most useful for the user is to provide good clear prompts and well validated input with clear error messages for when incorrect actions are taken. In addition to this it is usually relatively simple to provide a link to a pdf file containing the full user documentation. A more comprehensive approach to providing help is to provide context sensitive help on a help menu, or function key (e.g. F1) using custom-programmed help procedures or through a system like the Windows help interface.

Think Which application that you use provides the best help? Why do you think the method used is so good?

REVIEW

A good programming team will attempt to create the best quality code possible by conducting formal reviews on code being written, and the finished code. This will involve a meeting between the producer and one or more members of the team to look through the code and analyse the suitability of what has been produced.

Reviews against specifications requirements

At the end of the development test the review team will inspect the final product to ensure it meets the requirements as written in the definition of scope and the functional specification. To do this they will take each requirement in turn and the producer will present how this has been achieved. The review team will analyse this and decide if this is correct with reference to the code and the finished product.

Interim reviews

Interim reviews will take place as the code is developed. Typically a moderator will be appointed to manage the meetings and report on what has been found, a recorder to keep notes of the inspection and ensure each defect is noted in detail, and possibly a presenter who will talk through the work, who may be the producer but need not be. The meetings aim to find any problems in the work prior to the product being released. A popular variation of this is a structured walk-through. This involves the team looking at the code for a routine, or a module and talking through it line by line. When a number of people look at the work line by line in this way they spot potential flaws, notice optimisations that can be put in place, routines that may be put into reusable code, or notice reusable code that exists already that could be used in place of the custom code that has been written. The real benefits are not only that the product itself is potentially improved a great deal, but also the team as a whole learns and improves together and over time their productivity grows enormously.

Developers could feel under threat when their code is reviewed in this way and 'defects' noted. It is important, therefore, that the process is conducted in a neutral manner, with no sanctions or penalties arising from these reviews. Finding errors and possible improvements has to be seen by all as a welcome challenge, rather than as a threat.

EVIDENCE ACTIVITY

P6, M3, D2

Special Tea Rooms: Test and review

Using the test plans from your designs for this project, test the completed application created for Special Tea Rooms.

Form a small review group and conduct a formal review of the solution, and provide minutes of the meeting(s) in your own words. These must document at least two improvements which could be implemented (note: these should ideally include improvements to the efficiency of the code and/or improvements to the interface).

Create a technical manual comprising annotated program code, test plans and test logs and minutes from the formal review.

Create a User manual including a getting started guide and annotated screenshots covering all the main functions of the application. **(P6)**

Any changes made must be confirmed by retesting and a second review. Provide annotated screenshots of the improvements made as a result of testing and review and minutes of the review. **(M3)**.

Provide a report to your manager to include a formal evaluation of the solution against the original specification covering the purpose, audience, benefits and limitations, and possible improvements and extensions. **(D2)**.

Digital Graphics and Computers

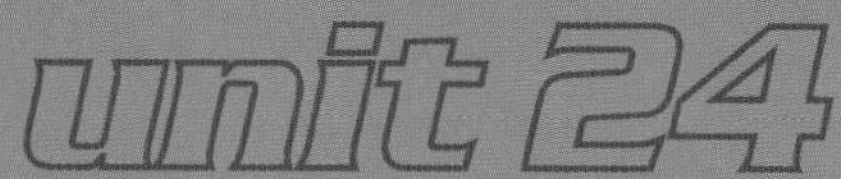

Images and graphics are part of our everyday world. From artwork on our breakfast cereal packet to website graphics, we are surrounded by images. The rapid development of computer processing power and graphic editing software allows the production and manipulation of images in ways and at speeds undreamed of a few years ago. The development of digital cameras, scanners, graphics tablets and photo quality printers assist in the production of high quality input and output.

This unit will teach you to identify suitable hardware and software to create and edit, store and print graphics. You will create original graphic images using a range of software tools and edit images you have captured electronically. You will learn about different file formats and their appropriate selection as well as file management and compression. Laws of copyright will be considered and discussed.

The IT practitioner may be expected to produce images for a client. You will learn about ensuring that you meet both client and user needs in the development of images. Reviews will need to be undertaken to ensure that the images are appropriate for use.

By the end of this unit you will:

So you want to be a...

Graphic Designer

My name Darren Phillips-Boyd
Age 26
Income £20,000–£24,000

What does a graphic designer do?

I create designs for CD cases, illustrations, books and magazines.

What are your day-to-day responsibilities?

I am given a brief with guidelines that include a deadline for completion. The brief is normally presented to me as text. Occasionally, there may be a sketch to work from, but often the design is left entirely to me. I usually start the design process by doing some research. I then create a draft prototype of the image(s). This then goes to the client so they can give feedback and make suggestions. The process is iterative and will go through first, second and third proofs before completion.

> "You need to be very creative and have a passion for design."

How did you get into the job?

I did A Levels and developed a portfolio of art work at school. I then did a foundation art course at college. I finally did a three-year degree in Graphic Design at university. After completing my degree I did some freelance design work, before joining my present company.

What training have you had?

I developed an interest in art and design when I was very young. I started using the computer in the development of graphic designs while studying for my A Levels. Since then, at college and university, I have developed skills using a range of computer applications. In my present job I use Photoshop, Illustrator, InDesign and Quark. I have only been in the job for three months, but I understand that I can request training courses when I have my first review.

What are the hours like?

I work from 9am to 5:30pm, Monday to Friday.

How good is the pay?

The salary for a Junior Graphic Designer is between £20,000 and £24,000.

It sounds like a complex role, what qualities do you need?

You need to be very creative and have a passion for design. A good understanding of colour and how colours work together is also vital. Also having the concept of space, where images/text can fit to create a mood that reflects the brief.

How do you see your career progressing?

It is possible to progress from Junior to Mid-weight then a Senior Designer. Top of the tree is the Art Director/Creative Director. I am not sure about the future, but may at some time want to run my own graphic design business.

Grading criteria

The table below shows what you need to do to gain a pass, merit or distinction in this part of the qualification. Make sure you refer back to it when you are completing work so that you can judge whether you are meeting the criteria and what you need to do to fill in gaps in your knowledge or experience.

In this unit there are four evidence activities that give you an opportunity to demonstrate your achievement of the grading criteria:

page 149 **P1, P2, M1**

page 156 **P3, P4, P5, P6**

page 165 **M2, M3, D1**

page 169 **D2**

To achieve a pass grade the evidence must show that the learner is able to...	To achieve a merit grade the evidence must show that, in addition to the pass criteria, the learner is able to...	To achieve a distinction grade the evidence must show that, in addition to the pass and merit criteria, the learner is able to...
P1 describe the hardware and software used to create and edit graphics	**M1** compare the limitations of at least two different hardware devices and two different software packages utilised for the capture, manipulation and storage of graphics	**D1** justify the following in connection with the production of graphic images to meet a client and user need: software and tools used, file format, image resolution, colour depth
P2 identify two graphics related hardware upgrades to an existing system and describe the potential benefits when working with graphic images	**M2** demonstrate the use of two advanced techniques in graphics manipulation	**D2** evaluate the impact of evolving output media on the designing and creation of graphic images.
P3 define and document a client and user need for three related graphic images	**M3** demonstrate the impact that file format, compression techniques, image resolution and colour depth have on file size and image quality.	
P4 create and review three original graphic images to meet a defined user need		
P5 capture existing images using a scanner and a digital camera and edit them to meet a given user need		
P6 explain potential legal implications of using and editing graphic images.		

24.1 Know the hardware and software required to work with graphic images

HARDWARE

Graphics cards and their features

Many modern motherboards have on-board graphics. This is sometimes referred to as 'an integrated graphics solution'. They share system RAM rather than having their own dedicated RAM. Integrated solutions on modern motherboards are capable of handling 2D and some 3D graphics. For high-end gaming and processor-intensive 3D graphics rendering, separate graphics cards are usually required. A graphics card performs three main tasks:

- geometry – the computation of shapes
- lighting – the creation of shadows, etc.
- rendering images – adding textures to surfaces.

Graphics cards are available as **AGP** or **PCIe**. AGP is slower and is being phased out. Motherboards come with either an AGP slot or PCIe slot(s). An AGP card cannot be installed in a PCIe slot, so a matching motherboard and graphics card is essential. For high-end processing, it is possible, using PCIe slots, to install two different graphics cards in a PC. This allows complex processing to be shared across both cards. This also allows up to four monitors to be attached to a PC (an OS that supports multi-monitors, such as Win XP is also required).

Figure 24.1 A graphics card

> **Key words**
>
> **AGP** – Accelerated Graphics Port, used to assist graphics performance.
>
> **PCIe** – PCI Express can support can support fast data transfers necessary for high-end graphics processing.
>
> **rasterising** – preparing an image for printing by reducing the resolution.
>
> **wireframe** – model composed of lines and curves.

The CPU, in conjunction with application software, sends information about an image to the graphics card. Graphics cards have the following features:

- A GPU (graphics processor unit), which is designed to process complex graphics algorithms quickly, freeing the CPU for other processing. It takes binary data from the CPU and creates a digital image by creating a **wireframe** and then **rasterising**, and adding colouring and lighting to it.
- RAMDAC, a chip that converts digital signals from the GPU to analogue signals to be output to the monitor.
- Dedicated memory, used to hold binary data sent from the CPU, and temporarily hold the image before it is output to the RAMDAC and then the monitor.

  Modern graphics cards commonly have 128, 256 or 512 MB of dedicated memory. The more dedicated memory installed, the fewer times data will need to be swapped into main memory and slow down proceedings. Performance can be affected by the width of the memory bus. Wider buses will transfer data faster than narrower buses. Most modern cards have 128 or 256 bit memory buses, although some cheaper cards have 64 bit buses.

> **Research tip**
>
> Find out about graphics cards. Look at reviews and buyers guides. www.itreviews.co.uk is a good starting point.

Role of internal memory

Cache

Graphics creation and manipulation is a processor-intensive activity. The cache temporarily stores the most frequently accessed data and instructions. When the processor operates, it looks for data in the cache prior to looking in RAM. Cached data and instructions can be accessed more quickly than those that have to be fetched from main memory.

L1 cache is located on the processor chip. It is usually 32 KB in total, divided into two 16 KB memory caches: one for data and one for instructions. (AMD K6 processors use 64 KB of L1 cache.) L2 cache is usually 256 or 512 KB, and is located on a separate chip. If the processor cannot find the data it is looking for in L1 cache, it will look in L2 and then in main memory.

RAM

Many graphics programs recommend at least 512 MB of RAM. Most PCs ship with 512 MB or 1 GB of RAM, so should cope with most general graphics requirements. This memory consists of modules that are inserted into slots on the motherboard, close to the processor. They can be removed or replaced as necessary.

Instructions and data are read from and written to RAM from the processor. RAM is sometimes known as 'primary' or 'main' memory and is vital to the operation of a computer. It is volatile, meaning that when the computer loses power or is switched off, the data held in RAM is lost.

Remember that graphics cards have their own dedicated memory. Without a dedicated graphics card, system RAM is used to hold data prior to processing and temporarily after processing, leaving less system RAM available for other activities.

Role of processors in relation to the manipulation of graphic images

The production of graphics is processor-intensive as many complex calculations need to be made. Without a dedicated graphics card, this activity is carried out by the main CPU. For a discussion of Graphics Processor Units, see the section on graphics cards. To use the latest graphics packages such as Photoshop CS3, Intel Pentium 4, Intel Centrino, Intel Xeon, or Intel Core™ Duo (or compatible) processors are recommended.

Other internal hardware devices

See the section on digital cameras.

File storage

CD ROM

Due to the large file size of high-quality graphic images, CDs are an excellent storage medium. Most modern PCs and laptop computers ship with DVD or CD writers. This makes it very simple to save large numbers of images on standard or rewritable CDs. An additional benefit is that they can store other types of media as well, such as sound and data.

Hard drives

The development of hard drives capable of storing very large volumes of data has made the saving of large numbers of graphic images on disk feasible. Some graphic software programs also require substantial amounts of disk space for installation. (Photoshop CS3 extended requires 1.5 GB of disk space.) SATA hard drives are available with disk sizes of up to 750 GB. External hard drives with similar capacities are also available, making it possible to keep huge libraries of images and clipart.

Remember that finding your graphic images requires some sensible file management!

Flash cards

Flash cards are small flash memory modules that are enclosed in a plastic case. They retain their data after they have been detached from their host. They are commonly used in digital cameras, pagers, laptops, mobile phones, PDAs and audio players. A number of different form factors are available including SmartMedia, CompactFlash and PCMCIA.

USB storage devices

The development of USB storage has made the connection of storage devices to computers very quick and easy. There are a number of different types of device available. These include external hard drives, CD and DVD drives, pen drives and card disks.

Input devices

Graphics tablet

A graphics tablet allows a user to draw images in a similar way to using a pen and paper. A cable (usually with a USB connector) connects to the computer. A stylus is used to 'draw' on the flat surface of the tablet. The drawn image appears on the computer monitor. Because the stylus resembles a pen, accurate drawings can be produced more easily than using a mouse.

Research tip

Investigate the range of graphics tablets that are available. They come in a wide range of prices. What additional features do the more expensive models offer?

Mouse

A variety of pointing devices, known as mice, are available. The mouse enables a user to control the position of an on-screen cursor. Most have two buttons and a scrolling wheel. Mouse actions include single-clicking, double-clicking, click and drag, drag and drop and right-clicking. Most mice use USB or PS2 connectors. Wireless versions are also available. Some mice have a small ball underneath them that rotates against two sets of rollers inside the mouse. This captures information about the direction the mouse is moving in and this is converted to movement on the screen.

Digital camera

A digital camera is an electronic device that can take pictures without the use of film. A huge range of models with varying features are available. When choosing a digital camera, a number of features should be considered.

Resolution – The resolution of most new cameras is 5 megapixels or more. The greater the resolution the more flexibility, but the larger the file sizes will be.

Zoom lenses – Many digital cameras provide two types of zoom, optical and digital. Optical zoom uses a lens to magnify an image. Digital zoom discards some of the pixels around the edge of an image and enlarges the rest, giving the appearance of zoom but reducing the quality of the image. For high-quality photographs choose a camera with a good optical zoom.

Storage – There are a number of choices of storage media. Compact flash cards are very popular. Additional and larger cards (up to 1 GB) can be purchased. The cards have a controller chip that enables the fast transfer of data between the camera and card.

Other types of storage media include:

Smart media cards: These are used by Olympus and Fuji and have a maximum storage capacity of 128 MB.

Memory sticks: These are used by Sony and are very flexible as they can store data and music as well as images, but are presently limited to 128 MB.

Microdrives: These are popular with high-end users as they can store up to 1 GB of images and are presently cheaper than similar-sized compact flash cards.

XD-Picture card: This is being developed jointly by Olympus and Fuji. It can presently only store 128 MB of pictures, but has the potential to store up to 8 GB. It is about the size of a postage stamp so has great potential.

Batteries – The cost of batteries should be considered when purchasing a camera as some consume batteries at an alarming speed.

Digital camera drivers – Digital cameras usually ship with a CD or CDs that include software drivers and additional photo editing software.

Example

Digital cameras that employ wireless USB for the transfer of images between camera and computer are beginning to appear on the market. See http://artimi.com/news.php?presrelease=000028

Think What camera features are important for wildlife, news or sports photography?

Scanner

A scanner can be used to capture a paper document as an electronic image that may then be edited using graphics software if required. A number of different types of scanners are available including hand-held and drum scanners, but the most popular for home office use is the flatbed scanner. The most popular size is A4, although scanners in varying sizes are available.

To scan a document using a flatbed scanner, the document is placed on a glass plate and the lid of the scanner is lowered. A lamp illuminates the document and a scan head passes down its length. In colour scanners, the light is passed through red, green and blue filters. Most support true colour (24 bit). Some support 30 or 36 bit colour. Mirrors reflect the image onto a lens. The lens focuses the light onto diodes that convert the light into electrical current that varies according to the strength of the light. An analogue to digital converter converts the voltage into digital pixels. The image is then transferred to the computer via a USB, parallel, SCSI or FireWire connection. A software driver, usually known as a TWAIN driver, allows any application that supports it to work directly with the scanner.

Figure 24.2 A flatbed scanner

OUTPUT MEDIUM

Printer

A wide variety of printers are available. Graphic designers often use printers differently to most office workers and home users. Quality, exact colour matching and layout are very important and frequently mean purchasing high-end printers. Colour laser printers are fast but expensive and the quality of output of cheaper models can be poor. There are many inexpensive inkjet printers on the market, although the cost of replacement cartridges can be considerable. Again, the quality of output can vary considerably.

Postscript printers are favoured by graphic designers as they allow for very accurate rendering of images, especially vector images and fonts.

Some photo printers produce very high-quality output and use the same paper and printing technology as the ones in photo kiosks. Many new printers have slots for different types of memory card. Some have Bluetooth, enabling photos to be sent from mobile phone to printer. Additionally, some printers have a dock for the camera, so that the memory card does not need to be removed prior to printing. Portable printers containing batteries are available. Some printers have small LCD screens that can perform simple editing tasks such as cropping, red-eye removal and resizing.

With the development of five to nine megapixel cameras, A3 colour printers have become more popular.

Computer monitor

The choice of monitor can make a large difference to the viewing experience of the user. There is a choice between two different monitor technologies: CRT and LCD.

Traditionally, digital graphics designers have preferred CRT technology because it supports a greater variety of screen resolutions and displays greater colour representation. However, more designers are now moving to high-end LCD monitors as the development of LCD technology has closed the quality gap. LCD monitors consume much less electricity, have a longer working life and take up less desk space. They weigh much less and can be moved easily. However, they are more vulnerable to damage and the viewing angle can be an issue, as the further from the centre of the display the screen is viewed, the poorer the quality of the image.

CRT (cathode ray tube) monitors have been around for many years. They work by sending a stream of electrons from three electron guns (each assigned a colour: red, green or blue) through a metal grille (used for focusing), and onto the monitor screen from behind, lighting tiny phosphor dots on the inside of a glass tube. There are three sets of phosphor dots in red, green and blue. Combinations of these dots allow the monitor to display a very wide range of colours. The stream of electrons passes back and forth in lines and from top to bottom, creating a complete image on the screen.

Dot pitch is used as a measure of the crispness of the display. It is a measure of the distance between the phosphor dots in millimetres. Therefore, a low dot pitch, such as .28 is considered to be good. A high dot pitch may mean that the image appears blurred.

Figure 24.3 A CRT monitor

LCD (liquid crystal display) monitors are becoming widely used as the technology has improved to provide output to compete with the quality of CRTs. The displays use two sheets of polarising glass (known as substrate) with a liquid crystal solution in between. A light passes through the first layer of substrate and an electric current causes the crystals to line up, effectively allowing varying amounts of light to pass through. When the light passes through the second substrate, the image and colours are produced. Most LCD monitors use active matrix technology. This allows faster screen refresh times than cheaper passive matrix technology. When using an LCD monitor, it should always be set to its native screen resolution in order to produce the crispest display.

Figure 24.4 An LCD monitor

Example

Plasma displays are now available. They are capable of displaying high definition graphics and are available in a wide range of sizes. They are presently very expensive.

Other

Mobile phone

The range of features available in mobile phones continues to expand. The ability to take photographs, record video footage, send photos and video to others, use your photos as wallpaper etc. is now well established. Phones that can be used for satellite navigation and live broadcast television are likely to be available soon.

PDA

A PDA (Personal Digital Assistant) is a small, handheld device that can be used to keep a calendar of appointments that can be synchronised with a calendar on a PC or laptop. Many PDAs have a wide range of facilities including reminders and alarms, notes, to do lists, calculators, applications, games, handwriting recognition and contact information. The trend is for these devices to become more multi-functional.

Figure 24.5 A Personal Digital Assistant

Plotter

Plotters are most frequently used for the production of high-quality vector scale drawings such as engineering drawings and building plans. They can be purchased in varying sizes and can produce colour drawings. Traditionally, they involved pens moving mechanically across a paper surface. Today these have largely been replaced with very large-format inkjet and laser printers. These are still called plotters even though they produce images as bitmaps. Some models produce very large photographic quality images.

SOFTWARE

It is possible to categorise graphics programs under headings such as vector, bitmap and photo manipulation software. However, as these products continue to be developed and new versions appear, extra features are added that lead to a blurring of the categories. For example, Paintshop Pro can produce both bitmap and vector images. This should be borne in mind while reading the sections below.

Dedicated vector graphics software

A number of well-established vector graphics programs are available, e.g. CorelDRAW, Adobe Illustrator, Adobe Flash and AutoCAD.

CorelDRAW is a suite of programs including:

- CorelDRAW: a vector graphics program
- Corel Capture: allows images to be captured using several methods
- Corel PowerTRACE: converts raster images to vector images
- Corel Photo-Paint: raster image creation and editing program.

CorelDRAW originally appeared in 1989 and has since been developed and improved.

CASE STUDY: PET PHOTOGRAPHER

Mike Dansom is a professional pet photographer. Many of his customers are breeders of pedigree show dogs. He also takes portraits of family pets. Photographs are normally taken in clients' homes and gardens. 'The important thing is to try to capture the character of the animal. You need to have an affinity with animals as they can be nervous or very fidgety. Some of my favourite photos are the action shots, showing the animals in motion. These are also the most difficult to get. I use Photoshop to enhance the image if necessary.'

QUESTION

What features need to be considered when purchasing a digital camera for taking action shots and portraits of animals?

Adobe Illustrator was first shipped in 1987 for the Apple Mac. The first Windows version appeared in 1989. It is presently considered to be the industry standard for illustration work.

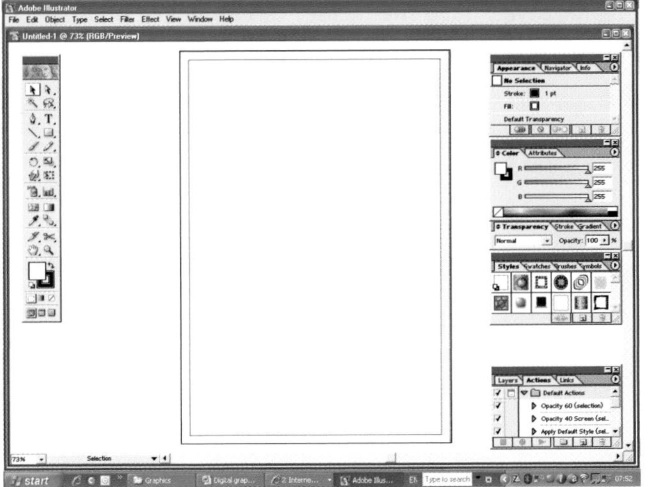

Figure 24.6 Adobe Illustrator

Adobe Flash is much more than a vector graphics program. It is a professional multimedia authoring program. It can be used to create graphic images, slideshows, games, movies and websites.

Applications for producing 2D or 3D engineering or architectural drawings use vector graphics. The best-known applications are produced by Autodesk. They produce a number of different versions of their **AutoCAD** program for different applications. These applications require a fast processor or processors, lots of RAM (frequently 2–5 GB), and a powerful dedicated graphics card.

Dedicated bitmap software

Microsoft Paint comes bundled with Microsoft Windows. It is frequently the first drawing program to be used by young children. The package has a number of simple drawing tools and allows pictures to be saved as bitmaps. Images such as .jpg, .gif and .bmp files can be created and then pasted into other documents if required.

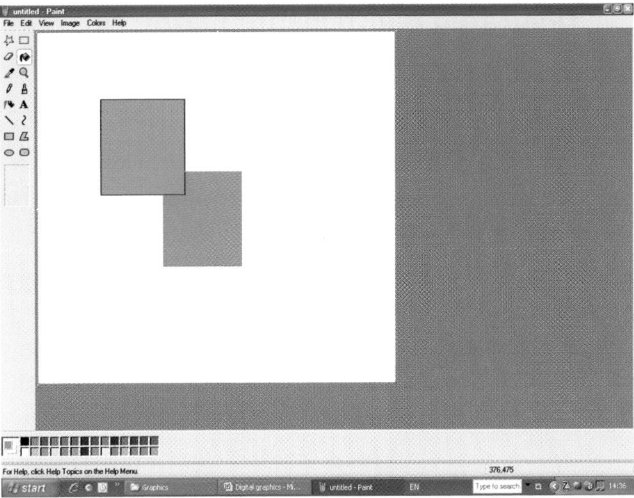

Figure 24.7 Microsoft Paint

Adobe Photoshop is most frequently used for the editing and manipulation of photographic images. See the section on dedicated photo manipulation software.

Paintshop Pro, originally published by Jasc Software but now owned by Corel, supports both bitmap and vector editing. It is far less expensive than Photoshop, but is not available in an Apple Macintosh version.

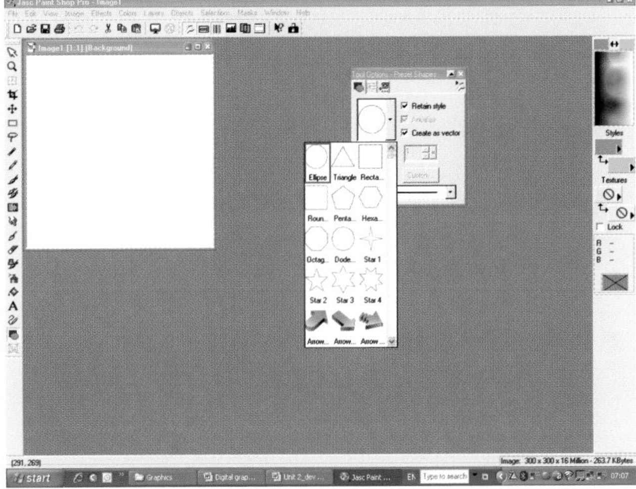

Figure 24.8 Paintshop Pro

Dedicated photo manipulation software

Adobe Photoshop can be used to edit images such as photographs and scanned images. It is currently considered to be the market leader in commercial bitmap and image manipulation. It also has a selection of drawing tools that can be used to create images from scratch. The colour depth of an image can be altered and the image can be compressed in a number of different formats. The extended version includes the ability to work with 3D and motion-based content.

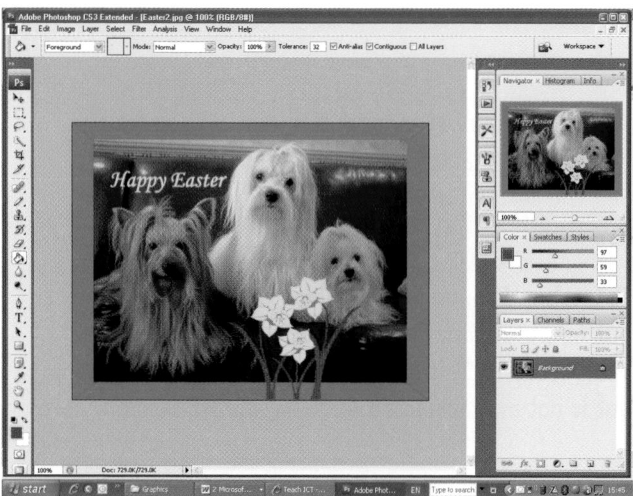

Figure 24.9 Photoshop CS3

Graphics facilities embedded within other application packages

Many applications have graphics facilities available within them. For example, in the Microsoft Office suite, Word, Excel and PowerPoint all have a drawing toolbar with facilities such as: shapes, 3D styles, shadow styles, lines, line styles, arrows, autoshapes, line colour, fill colour, WordArt, grouping and ungrouping, ordering of objects, clipart and picture insertion, rotating, flipping and a diagram gallery. It is also possible to insert charts and graphs and to recolour some drawings. Images can be animated in PowerPoint. Microsoft Access does not have a drawing toolbar, but it is possible to store images within a database, add images to forms and add charts and images to reports.

Some web-authoring programs, such as Dreamweaver, have the facility to produce graphic buttons and animated gifs.

> **Research tip**
>
> Open two different graphics programs. Look at the toolbox in each. Compare and contrast the tools and facilities in each.

Other tools

Image viewers

A large number of image viewers are available. Many have been developed to support single desktop environments such as Windows, MacOS etc. A few, such as **Adobe Bridge**, have been developed for both Windows and the Mac.

Windows XP comes with its own image viewer, **Windows Picture and Fax Viewer**. Double-clicking on an image file will open the image within the viewer by default unless that file type has been associated with another application. The viewer allows the user to preview, zoom, print, save, delete, view a slideshow of images in the same folder, rotate the image by 90° and to open the image in an editing program.

Versions of Microsoft Office from XP onwards ship with a viewer called **Microsoft Office Picture Manager**. Picture Manager allows the user to add shortcuts to locations where images are stored, adjust settings such as brightness, contrast, resize, rotate and flip, red-eye removal and crop. It can also compress images.

Photo galleries

A large number of different programs, including many freeware programs, are available for creating photo galleries for viewing on websites. These tools will generate web pages, optimise and resize images as thumbnails and create hyperlinks to full-size photos. Photoshop CS2 and CS3 has this capability. Many examples of these galleries can be found by searching on the Internet. Some allow images to be uploaded to their sites.

Research tip

Go to www.sxc.hu/ to see an example of an online photo gallery with over 250,000 photographs. Check the legal restrictions on individual photographs.

File conversion software

Sometimes a graphic file needs to be converted from one format to another. For example, a drawing may be saved as a .bmp file. If this image is to be displayed on a website, the .bmp file type is not recognised by web browsers, so the file must be converted to an appropriate file type such as .gif.

Dedicated graphics packages have the facility to export images in a variety of formats. A number of third-party tools are also available for this purpose.

File conversion is discussed further in the next section.

EVIDENCE ACTIVITY

P1 – P2 – M1

You are working for a marketing company. You have been asked to create a number of graphic images (minimum of three) for one of several new clients. You will need to choose one of the following projects:

- a new range of cosmetics
- a new all-weather holiday resort
- a new theme park
- a vintage teddy bear shop.

You will need to meet the client to discuss their requirements. You will need to determine:

- The purpose of each image
- Any particular aspect of the product that they wish to be included
- The target audience and how their needs could be met
- How the images will be used. Will the images appear on billboards, in glossy magazines, leaflets or on a website?
- Does the client require a logo?
- Whether a particular house style needs to be adhered to
- Minimum and maximum file sizes
- Cost of production
- Timescale for the project including dates of future meetings to monitor progress.

Describe the hardware and software you could use to create your images. Describe the features of each device and program used. Ensure that the following are included: graphics cards, memory, processors and cache, input and output devices, file storage, vector software, bitmap software, photo-manipulation software, embedded software and other tools. **(P1)**

Explain two possible hardware upgrades that would be beneficial to the production of graphic images and discuss the potential benefits. **(P2)**

Write a short report to compare the limitations of two different hardware devices and two different software packages used for capturing, manipulating and storing graphics. **(M1)**

24.2 Understand types of graphic images and graphical file formats

FILE HANDLING

Converting files

In general, vector graphics programs have the capacity to export to other vector formats, while bitmap graphics programs export to other bitmap formats. It is relatively easy to convert a vector image to a bitmap, but more problematic to convert bitmap images into vector images. Although the conversion is possible, using Flash or Illustrator, the quality of the result may be disappointing.

File sizes

If images are being produced for high-quality printing, then large file sizes cannot be avoided. However, if images are being produced to be viewed on screen, such as part of a web page, then optimising the image is important. The size of a file correlates with the time it takes it to download from the Internet and display on the screen. A resolution greater than 72 dpi results in larger file sizes without appreciable improvement in on-screen viewing. Resizing or cropping an image or using thumbnails can significantly reduce download time. Controlling the number of colours used in an image can also reduce file size. If your image is saved as a .gif file, try reducing the image to 128, 64, 32 or 16 colours. If your image is a .jpg file, experiment with different compression ratios. The aim is to reduce the size of the file, but to still be able to view an image of acceptable quality. Another method that can speed up the download of images is to create interlaced gifs or progressive .jpg files.

Think When visiting a website, how long are you prepared to wait for images to appear on your screen?

File management

When working with graphic images, it is easy to generate many files. Digital cameras generate fairly meaningless file names which make it difficult to identify particular ones. It is also sometimes necessary to save an image that is being edited several times and in different file formats. Therefore, good file management is very important. Adobe Photoshop has its own file management application known as the Bridge. This can be used as a cataloguing tool as well as a way of previewing images. It has facilities for creating and managing folders, creating a Favourites list and viewing or adding **metadata** to images.

Key word

Metadata - additional information that is stored within an image, such as: author, copyright notice, file size, date created and modified, resolution, colour mode, bit depth, etc.

Naming files

It is good practice to save files using appropriate filenames that will make it easy to identify required images. All graphics packages allow for files to be named and renamed. If an image needs to be saved several times while being edited, adding V1, V2, V3 etc to a filename will help to identify the latest version.

Files can be renamed without opening them. In Windows, right-mouse click on the filename and select Rename from the context-sensitive menu. Type in the new filename. Alternatively, click on a file, then click on its filename textbox to allow the filename to be edited. Type in the new filename, then press Enter.

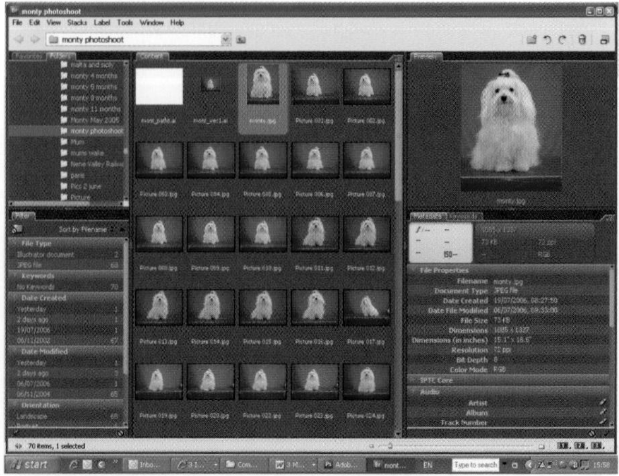

Figure 24.10 Adobe Bridge

- Multiple files can be renamed. Open a folder and select the files to be renamed. (Press Ctrl+A to select all files.)
- Press the F2 key. It will appear that only one file has been selected.
- Type in the filename required, then press Enter.

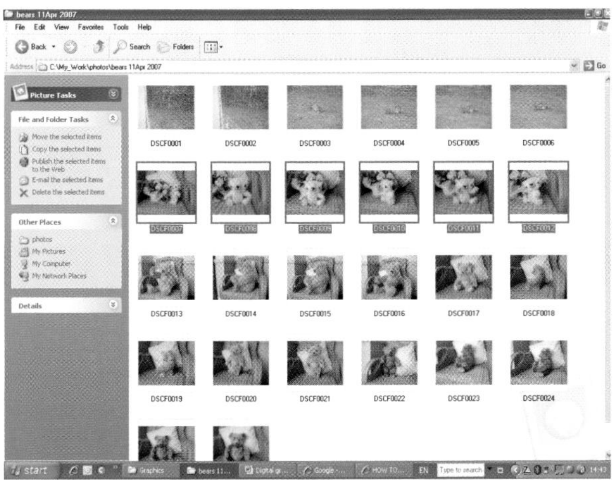

Figure 24.10(a) Images of Pip (small bear) have been selected by clicking the first image, holding down the Ctrl key, then selecting the other images to be renamed.

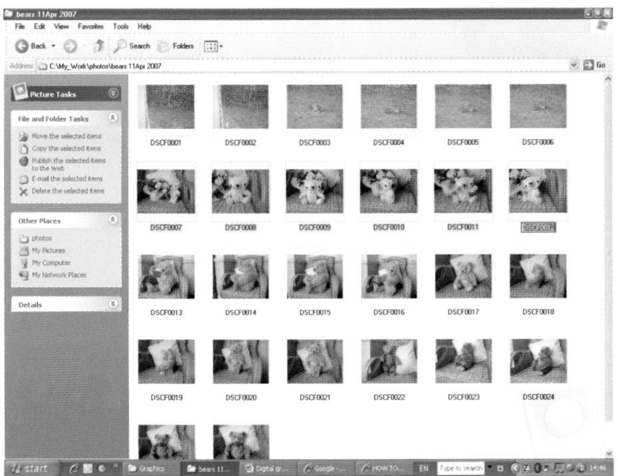

Figure 24.10(b) Pressing F2 causes the selection to become grey. The image at the end of the row is in editing mode. Type in the filename. Press Enter.

Figure 24.10(c) All the selected files have been renamed.

Folder structures

It is important to develop a sensible structure for managing your files. Create folders with meaningful names. In Windows XP, inside the My Documents folder, a folder called My Pictures can be found. This folder is used by many users to store their images. In time, this folder can contain hundreds of images, making it difficult to find the one required. To create folders to make the management of images easier, go to File > New > Folder. Name your folder, then press Enter.

Folders can be created where you want them. Some people save their images to a separate, external hard drive.

It is a good idea to create a folder for images before downloading them from a digital camera.

Moving and deleting files

To move images, select them (Ctrl+A for all files in a folder **OR** click first file, hold down the Shift key and click last file to select a block of files **OR** click first file, hold down the Ctrl key and select other files), then Edit > Cut or press Ctrl+X to move files into the Windows clipboard. Move to the required location for the files, then Edit > Paste or Ctrl+V to paste them into their new position.

Compression techniques

Images intended for web pages need to be compressed in one of three file formats: .jpg, .gif or .png.

To optimise a .jpg image in Paintshop Pro:

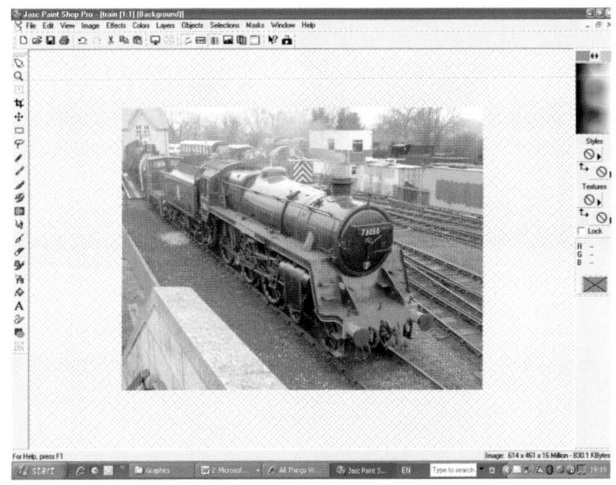

Figure 24.11(a) Open the image to be optimised. Go to File > Export > JPEG optimizer. The initial size of the file is 86 KB.

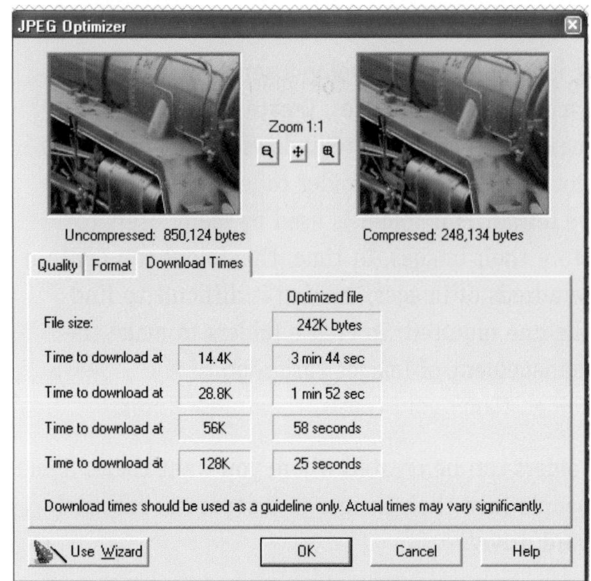

Figure 24.11(b) The JPEG Optimizer window appears. There are three tabs: Quality, Format and Download Times.
The Format tab allows the file to be encoded as progressive or standard.
Click on the Download Times tab.
This shows that an optimised image will be approximately 25 KB and on a 28.8 K modem, will download in 1 minute, 52 seconds.
Click the OK button to accept these settings.

Figure 24.11(c) To choose a different level of compression, click the Use Wizard button.
Drag the slider to choose between quality and file size.
Click the Next button.

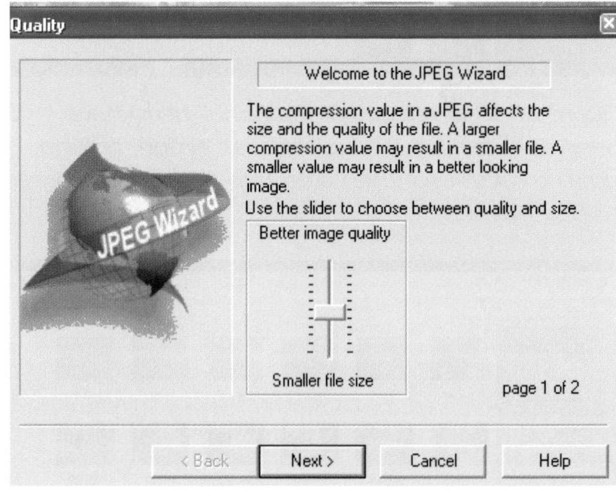

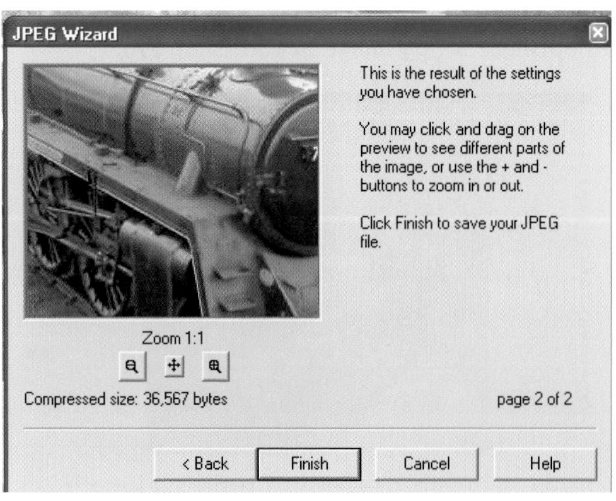

Figure 24.11(d) This screen allows the image to be previewed. It also displays the image size – in this case about 36.5 KB.
At this point, a different level of compression can be chosen, the operation can be cancelled or the settings accepted by clicking OK.

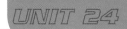

To optimise a .gif image in PaintShop Pro:

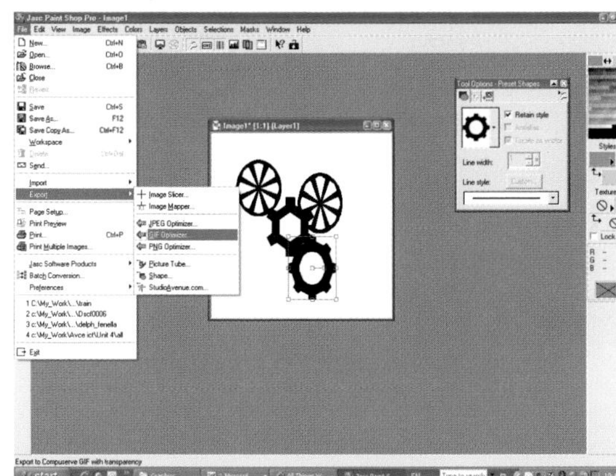

Figure 24.12(a) This file was saved as a 90 KB .bmp file.
To optimise it as a .gif image, go to File > Export > GIF Optimizer.

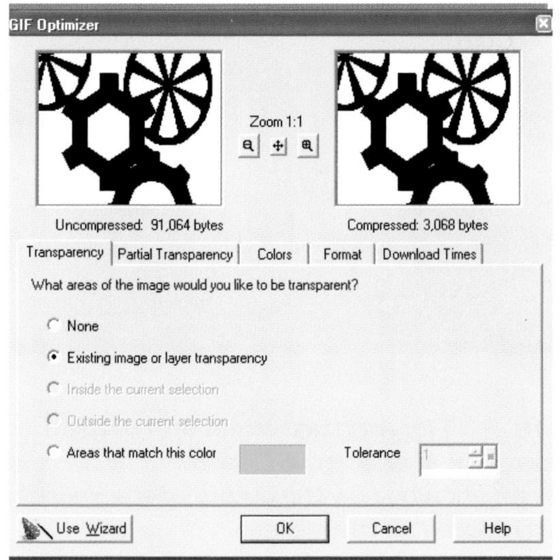

Figure 24.12(b) The GIF Optimizer window opens. There are five tabs of options.
By accepting the choices the optimizer has made, the image will be reduced to 3 KB.
Alternatively, click the Use Wizard button to make your own choices.

Instead of compressing individual files, several files or folders containing files can be compressed. A popular format is .zip. A software program is required to compress the data and to uncompress it. A number of free compression utilities are available on the Internet. Windows XP has its own compression utility.

Example

To compress a file or folder in Windows XP:
Right-click on the file or folder and select
Send to
Choose Compressed (zipped) folder from the fly out menu.

To unzip a file or folder in Windows XP, double-click the zip file.

GRAPHIC IMAGES

Vector graphics

A vector graphic is held by the computer as a list of mathematical equations. Images are composed of simple geometric lines, polygons, curves and points to define the shape, location and properties. This method of storing images allows them to be resized, deformed and printed without degrading the quality of the image. Curves, sometimes referred to as Bezier curves, can be created very precisely by dragging handles of the selected shapes. It takes some time to get familiar with these tools (the Pen, in Figure 24.13), so give yourself time to practise.

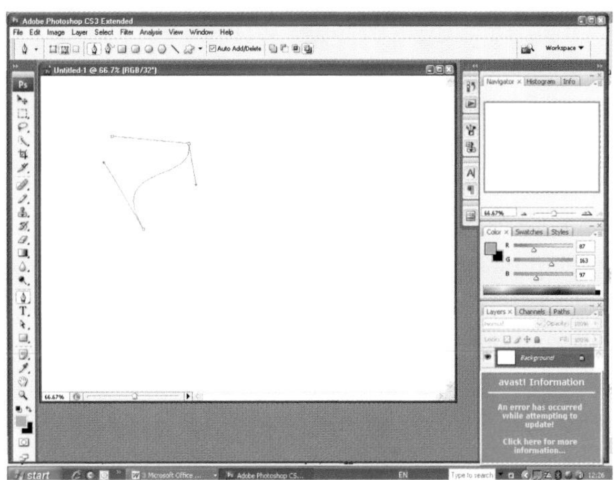

Figure 24.13 Bezier curves

Vector graphics are particularly useful where the same image needs to be produced in a number of different sizes, such as a logo. A similar image saved as a bitmap is likely to produce a larger file. The vector image only needs to store mathematical instructions, while a bitmap holds information about the position of each pixel.

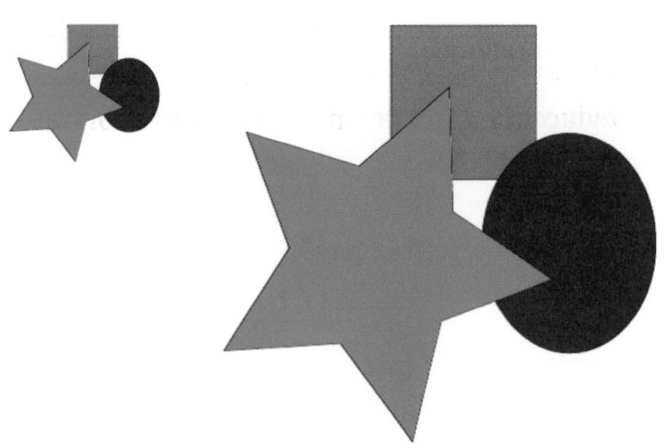

Figure 24.14 When a vector image is enlarged, it maintains its quality.

CorelDraw, Freehand, Illustrator and Flash are examples of vector graphics editors.

Bitmaps (raster images)

A bitmap image is composed of small squares, known as pixels. Each pixel has a colour and position associated with it. Bitmaps are dependent on resolution. This is often displayed as dpi (dots per inch) or ppi (pixels per inch). Files with a .bmp extension are not compressed and can have very large file sizes. Therefore, many bitmaps are saved in compressed file formats such as .jpg, .png and .gif. Computer monitors normally display images at 72 or 96 dpi. Therefore, images to be used on websites need only to be saved at this resolution. Higher resolutions will lead to larger file sizes and longer download times. Images to be output to a printer will produce reasonable results with 72–185 ppi. Photographs are commonly stored as bitmapped images, as many different shades of colour can be incorporated into an image. When bitmap images are increased in size, extra pixels are created. This process is called interpolation. The program chooses colours for the extra pixels based on surrounding colours. This results in **pixilation** and the quality of the resulting image may be reduced. When the size of a bitmap is decreased, pixels are dropped. This also results in the quality of the image being reduced.

Adobe Photoshop and Microsoft Paint are examples of bitmap graphics editors.

> **Key word**
>
> **Pixilation** – when a picture appears to be constructed from small blocks of colour, as in Figure 24.15 (b).

(a)

(b)

Figure 24.15 (a) An image taken with a digital camera. (b) A section of the image that has been resized, showing how the quality of the image has been reduced by the process.

Comparison between types of images

Vector graphics are excellent for drawings, particularly if they are to be resized. Their file size is usually smaller than that of a bitmap of the same object. They are easy to resize while maintaining the quality of the image. They can be converted to bitmap images.

Bitmap images are excellent for photographic images. They can also be used for drawings. Without using a file type that incorporates compression, file sizes may be large. When scaled up, the image may lose quality and become pixilated or 'blocky'. When scaled down in size, the image may become indistinct and 'fuzzy'. A bitmap can be embedded in a vector graphic, but a vector graphic cannot be embedded in a bitmap image.

File format features and typical uses

There are many different graphic file formats. Many image manipulation programs allow conversion from one file type to another.

Three different file types, JPEG, GIF and PNG, can be used for images intended to be used in web pages.

JPEG – Joint Photographic Experts Group

This format is usually used for saving full colour, complex images such as photographs. It stores pixels as 24 bits (16,777,216 colours). (It uses lossy compression. This involves some loss of quality as the image is saved, but results in much smaller file sizes. It averages colour changes and discards changes not easily seen by the human eye to obtain impressive compression ratios.) When saving an image as a JPEG, the user can choose the amount of compression to be used. This decision is likely to be based on the quality of image needed versus the size of file that is acceptable. There is a progressive version that allows large images to be displayed while the file is still being loaded, but it is not fully supported by early browsers.

GIF – Graphic Interchange Format

This format is principally used for simple drawings, cartoons, logos and buttons that are made up of relatively few colours. It supports 8 bit graphics (up to 256 colours) and uses lossless compression to reduce file size. The normal compression rate achieved is about 4:1. GIF89a allows the storage of multiple images in a file along with control information to produce animations known as animated gifs. It has an optional interlacing feature, which allows an image to gradually appear as the image loads into a web browser. This is particularly useful when using slow Internet links. The interlaced GIF is slightly larger than a non-interlaced version of the image.

PNG – Portable Network Graphics

This format was developed to be a replacement for GIF. It uses lossless compression, supports more colours (16.7 million) and 2D progressive rendering, multiple layers for transparency and gamma correction. It is not fully supported by older browsers. The file sizes of similar images saved as JPEGs are smaller.

Research tip

Look for images such as photographs, line drawings and clipart on the Internet. Find some 'good' and 'bad' examples. Think about what makes a good or bad image.

Table 24.1

Other common file formats		
.bmp	Windows bitmap	Uses lossless compression Used by Microsoft Paint
.fla	Flash native format	Only usable within the Flash application
.psd	Photoshop native format	Bitmap-based Supported by some other graphics programs Stores information in layers
.psp	PaintShop Pro native format	Primarily bitmap program, but has some vector tools Supported by few other programs
.swf	Shockwave Flash format	Vector-based applications viewed using Flash plug-in
.tiff	Tagged image file format	Bitmap-based lossy and lossless implementations Commonly used for print graphics
.wmf	Windows metafile	A vector graphics format that can include bitmap graphics

EVIDENCE ACTIVITY

P3 – P4 – P5 – P6

Task 1
Define and document the client and user needs for three graphic images from the findings of your meeting, as outlined in the previous evidence activity on p.149. Ensure that you address each bullet point in that activity and that you clearly differentiate between the needs of your client and their users. Your document should include drafts of the images you intend to develop for the client. Explain the legal implications of the use of images that have been produced by others. **(P3, P6)**

Task 2
Create your three images for the client. Use a digital camera and scanner in the production of some aspect of your images. Edit them to meet the needs of the user. You should save your drafts in your portfolio, annotating them to explain the reasons for changes you have made. You must create your images using a range of software and file types. Ideally, use dedicated vector, bitmap and photo manipulation software to produce your images. Include and document the use of a number of different techniques such as freehand draw, rotate, flip, group, ungroup, soften, sharpen, watermark, invert, appropriate choice of colour depth and layering. Ensure that there is a good reason for using these techniques to meet client and user requirements. **(P4, P5)**

Review the three images, describing how they meet the client and user needs.

Key word

TWAIN – the interface between a scanner or digital camera and image processing software.

24.3 Be able to use editing tools to edit and manipulate technically complex images

GRAPHIC CREATION

Image obtaining

It is not always necessary to create images from scratch. If an image is not in electronic format, a scanner can be used to convert paper-based documents, pictures and photographs to images. Sometimes, image files or photographs may have to be imported into a graphics package for editing.

Scanning

Two main methods are used for scanning images. The software that is supplied with the scanner can be used to capture and save the image, or another application that supports TWAIN devices can be used. Most graphic programs support this feature. For example, Photoshop can import images from a scanner that supports the TWAIN interface.

Microsoft Office Document Scanning is a program that comes bundled with Microsoft Office (All Programs > Microsoft Office > Microsoft Office Tools > Microsoft Office Document Scanning).

Importing

Most graphics programs will open a wide variety of image file types, through File > Open. If All files are selected, then all files, regardless of file type will be visible. Alternatively, the file format can be selected from the drop-down list.

The Import feature in graphics programs usually allows the user to acquire images directly from scanners, digital cameras and video cameras. The Adobe Flash Import option allows images, sound and video to be imported either directly to the 'stage' or to a library.

Digital camera

Photographs taken with a digital camera can be downloaded onto a computer and saved into a folder, or imported directly into the program via the Import menu option. This usually involves the use of a cable to connect the camera to the computer, although, depending on the camera, there may be other ways of doing this, including the use of wireless USB and card readers.

Image creation

Images can be created from scratch in a number of ways. An image may be drawn by using a digital tablet or a variety of drawing and editing tools available within graphics programs. Choices must be made about the file format. This is discussed in greater depth elsewhere in the unit.

TOOLS AND TECHNIQUES

Standard software tools

This section discusses a variety of standard graphics tools. The examples shown are from Adobe Photoshop CS3 Extended, but other graphics programs will have similar features.

When a tool is selected, a range of options and settings for that tool appears at the top of the screen, below the menu bar.

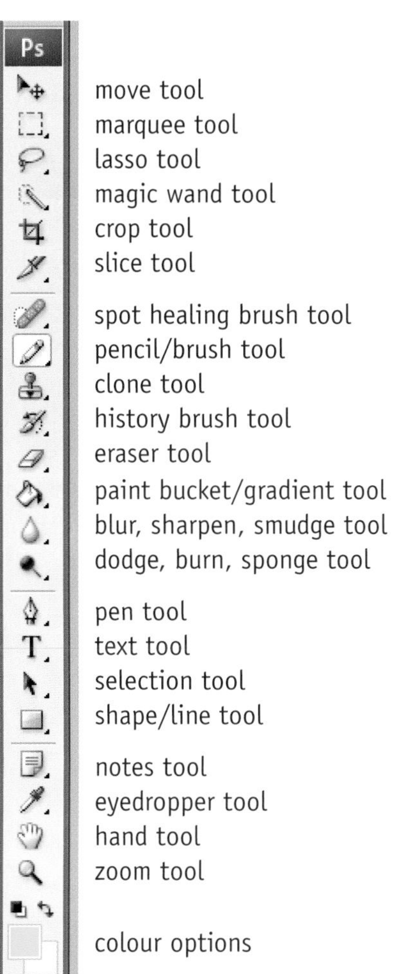

Fig 24.16 Photoshop tool box

Freehand draw

Freehand drawing can be done using the pencil or freehand pen tool. Each tool has a range of options (such as the thickness of the line) that can be selected from the option toolbar that appears on the screen when a tool is selected.

These tools are useful for producing naïve drawings, such as Figure 24.18. A digital tablet is usually preferred for producing professional-looking images.

Figure 24.17 A freehand drawing

Rotate

There are two options, a fixed 90 or 180 degree rotate, or a free rotate.

This example shows how to fixed rotate an object.

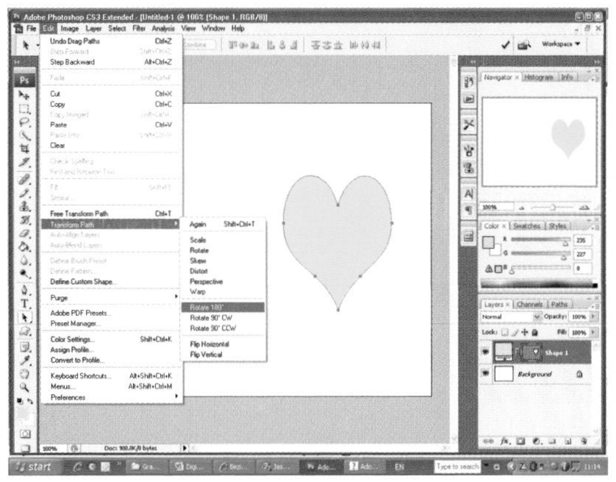

Figure 24.18(a) First select the heart shape. Select the Path Selection button and click on the heart shape

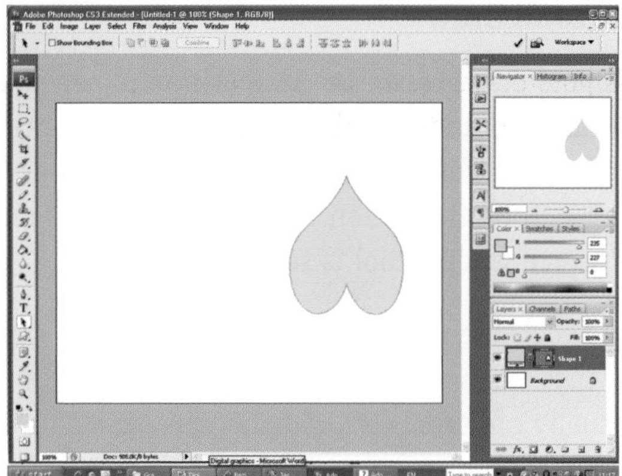

Figure 24.18(b) Select Edit > Transform Path > Rotate 180 degrees.

To freely rotate an object, select Edit > Free Transform Path. Move the mouse pointer outside the boundary of the shape. It becomes a curved two-headed arrow. Hold down the mouse button and drag the mouse until the shape has rotated the required amount.

Flip

To flip a shape vertically or horizontally, select the shape. As with fixed rotate above, Edit > Transform Path. This time select Flip Vertical or Flip Horizontal.

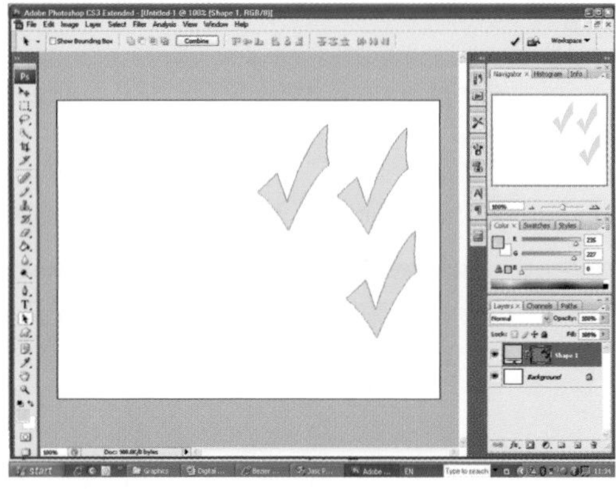

Figure 24.19(a) Three copies of the shape.

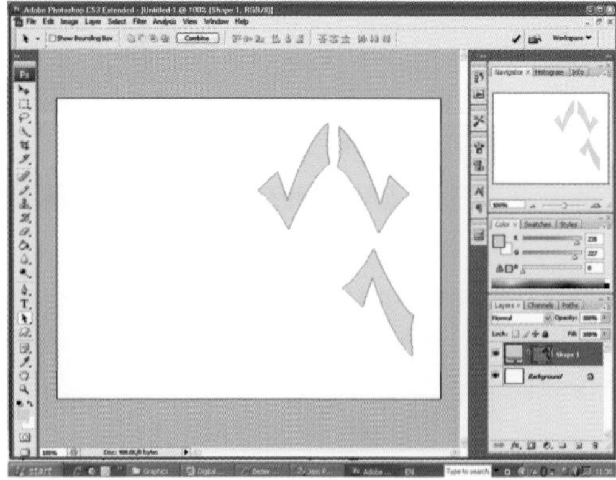

Figure 24.19(b) The first image remains the same, the other two have been flipped.

Crop

Cropping is the process of removing areas of an image, usually to create a focus or to improve a composition.

Figure 24.20(a) Select the crop tool from the toolbox.
Click and drag out a rectangle around the area to be kept. The area that will be lost appears shaded.

Figure 24.20(b) Press the Enter key to delete the rest of the image.

Group and ungroup

Objects that are in different layers can be grouped together, so they can be transformed in some way or so they remain in the same position relative to each other.

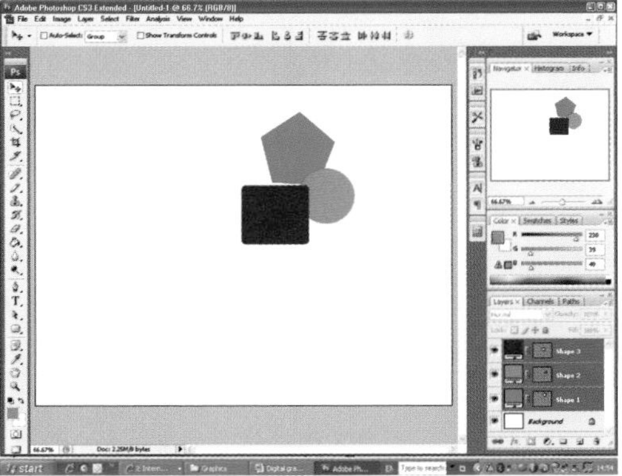

Figure 24.21(a) To move several objects together, go to the Layer palette. Select the layers with the objects to be moved. Click in a layer, then Ctrl and click into each of the other layers. The selected layers in the palette should turn blue.

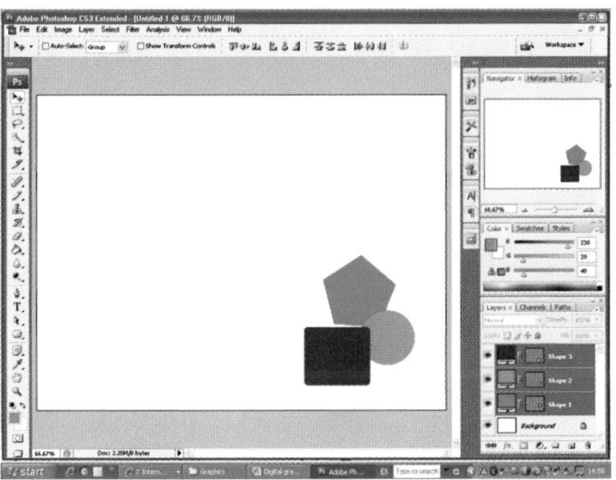

Figure 24.21(b) Select the Move tool in the toolbox. Click on one of the objects and drag. They will move as one.
To ungroup the objects, click on one of the layers in the palette. The blue selection will be removed from the other layers.

Resize

It is possible to resize the image (canvas) as well as resizing objects within the image.

Reducing the size of an image, prior to inserting it into a web page, reduces its file size. Inserting a large image in a web page, and then setting its size does not reduce its file size.

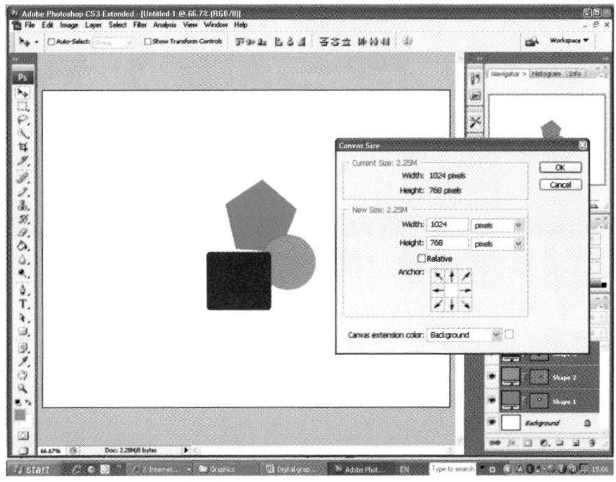

Figure 24.22(a) To change the size of the image: Image > Canvas Size
In the example above, the image was 1024 x 768 pixels

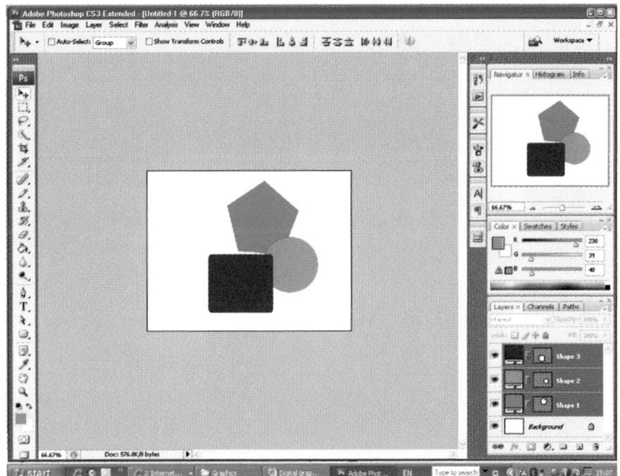

Figure 24.22(b) The width and height values were changed to 512 x 364 pixels.
The original larger image was 147 KB. The image with the smaller size was 84 KB. Both images were saved in .psd format

Resizing an object is referred to as scaling. Objects can be scaled larger or smaller.

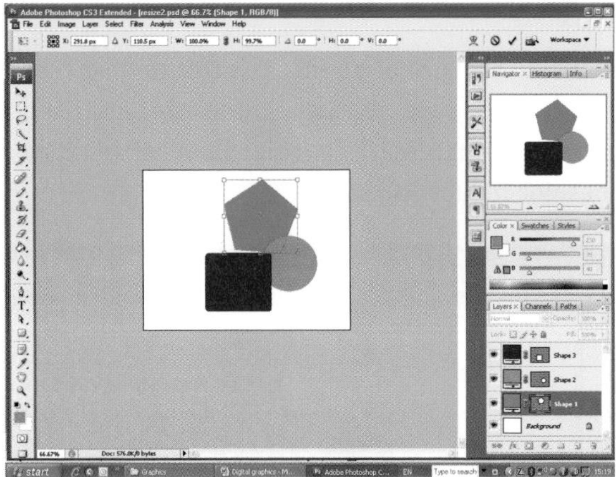

Figure 24.23(a) Select the object. Then choose Edit > Transform Path > Scale.

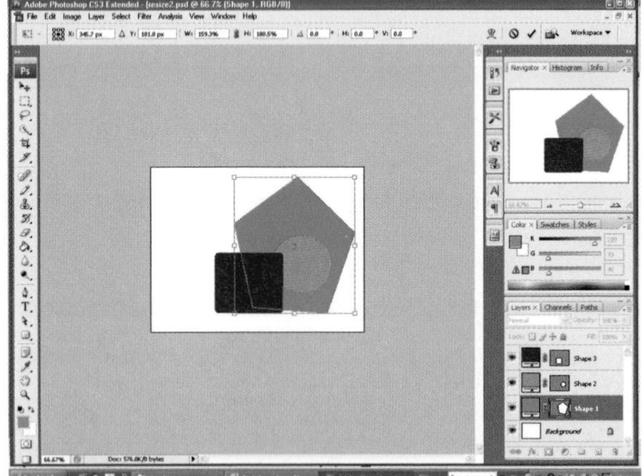

Figure 24.23(b) Click and drag on a corner handle to resize the object.

Special effects

Soften

One way of softening the appearance of an image is to use the Blur option.

Figure 24.24(a) This is the original image.

Figure 24.24(b) Filter > Blur > Gaussian Blur. In this example 2 pixels have been selected, but experiment to get the desired effect.

Alternatively, anti-aliasing can be applied to soften the jagged edges that occur between the edge pixels of an object and the background pixels. The Lasso, Marquee and Magic Wand tools have the anti-alias option.

Feathering can be used to create a soft, blurred edge between a selection and its background. The Marquee and Lasso tools can be used to create this effect.

Figure 24.25 Example of feathering

Sharpen

If images appear blurred they may benefit from being sharpened. The Sharpen options include Sharpen, Sharpen More and Smart Sharpen. The changes are often subtle and show best when the images are printed and compared.

Figure 24.26(a) Open the image.

Figure 24.26(b) Filter > Sharpen > Smart Sharpen. Smart Sharpen has been selected as this gives the option to correct Gaussian, movement or lens blur. Each can be previewed before making a final selection.

Watermark

A number of methods can be used to create watermarks. These are frequently used to show copyright information and stop your images being used without permission.

Figure 24.27(a) Select the text tool and the colour, font and text size required. Type in your text. For the copyright symbol, hold down the Alt key and type 0169.

Figure 24.27(b) With the text tool still selected, highlight your text.
Layer > Layer Style. Drag either of the Opacity sliders. The text starts to fade.
Click OK.

Invert

Some very interesting effects can be created using the Invert command.

Figure 24.28(a) Open the image to be inverted.

Figure 24.28(b) Image > Adjustments > Invert

Research tip

Within the Layer Style options are many interesting effects such as bevels, embossing, shadows etc. In your graphics program of choice, look to see what special effects are available.

Colour

Most graphics software allows the user to choose from several different colour modes including HSB, RGB and CMYK. (Screenshots of colour palettes from Adobe Illustrator 10.)

HSB model (Hue Saturation and Brightness)

This model uses three characteristics of colour:
Hue: This is based on a colour wheel, with 0° representing red, 60° representing yellow, 120° representing green and 240° representing blue.

Saturation: This is the strength of the colour. The amount of grey in proportion to hue is measured between 0 and 100%. A highly saturated colour is vivid, whereas a muted colour has a low saturation value.

Brightness: This is the relative lightness or darkness of the colour. It is usually measured between 0 (black) and 100%.

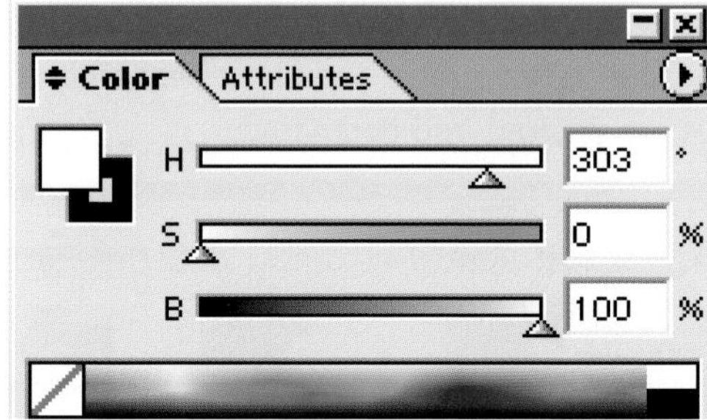

Figure 24.29(a) HSB model

RGB model (Red, Green, Blue)

This model is based on the principle that most colours can be created from mixing different combinations and intensities of red, green and blue. This model has been implemented in television and computer screens and lighting.

Each colour can take a value between 0 and 255. If all three are set to 0, the resulting colour is black. If all three are set to 255, the resulting colour is white. One slider set to 255 with the rest set to 0, will result in red, green or blue being displayed respectively.

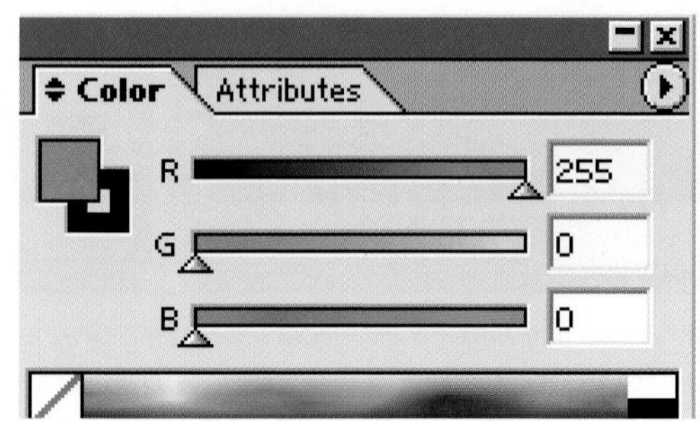

Figure 24.29(b) RGB model

CMYK model (Cyan, Magenta, Yellow, blacK)

This model is sometimes called four-colour process printing as it is used to print images with four passes through a printing press. The model is based on the principle that as light falls on colour, some is absorbed and some is reflected back to the eye.

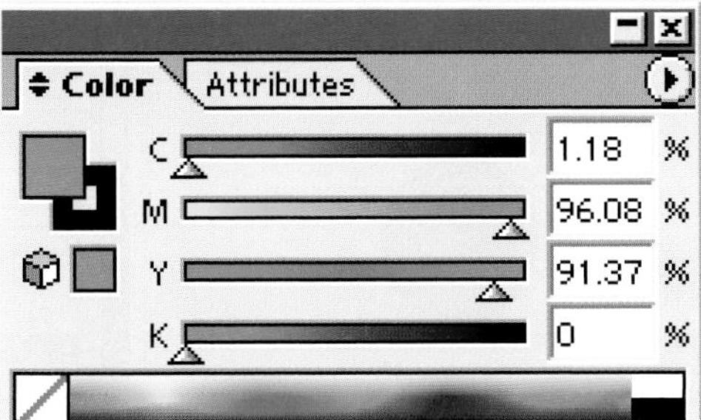

Figure 24.29(c) CMYK model

Colour balance

To obtain colour balance, it may be necessary to adjust the amounts of blue, red and green colours in an image so that neutral colours can appear natural.

Figure 24.30(a) In this image blue is the predominant colour.

Figure 24.30(b) Ctrl+B opens the Colour Balance window. Move the three sliders until the required colour balance has been achieved. Click OK.

Colour depth

Colour depth is the term used to describe the number of bits used to represent the colour of a pixel.

When creating a new image, the colour depth can be specified. The greater the number of bits used to represent a pixel, the larger the file size.

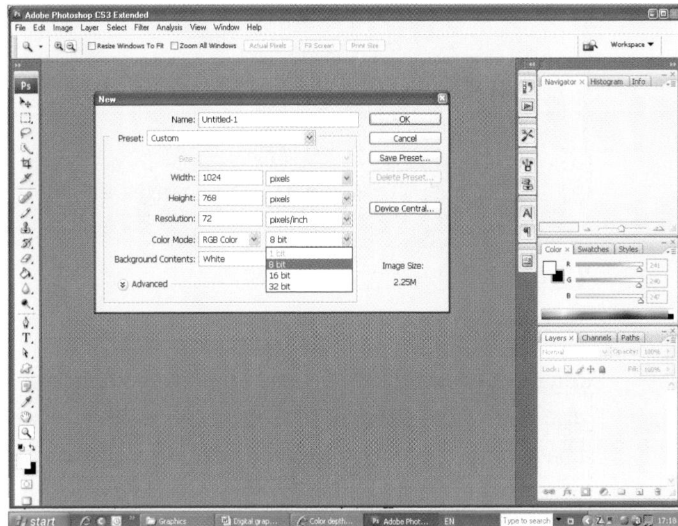

Figure 24.31 Specifying colour depth

The following table shows the number of colours available at each bit depth.

Table 24.2

Bit depth	Number of colours
1	2
2	4
4	16
8	256
16	65,536
24	16,777,216
32	16,777,216 plus transparency

Layers

Most graphics programs use layers as a means of organising the different elements of images. Layers also enable the designer to work on an element of an image in a layer without affecting other elements in other layers. To make editing easier, it is possible to hide and/or lock layers when required. Effectively, multiple layers stack on top of each other.

Photoshop has a background layer that behaves differently to other layers. It cannot be moved and is locked by default.

When an image is complete, the image can be 'flattened'. All layers are merged into the background layer.

Research tip

Photoshop has a large number of features for working with layers and it is easy to become confused and overwhelmed. Familiarise yourself with how Photoshop uses layers for individual parts of an image, then investigate specialised layers, layer styles and layer modes.

In Flash, objects to be animated are inserted on different layers. This enables them to be animated individually and, if necessary, to have their own timelines.

Advanced techniques

Representation of three-dimensional images

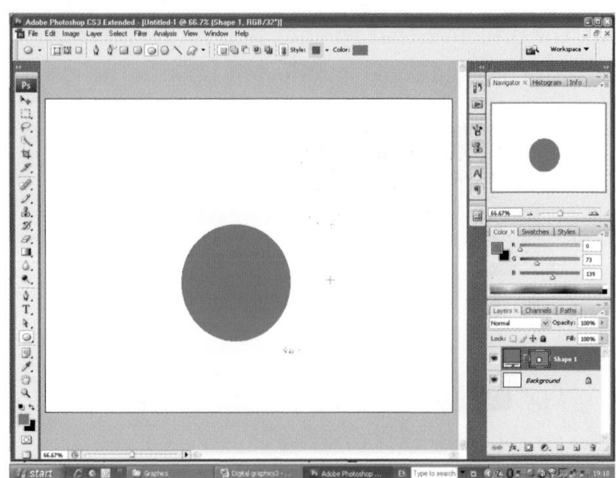

Figure 24.32(a) Create a new image and draw a circle.

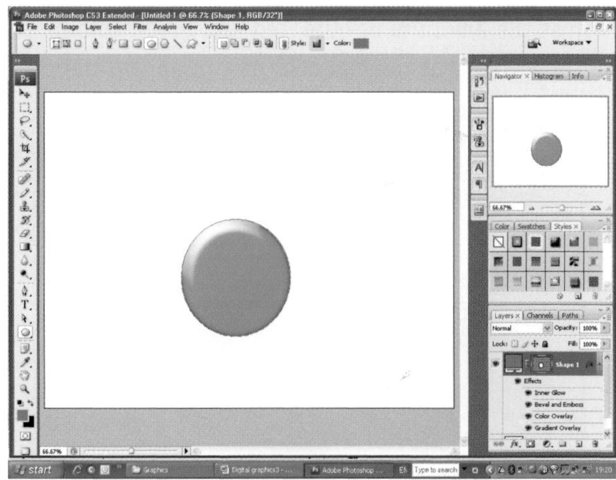

Figure 24.32(b) Go to the Colour palette and click on the Styles tab.
Select one of the options. The fifth option from the left on the top row has been chosen to create a bevelled 3D effect.

Research tip

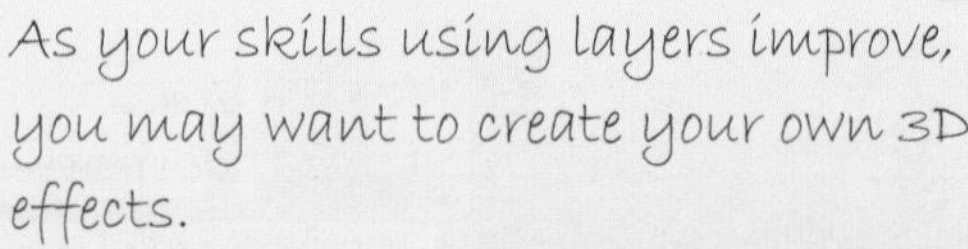

As your skills using layers improve, you may want to create your own 3D effects.

Masking

A mask is like a stencil where only the cut-out area is editable. Masks can be used in many ways.

Figure 24.33(a) A soldier is to be extracted from this image.

Figure 24.33(b) Filter > Extract. This opens the Extract window. A pen size is chosen to mark the edges of the part of the image to be extracted. Then the Fill tool is used to select the inside of the selection. Then OK is clicked.

To mask part of a layer:

- Select the layer.
- Select the area to be masked.
- Click the New Layer Mask button in the Layers palette to create a mask that shows the selection or Alt+Click the New Layer Mask button to create a mask that hides the selection.

In this example, the Extract feature is used to move a selection from one image into another.

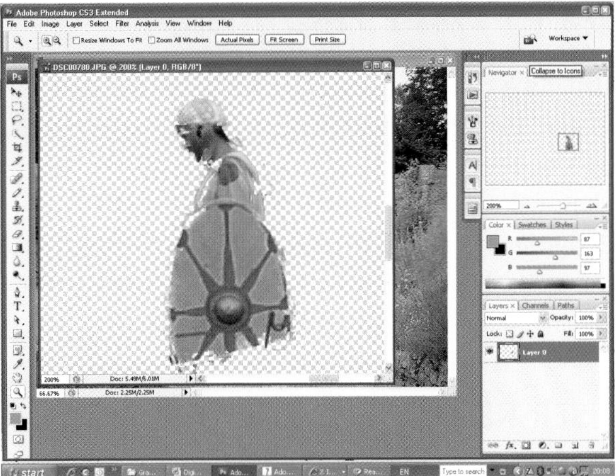

Figure 24.33(c) The selection appears in its own window with a transparent background.

Figure 24.33(d) The soldier selection has been dragged into another image. It was a little small, so Edit > Transform > Scale was used to resize it.

EVIDENCE ACTIVITY

M2 – M3 – D1

Use two advanced techniques, such as masking and the development of 3D images, in the development of your images. Create several annotated screenshots to demonstrate how you applied the techniques to your images. (**M2**)

Demonstrate the impact that file format, compression techniques, image resolution and colour density have on file size and image quality. Justify your use of software and tools, file format, image resolution and colour depth to show how you have met client and user needs. **(M3, D1)**

24.4 Be able to create and modify graphic images to meet user requirements

Usually a client requests the designer to create images for a particular purpose. This is referred to as 'the brief'. This starts a sequence of activities that make up the design process. Some of the activities may need to be repeated as the designs are refined. The designer is required to assess the scope, complexity and cost of an assignment.

USER NEED

Client needs as opposed to user needs

The client will often only describe their requirements in fairly general terms. They will expect the designer to produce the creative ideas and flair! It is important that the designer obtains an understanding of the client's business and customers, by listening carefully to the client and asking relevant questions, before starting to draw the designs.

What problem needs to be solved? What message needs to be communicated? This may involve some research such as looking at the client's and his competitors' websites, advertising material etc. The designer must ensure that he understands the purpose of the images. Are the images intended to create a corporate image, to market a product, to be informational or provocative?

> ***Think*** In what other ways can images be used?

Identifying the target audience

Who will be viewing the images? There will be different demographics of people with a need for the client's products or services. Demographics are characteristics that can be used to categorise segments of the population. This can include age, gender, race, income, postcode, occupation etc.

> ***Think*** There is evidence of demographic changes occurring in the UK. For example, people are living longer and the number of non-traditional households is increasing. Can you identify two other changes?

User requirements

The designer needs to be able to tune into the likes and dislikes of different audiences. Further research and analysis may need to be done to ensure that the designs will appeal to the client's target audience.

Sometimes, images will be used to encourage a need that the viewer had not been aware they had until that moment! Statistics, such as the General Household Survey (available at www.statistics.gov.uk), can form a useful starting point for research. Your client may make available some research they have done themselves.

Constraints

Although designers may have a reasonably free hand when it comes to many of the design elements of their images, there are likely to be some constraints.

House style

Many organisations have house styles and may require images produced by a designer to conform to them. A house style is a set of standards used to produce documents for an organisation. It may specify fonts, colours, font sizes, particular sizes of logos for different purposes etc.

Image size

The sizes of the final images are likely to be determined by their intended use. Size may range from the design of custom bullet points for a website to large billboards that may be 40 metres by 10 metres or more in size. For printed media, the size will determine the specification and size of the output printer or plotter. For screen output, the size will be determined by the screen resolution used by viewers.

Intended use

The images may be used for a wide range of purposes, for example, book, leaflet or magazine illustrations; posters or billboards; web pages; exhibitions; packaging etc. Each purpose has its own unique requirements. Producing images for viewing on screen requires different production methods from creating images for print where colour separations may be needed. The requirements need to be considered carefully, as the intended use will affect the production method used, output device used, costs and timescale.

File size

This is particularly important when considering images being produced for websites. Images need to be optimised for web use. This involves making choices between file size and the quality of the image.

Production costs

A number of costs will need to be considered. Labour, overheads (heating, lighting, rent), travel to meetings, cost of materials, packaging and printing all need to be factored in to the final cost of producing the images.

Timescale

How long will the process take? Research and analysis, meetings with the client, development, production and review time all need to be considered in the planning process. Unfortunately, in the real world, the client will often decide the deadline for delivery of the images, and it will be up to the designer to fit all of the processes into that time frame.

Output media

- Will the images be viewed on paper or on screen?
- If on paper, will the printing be done in-house or by a printing bureau?
- Are colour separations needed?
- Will specialist printers or plotters be needed?
- What quality of image will need to be produced?
- What preparations will need to be made?

If using specialist equipment or a bureau, the use of the printers will need to be booked. Paper and ink of the required quality and quantity will need to be sourced.

CASE STUDY: SPECIALIST SCHOOL NEWSLETTER

A twice-yearly newsletter is produced to inform parents, students, governors, link schools and others about events and activities related to Specialist status. The newsletter is A4 in size and full colour. The school has four specialist subjects, so each subject needs to supply copy for a page. Many photographs are taken in the course of these activities.

- The selected pictures may need cropping or other editing to ensure that they will fit into an allocated location on the page.
- If a photograph contains images of individuals, checks need to be made to ensure they are happy to have their picture included.
- Where children have been photographed, parental permission has normally been sought in advance, but this is checked before the picture can be included.
- The files need to be converted into a CYMK press-ready PDF format.

QUESTION

Look at some examples of newsletters containing images. What elements make a pleasing design?

For images to be used on a website, meetings and coordination with the client's webmaster will be needed. The images will need to be provided in an agreed format.

REVIEWING

Check against client need and user need

It is important that the designer always keeps client and user need in the forefront of their thoughts while developing their designs. It is easy to be overcome with creative zeal. The designer should return regularly to the original brief, and to research notes taken in discussion with the client.

Proofing

The client is normally given the opportunity to monitor the progress of the development of images. Proofs can be sent to the client for approval and/or further discussion. This is an iterative process that may involve second and third proofs being sent. The client may also want proofs shown to their customers for additional feedback.

Image resolution

The required resolution of the images should be agreed when the original brief is discussed. It is important that the designer delivers the images as originally defined. The resolution of images for the screen (usually 72 dpi) is usually lower than that required for print (may be 1200 dpi or greater).

File formats

The designer must check that all images are provided in formats as agreed with the client, the client's webmaster and the print bureau where appropriate.

LEGISLATION AND GUIDELINES

Identifying ownership

It is not always easy to determine the ownership of materials. Images will often contain copyright information that has been saved as metadata. In Photoshop, this information can be viewed by clicking File > File Info.

Copyright, Designs and Patents Act 1988

This UK law gives writers, playwrights, musicians and artists the rights to control the use of works they have created. These rights cover copying, adapting, broadcasting and public performance, renting and lending to the public. Photography, drawings, diagrams, paintings, maps and logos are protected. Copyright is conferred automatically when an individual or organisation creates a new work, if the work is original and shows some skill, labour or judgement. Copyright for artistic works lasts for 70 years from the end of the year in which the author dies. If the work is made available to the public during that time, the duration will be 70 years from the end of the year in which the work was made available. Penalties for copyright infringement or plagiarism include legal charges, fines or imprisonment. Many designers add copyright information, including the copyright symbol to metadata that is saved with the image file.

Copyright free

Some designers and photographers offer copyright-free images to others, usually on websites. Always carefully check any terms of use on these websites, before copying and using them. Some designers will allow use of an image if it is credited to them; others insist that no changes are made to the original.

Gaining permissions

An author's work or extracts of their work cannot be sold, published or distributed without their permission. Where possible, apply to the publisher or author for permission to use their work. For photographs, contact the photographer. For images on websites, contact the webmaster. Give them a description of the work and tell them how it will be used. Get the permission in writing to avoid later disputes. Always attribute the work by stating the name of the owner.

CASE STUDY: FREELANCE WEB DESIGNER

Marie Blanche designs websites for small businesses. The customers' requirements vary greatly. Some want her to produce all the images on the site, while others supply images.

Some sites consist of one page while others contain up to 20 pages. Marie charges a set fee per page and also charges fixed amounts for maintenance and web hosting if required. She will also produce high quality images and Flash animations for use on the website. These are priced individually depending on the brief and expenses incurred. The initial consultation is usually free.

QUESTIONS

1. What qualities do you think a web designer needs to run a business?
2. What information will Marie need from a customer?

EVIDENCE ACTIVITY

D2

Write a report to evaluate the impact of evolving output media on the designing and creation of graphic images.

unit 26

Animation is the creation of a series of images which, when shown in a sequence at speed, give the impression of movement. Computer animation involves the use of the computer to create the animations. The continuing development of more and more powerful computers and sophisticated software is leading to progress in speeding up the process of creating animations, including the development of photorealistic animation. At the same time, it makes increasing demands on processing power and storage.

Computer animations are used for a wide range of purposes including enhancing the appearance of websites, the production of advertisements and trailers, computer games, special effects, animated films and cartoons.

In this unit, you will explore the history and development of animation. You will find out about the different types of animation that have developed over the past 120 years.

You will also learn a number of software techniques that are used in the production of animations and how to plan, create, test and review your animations.

On completion of the unit, a learner should:

So you want to be a...

Computer Animator

My name Andrew Smith
Age 26
Income £18,000–30,000

What does an animator do?

I work on a variety of projects for a number of different clients. Much of my work involves the development of web-based advertising. Mostly I work on my own but sometimes as part of a team. I have friends that have found work in different areas, such as film and television effects and computer game development.

What are your day-to-day responsibilities?

I usually start with a brief. Sometimes I am given existing models or drawings to work from. For certain projects, the timings are critical, so careful planning is needed. I usually draw on paper initially and scan the drawings onto the computer or redraw using a digital tablet. I then use software to create the animation. I sometimes have to work long hours close to a deadline. As I run my own business, I have to keep track of all my income and expenses and make payments into a pension plan.

How did you get into the job?

I have always loved drawing, particularly cartoons and caricatures. I developed an interest in computer art and web design while I was at school and designed a website for my Dad's business when I was 16. My first animations were animated GIFS that were caricatures of famous characters. I completed a degree in Animation at university. After completing my degree, I sent examples of my work, called show-reels, to a number of well-known animation studios. It has been very hard work, but I am gradually building up a reputation and am getting repeat contracts.

What training have you had?

I guess I have been training for the job since I first picked up a pencil and started drawing. I specialise in 2D animation, although my degree course covered 3D animation as well. I would consider myself to be mainly self-taught.

> "You need to be very creative"

What are the hours like?

I work from 9am to 5:30pm, Monday to Friday. When required, I will just work through until the job is finished.

How good is the pay?

I earn between £18,000 and £30,000, but have earned more from occasional bonuses.

It sounds like a complex role, what qualities do you need?

You need to be very creative and be a careful observer of the way objects, creatures and people move. You also need to be able to work to a brief, meet deadlines and be professional in dealing with clients.

How do you see your career progressing?

I'm not really sure what the future holds. At the moment, I am enjoying the freedom of working freelance, but in the future I might want the security of a salaried job.

Grading criteria

The table below shows what you need to do to gain a pass, merit or distinction in this part of the qualification. Make sure you refer back to it when you are completing work so that you can judge whether you are meeting the criteria and what you need to do to fill in gaps in your knowledge or experience.

In this unit there are six evidence activities that give you an opportunity to demonstrate your achievement of the grading criteria:

page 178	P2
page 181	P1, D1
page 191	P3, M1, M2
page 195	P4
page 198	P5
page 201	P6, P7, M3, M4, D2

To achieve a pass grade the evidence must show that the learner is able to...	To achieve a merit grade the evidence must show that, in addition to the pass criteria, the learner is able to...	To achieve a distinction grade the evidence must show that, in addition to the pass and merit criteria, the learner is able to...
P1 describe how persistence of vision is used in animation	**M1** compare two different animation formats	**D1** evaluate one software package or technique that is used to create animations
P2 describe three applications for animations	**M2** compare two different specialist software package or programming techniques used to create computer animation	**D2** evaluate the tools and techniques used to create finished animations.
P3 describe the features, advantages and limitations of animated GIFs and one other animation format	**M3** adapt and improve animations based on formal reviews	
P4 describe two different types of animation techniques	**M4** explain particular techniques that are used to minimise the file size of animations.	
P5 describe the special factors that need to be taken into account when creating animations for the web		
P6 design, create and review animations for particular purposes that use both vector and bit map graphics		
P7 design, create and review animations for particular purposes that are designed to be incorporated into web pages.		

26.1 Understand the origins and types of animation

BASIS OF AND ORIGINS OF ANIMATION

Persistence of vision

This is a theory that suggests that showing a sequence of still images at speed (such as film or video) appears to us as motion rather than discrete images because the human eye retains an image for a short period of time. A form of visual memory is believed to be the cause of this phenomenon. The theory, although often quoted, does not have universal acceptance. Some scientists believe it to be a myth.

> **Research tip**
>
> Go to www.uca.edu/org/ccsmi/ccsmi/classicwork/Myth%20Revisited.htm to find out more about 'The myth of persistence vision.

Pioneers and Techniques

The origins of animation are intrinsically linked to the origins of film.

Athenean horsemen from the Parthenon frieze give a strong impression of movement. This style is repeated on many vases of the same age.

Fig 26.1 Athenean horsemen from the Parthenon frieze

Examples of series of figures showing progressive movement have been found on monuments in Egypt dating back to ancient times.

The earliest form of slide projector is believed to be the Magic Lantern, which dates back to the 1600s. It was a device that projected light through a transparent image (such as an image painted on glass) onto a wall or screen. Over time, they gradually became more sophisticated, replacing candle light with oil or gas lamps and were eventually replaced by electric light bulbs after 1910.

Figure 26.2 Magic lantern

> **Research tip**
>
> An excellent source of further information about Magic Lanterns can be found at http://www.luikerwaal.com/ This site includes many photographs of slides used in the lanterns. Many are miniature works of art.

The phenakistoscope was developed in 1832 by Joseph Plateau of Belgium. In the same year, Simon von Stampfer invented a similar device that he called a stroboscope. The phenakistoscope is composed of two circular discs. One has slots cut around the edge, while the other has a sequence of drawings placed around the disc in concentric circles. When the discs are spun in the same direction, and viewed through a mirror, the drawings appear to move.

The zoetrope was developed by William Horner in 1834. This was similar to the phenakistoscope, but used a drum instead of discs, and did not require a mirror for viewing the images. It consisted of a drum with an open top. Thin slots were cut around the side of the drum and a sequence of images on paper strips were placed around the edge of the bottom of the drum. When the drum was spun, the viewer looked through the slots on the side of the drum to see the animation. As it did not matter which side the image was viewed from, this design allowed several viewers to use the device at one time. The zoetrope fell into disuse after the introduction of the praxinoscope in 1877.

The praxinoscope was invented by Emile Reynard. This was similar to the zoetrope, but used mirrors in the centre of the drum to view the images, instead of viewing them through slots on the outside of the drum. The use of mirrors improved the clarity and brightness of the images. Reynard continued to develop his invention and designed a version that would allow a long strip of paper to be used, resulting in the ability to show much longer animations.

Figure 26.3 Praxinscope

Research tip

You are likely to find examples of some of these early devices in your local museum. There are also a number of websites devoted to these 'toys'.
Try: http://courses.ncssm.edu/GALLERY/collections/toys/opticaltoys.htm

Many of you will have had the experience of creating a flip book at school. Flip books were first patented in the US by Henry Van Hovenbergh in 1882. These books consist of a stack of small pages, stapled together at one end. Each page contains an image in a sequence. When the pages are flipped, the illusion of motion is created. They were frequently given away as promotional novelties and were popular up until the 1970s.

Research tip

A few companies still produce flip books. The site, http://www.fliptomania.com has some excellent movie clips showing flip books in action.

In 1888, Etienne Marey built a box camera that used an intermittent mechanism to allow a sequence of images to be recorded on a strip of paper film. This was seen by Thomas Edison in Paris in 1889.

With his assistant, W. K. L. Dickson and the newly developed Eastman film, Edison returned to the US and developed the Kinetograph camera and Kinetoscope viewing box (1891). Dickson cut the Eastman film into inch-wide strips and punched holes into each side to allow toothed gears to push the film through the camera at 46 frames per second.

In 1894, the Lumière brothers, Louis and Auguste produced a device called the Cinématographe. This device was able to act as both a recorder and projector of film. It used 35mm film and ran at 16 frames per second.

Films using the new technology began appearing in the late 1890s.

Research tip

Early pioneers of film animation include:

Georges Méliès: Le Voyage dans la Lune (1902)

Emile Cohl: Fantasmagorie (1908)

J. Stuart Blackton: Humorous Phases of Funny Faces (1906)

Winsor McCay: Little Nemo (1911), How a Mosquito Operates (1912) and Gertie the Dinosaur (1914)

Take a look at some or all of the above. At the time of writing, all the above-mentioned films could be viewed on www.youtube.com

A technological advance in the production of animations was made with the development of the use of cels. These are panes of celluloid on which images are painted. Each represents a single frame of an animation. Several cels can be laid over a background, rather than having to redraw the entire image. This technology was patented by Earl Hurd in 1915. John R Bray took over a number of patents on the use of transparent sheets for backgrounds in 1914 and to avoid a lawsuit with Hurd, they formed the Bray Hurd Process Company in 1917, which licensed the use of the cel technique to animators.

Figure 26.4 Cels image

A technique called rotoscoping was developed by Max Fleishe (Betty Boop) in 1915 and patented in 1917. This technique involved tracing images from previously recorded live action onto cels.

The Disney studio was responsible for further advances in animation, including the multi-plane camera stand, the use of storyboards, and pencil sketches for reviewing motion. They were masters of developing personalities for their cartoon characters.

Computer animation

The development of the SketchPad program in 1963 by Ivan Sutherland is considered to be a milestone in the development of computer graphics and animation. This program was able to animate line drawings. It used objects and instances (early object-oriented programming), and was the first to use a complete graphical user interface. It also made use of the recently invented light pen as an input device. A demonstration of its amazing capabilities can be viewed on YouTube.

Many early breakthroughs in the development of computer graphics came directly from research done in university laboratories. This research continues today, with additional support from many computer animation studios.

The first computer-animated film was 'Hunger' or 'La Faim' by Peter Foldes. This can be viewed on YouTube.

In the early 1980s, CGI (computer generated imagery) effects started appearing in mainstream movies such as Star Trek II and Tron. The first completely CGI film was Toy Story, produced in 1995. Final Fantasy – The Spirits Within was the first film to attempt realism in animating characters and clothing in 2001. In 2002, Monsters Inc. was the first film to attempt to produce realistic fur on screen.

Traditional techniques

Drawn (traditional) animation

This is the classic animation method. The animation process usually begins with a hand-drawn storyboard (rather like a comic strip). The storyboard is used to plan the scenes and flow of the plot. A soundtrack is recorded. This may contain voices as dialogue, music and special effects.

The drawings from the storyboard and the synchronised soundtrack are combined to create an 'animatic'. From the animatic, timings and the layout are developed. This contains the frames of each scene with the soundtrack synchronised to the action.

Model sheets, showing the main characters from different angles, are produced. Backgrounds, styles and colour schemes for the scenes are also developed.

A senior animator will create key drawings. These may be passed to assistant animators to create the 'in between' drawings. In a large studio, many animators may be working on different aspects of the animation. The work is regularly reviewed and may involve some stages being reworked until the director approves each stage of the work.

The drawings are cleaned up, and transferred to clear sheets of cellulose acetate called cels, either using pens or by photocopying. Colours are painted on one side of the sheet. Because several layers of the transparent cels can be laid on top of each other, different objects or characters in a frame can be painted on different cels and then laid over each other (in the same way that different parts of a computer image can be drawn on different layers).

A stack of cels for each frame, including the background at the bottom of the stack, is covered with a plate of glass and then photographed using a rostrum camera. Each frame of the animation is photographed in this way. Once the photography is complete, the individual frames are spliced together to create a reel. The film is sent for processing and the soundtrack is added.

Today, the drawings are no longer transferred to cels, but are scanned into the computer and coloured and processed digitally. The 'film' is then exported as a digital video format.

Cut-out animation

This involves flat, cut-out shapes being moved in front of a background. Paper, card, fabric and photographs are used. One of the best-known examples of this method can be seen in the opening credits of Monty Python's Flying Circus. Early versions of South Park were also created using paper cut-outs.

Example

Look at the following web page. It describes the production process for an episode of South Park. Compare and contrast it to other animation methods and processes.

http://www.southparkstudios.com/behind/production_process.php

Model animation or stop motion animation

Models are made from a variety of materials such as Plasticine, clay or wire. These are photographed, moved slightly, and then photographed again. There are a number of early examples of this method from the early 1900s, including Edison's 'Fun in a Bakery Shop'. The history of film is peppered with examples of the method, including Lost World (1925), the 1933 version of King Kong, Jason and the Argonauts (1963) and more recently The Nightmare before Christmas (1993) and in 2005 The Corpse Bride (Tim Burton). The Wallace and Gromit films (Aardman) are examples of clay animation or 'claymation'. This is the use of clay or Plasticine that is usually modelled around a wire armature (skeleton). The beauty of this method is the ease with which a character can be posed in different positions and with different expressions. The creation of animation using this method is very time-consuming and painstaking as a frame rate of 24 fps will require a minimum of twelve changes per second of film. Very careful object placement and maintaining a constant source of lighting is critical to achieving a convincing animation.

Computer animation or computer generated imagery (CGI)

This is an area of 3D computer graphics involved in the production of special effects that would usually be difficult, impossible or extremely expensive to produce in any other way. CGI has been used in many different fields, such as films, simulations, television programmes, printed media and commercials.

Example

The production of CGI special effects requires seriously high-end computers. Take a look at http://news.bbc.co.uk/1/hi/technology/6584075.stm to read about the equipment LucasFilm, Industrial Light and Magic and LucasArts use to produce movies, special effects and games.

Go to http://news.bbc.co.uk/1/hi/technology/6571491.stm to find out how CG visual effects are created.

APPLICATIONS OF ANIMATION

Advertising

Computer animation is used extensively for advertising goods and services. Animations are frequently used for television commercials, television trailers, and web advertisements. A very wide range of techniques are used, including cut outs, stop motion, 2D and 3D modelling, special effects, logo animation, etc. Many use novelty and humour to sell their products.

Example

Many companies with web presences have posted their television advertisements onto their websites. As a starting point, look at www.citroen.co.uk/c4/ and the Cadbury Smash 'Martians' advert of 1976 on www.youtube.com

Take a look at the advertisements between television programmes for one evening. What percentage use animation in some form?

Creative arts

Animation can be used to represent characters, forms and events that are only constrained by imagination. Because to this, it is of great interest to the creative arts, as demonstrated by a recent international conference at the Tate Modern. Artists are increasingly including animation in their exhibitions and installations.

Entertainment

Probably the best-known use of computer animation is in the area of entertainment. Animations can be seen in cartoons, television programmes and films. It is also used extensively in video and computer gaming and to add interest to websites.

Education

Animations are used frequently to demonstrate principles in a simple, effective and immediate way. Animation can enhance a learning experience and is particularly valuable for visual learners. In scientific visualisation, specialised computer software is used to display scientific data visually, with a view to gaining understanding of the data. It is used in a wide variety of applications including engineering, medical imaging, oil and gas exploration, meteorology, etc.

Simulations

Computer simulations are used to model either real-life or imaginary situations. A model is created that operates according to a set of rules, with a number of variables that can be changed. The best known simulations are games where the player is able to pilot a fighter plane or drive a racing car. There are many examples of simulations that have been developed to show how events have happened that could not easily be captured at the time, such as earthquakes, aircraft or rail crashes. Simulations are sometimes used to predict what might happen if certain events were to take place, such as traffic or population models. They may also be used as a training tool, such as a flight simulator for pilots.

Research tip

Go to the California Institute of Technology site to see near-real-time simulations of recent seismic events. http://shakemovie.caltech.edu/
A traffic flow simulation at http://www.traffic-simulation.de/ allows you to see the effects of changing different values on the flow of traffic on a road.

CASE STUDY: CYBER POLICE

(September 2007) News reports indicate that animations of police officers are popping up on thirteen of Beijing's most popular web portals to warn Chinese surfers to avoid viewing illegal content. The animated police walk, drive or cycle across the screen within the web browser to remind users that their Internet usage is being monitored. It is believed that the animated characters will be appearing on all websites registered in Beijing by the end of the year.

As a group, discuss:

1. Is it right to use friendly-looking cartoon animations to monitor Internet users browsing habits?
2. Is it an invasion of privacy?
3. Do you think it could happen here?

CASE STUDY: VIRTUAL WORLDS

Warner Bros has announced (September 2007) that it is developing a web entertainment site, called T-Works, that will contain a virtual world where users will be able to create avatars from the company stable of cartoon characters, and interact with other users in a similar manner to Second Life. They will also be able to access other content such as games, cartoons, films, etc.

In a small group, discuss:

1. Why has animation embedded itself into modern culture?
2. Do you feel that the future of animation will involve the convergence of different technologies?

EVIDENCE ACTIVITY

P2

Research three **different** applications of computer animation.

Describe the applications using web pages, a report or a presentation.

TYPES OF ANIMATION

Movement

Animating the movement of objects, text or characters is probably the most common application of animation. In computer animation, this is done frame by frame, by motion tweening or frequently by using a combination of frame by frame and tweening.

The following Flash tutorial shows:

- creating a motion tween
- applying rotation to an object
- applying easing (acceleration and deceleration) to an object.

Tips

The most common mistakes made by beginners are:

- When converting an object to a symbol, not selecting the entire object. Use the selection tool to draw a rectangle around the entire object. Flash treats the fill and stroke (border) of a shape as two separate objects! Ensure you select both.
- Forgetting to convert an object to be animated into a symbol.
- Forgetting to create a key frame where you want an action to start or finish.
- Adding additional objects into a layer. Make layers your friend. If you are using tweens to animate the eyes, nose, ears and hair of a character, put each in a separate layer.

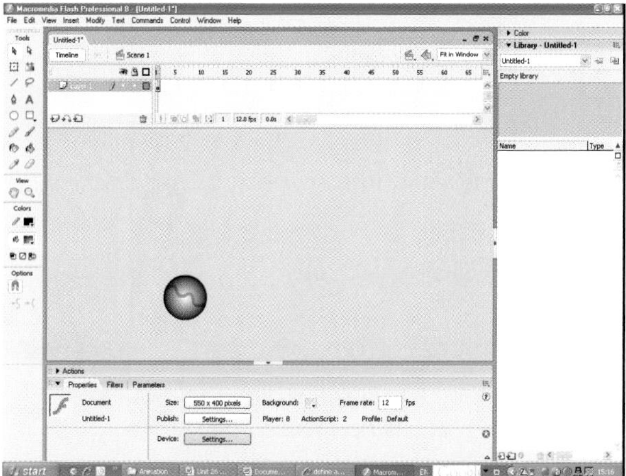

1. Draw a ball using the Oval and Brush tools.

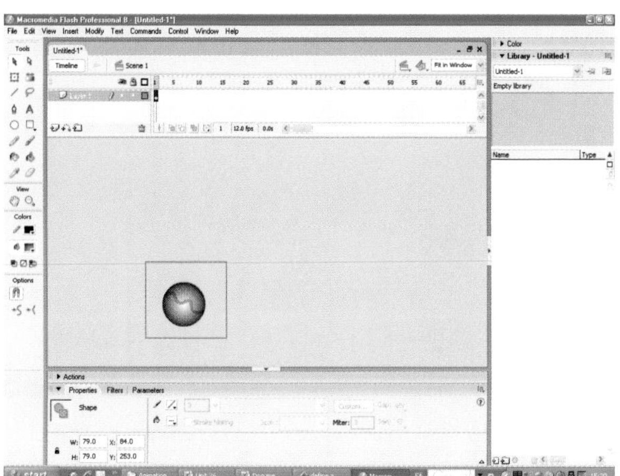

2. Use the selection tool to drag a rectangle around the ball to ensure the entire ball is selected. Note that the property panel shows that a shape is selected.

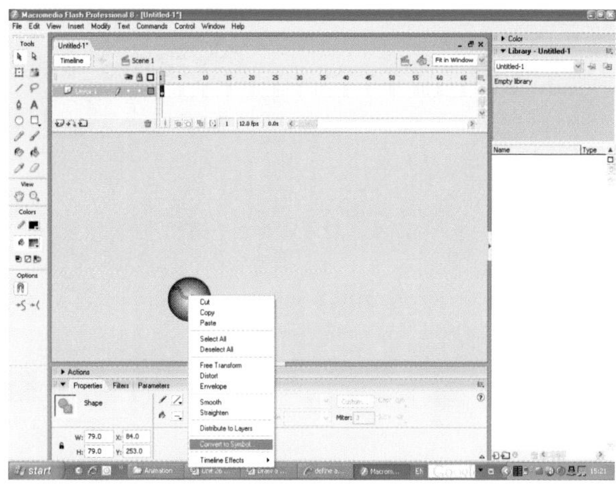

3. Right-mouse click on the selected ball, then select Convert to Symbol.

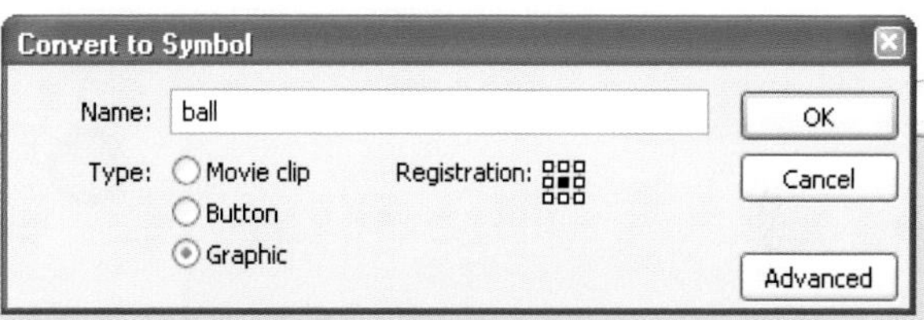

4. Choose Graphic symbol, give the symbol a name and ensure the registration point is in the centre as shown above.

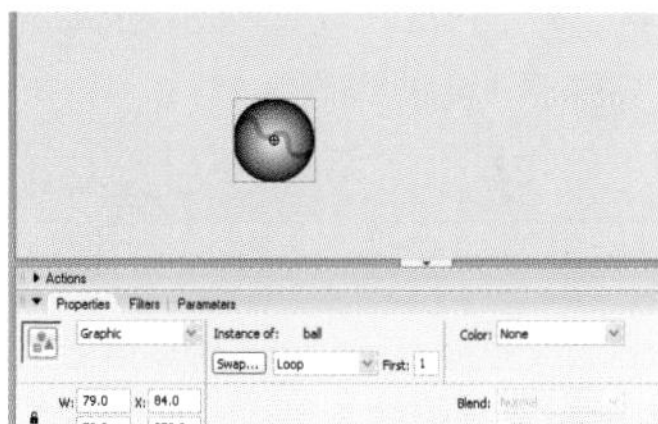

5. The ball now has a blue square surrounding it. Note that the property panel below now shows the properties of a graphic symbol.

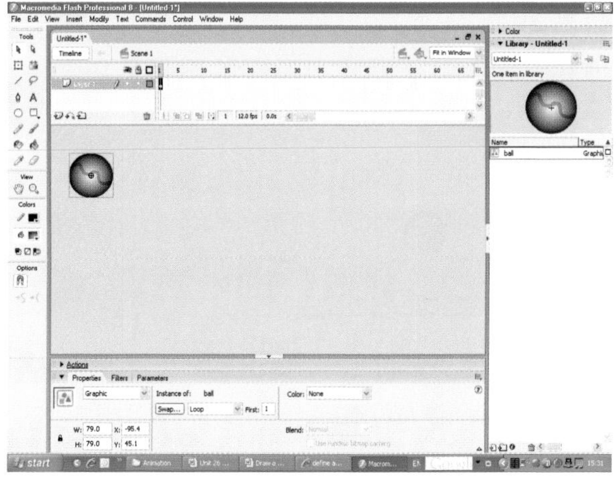

6. Move the ball symbol to its starting position in the movie.

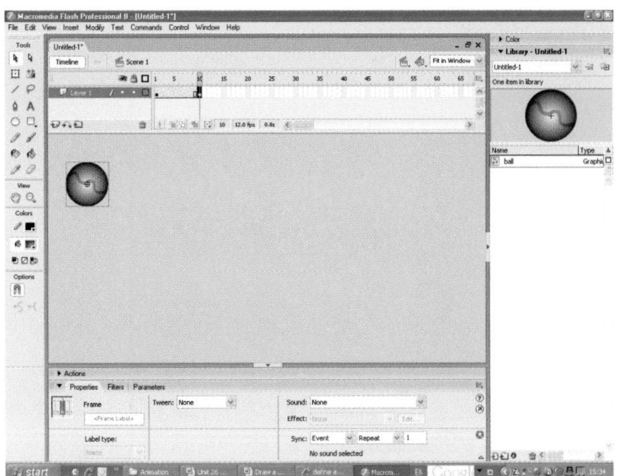

7. Click in frame 10 on the timeline, then press the F6 key on the keyboard to create a key frame.

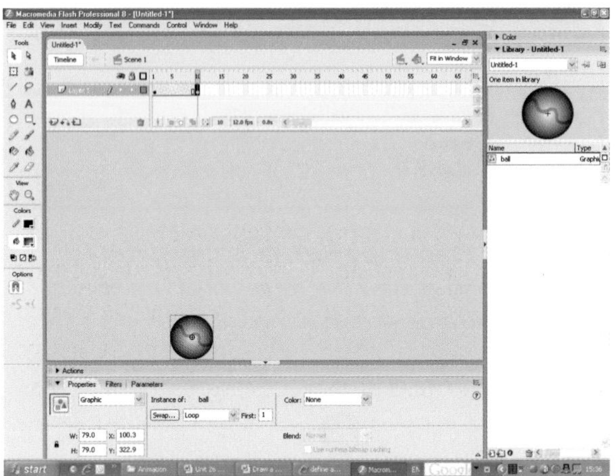

8. Move the ball symbol to its next position. I want it to appear that the ball is bouncing at the bottom of the stage.

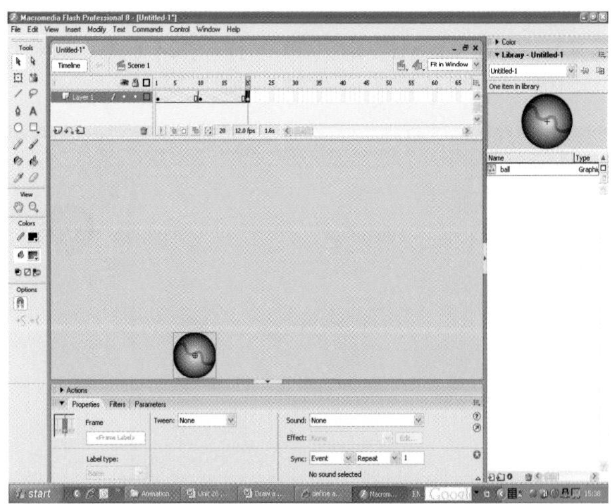

9. Add another key frame in frame 20 (F6).

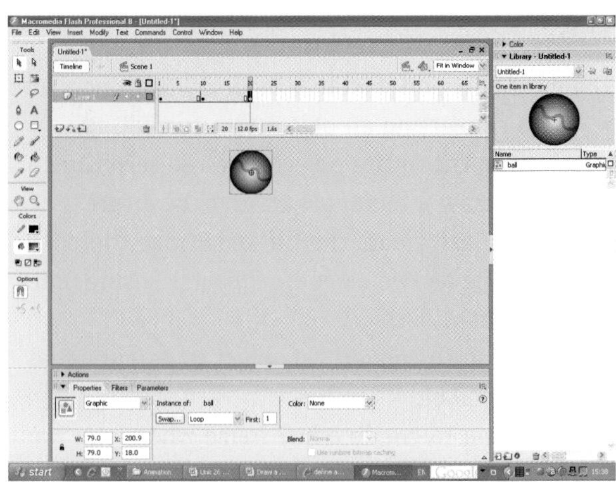

10. Move the ball to its new position.

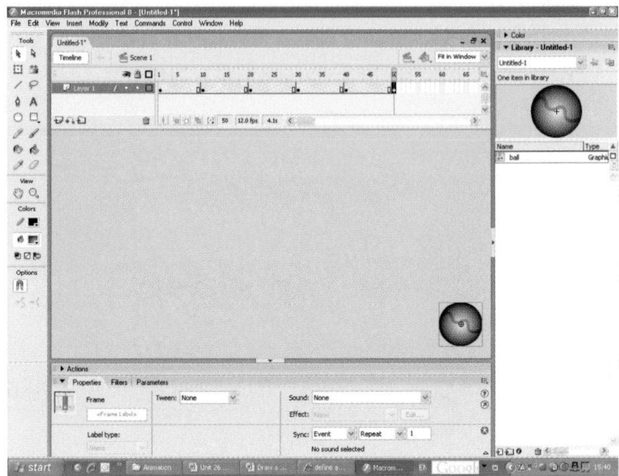

11. Continue adding key frames and moving the ball until the ball has exited the stage.

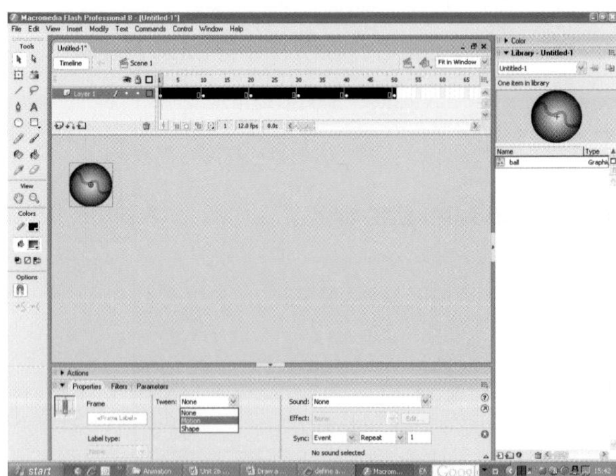

12. Select all the frames on the timeline. In the properties panel, select Motion from the Tween list box.

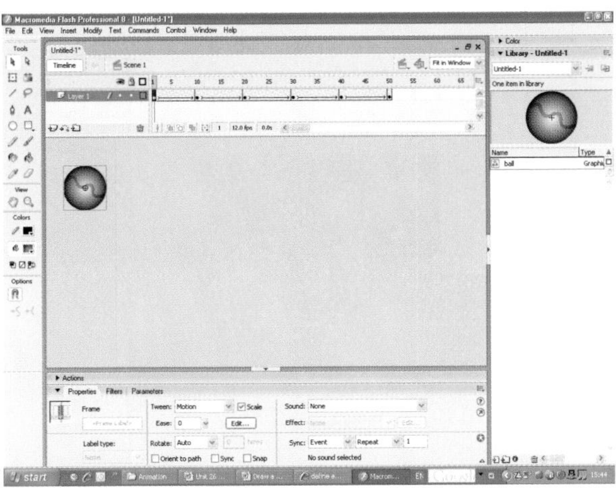

13. Arrows should appear between each pair of key frames on the timeline. If the arrow line is broken, there is a problem with the tween.

    Press Enter on the keyboard to preview your animation. Our ball has a pattern on it. The animation would look more realistic if the ball rotated as it travelled through the air.

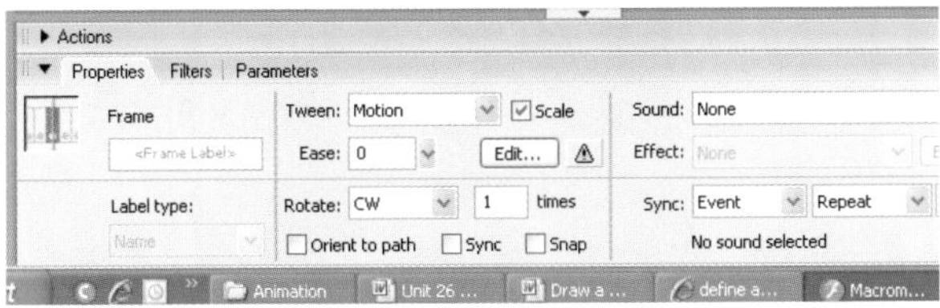

14. Select all the frames on the timeline, and then select CW (clockwise) or CCW (counter-clockwise) from the Rotate list box. Then select 1 from the 'Times' box next to it. Press Enter to watch your ball rotate as it moves.

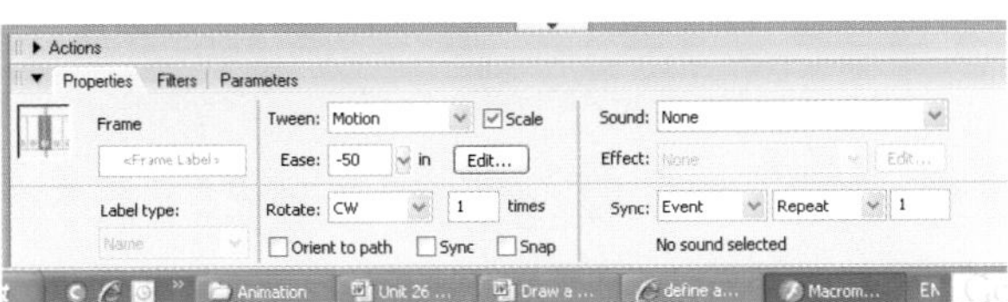

15. A ball accelerates as it falls and loses speed as it rises after bouncing. This effect can be produced using easing. Select the first key frame where the ball is at its highest point. In the properties panel, drag the Easing slider to -50. Then select the next key frame (where the ball is at its lowest point), drag the Easing slider to +50. Continue until you have applied Easing to each key frame. Press Enter to view the animation.

EVIDENCE ACTIVITY

P1, D1

Create a simple animation containing motion tweens. The animation should consist of about 200 frames. Experiment by changing the frame rate within your animation. If possible, run your animation on a variety of computers with different processors and amounts of RAM. Write a short report of your findings. Describe how the theory of persistence of vision is relevant to the design of computer animations. Include recommendations about the best frame rate for your animation. **(P1)**

Evaluate a software package or technique used to create animations. **(D1)**

Masking

Masks can be used to selectively block an area in a layer on the timeline. This can be used to create a number of different effects. For example, the mask or the area under the mask can be animated. Common examples of masks being used include a spotlight effect that appears to move, lighting up certain areas on the stage or a magnifying glass that enlarges items as it passes over them.

Masks are created on special mask layers. The following tutorial shows:

- how to create a spotlight mask effect

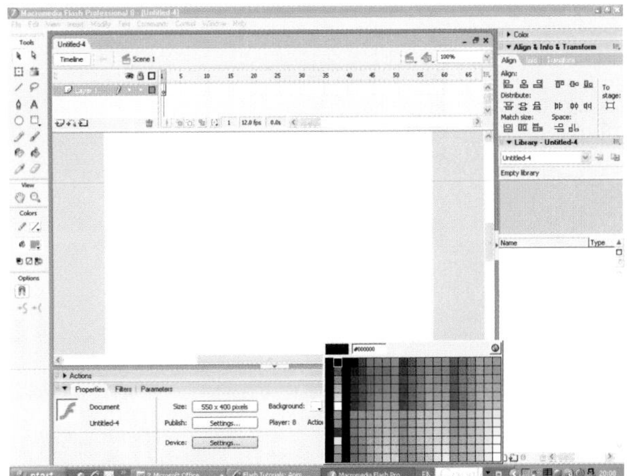

1. Choose a background colour for the document by selecting a colour in the properties panel.

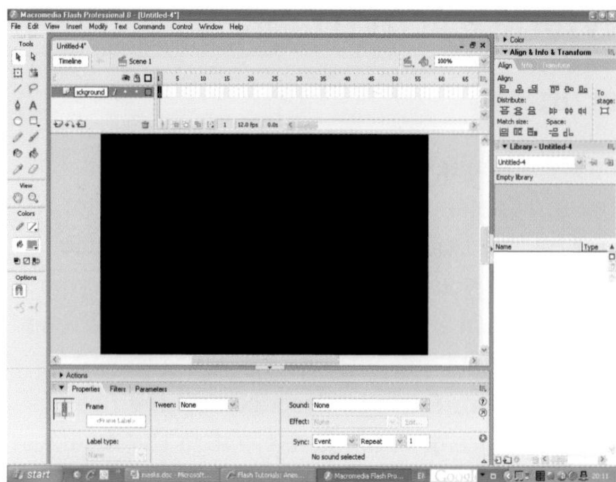

2. Double-click on Layer 1 to rename as Background.

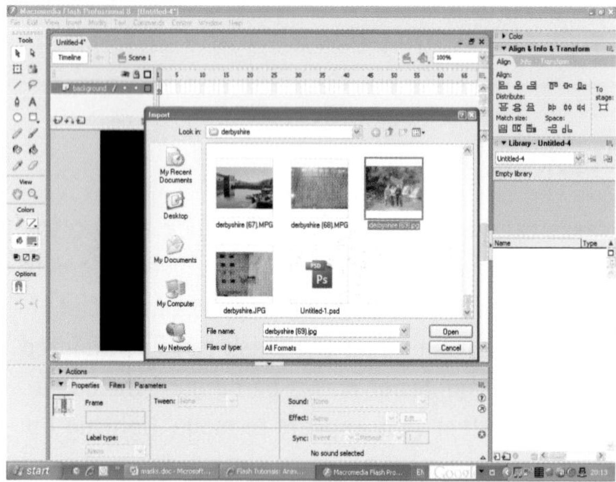

3. Import a photograph to act as the background to the mask. File > Import to Stage, then select the image.

4. File > Import to Stage, then select the image.

5. Select the rectangle tool. Choose a colour that is different to the colours in the photo.

6. Draw out a rectangle that is larger than the photo.

7. Lock the Background layer by clicking the padlock on the Background layer.

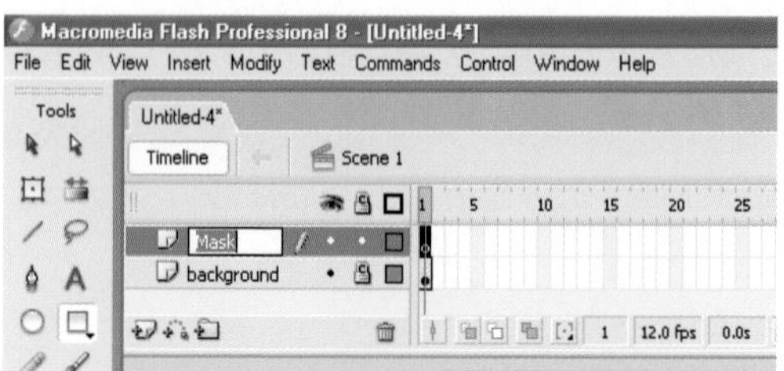

8. Add a new layer and rename it 'Mask'.

9. Select the Oval tool and choose a colour for the fill. Ensure the stroke is turned off as shown above. Draw a circle at one side of the stage at the height you want to eventually be exposed.

10. Convert the circle to a graphic symbol. Right-mouse click on circle or press [F8].

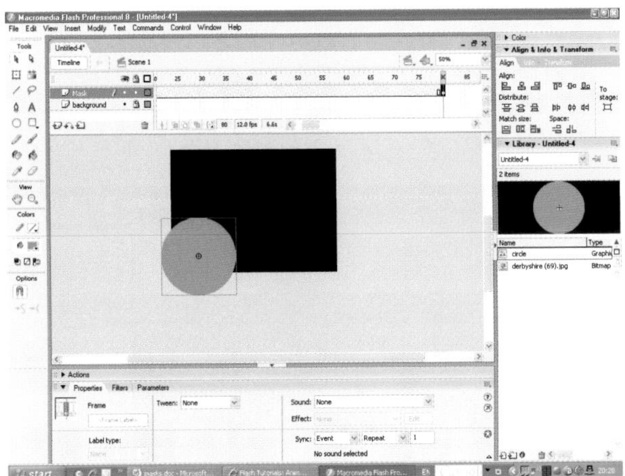

11. Add a key frame [F6] at frame 80.

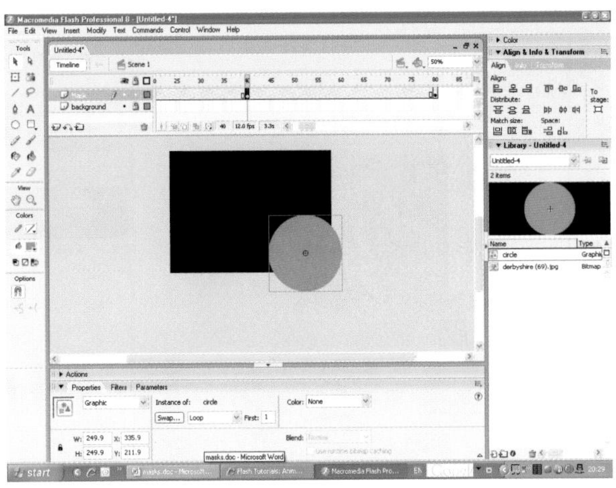

12. Add another key frame at frame 40 and move the circle symbol to the other end of the stage.

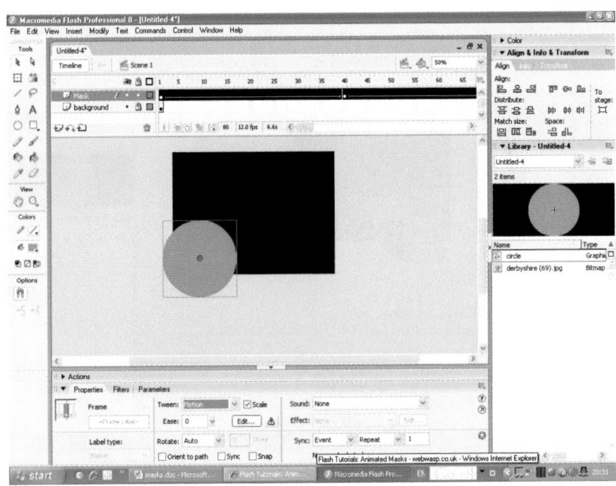

13. Select all the frames in the mask layer and select Motion Tween in the properties panel.

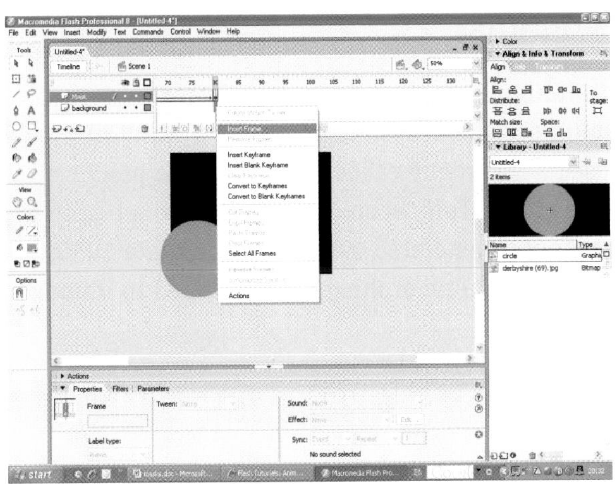

14. Unlock the Background layer. Right-mouse click in frame 80 of the Background layer and select Insert Frame.

15. Right-mouse click on the Mask layer label and select Mask from the menu.

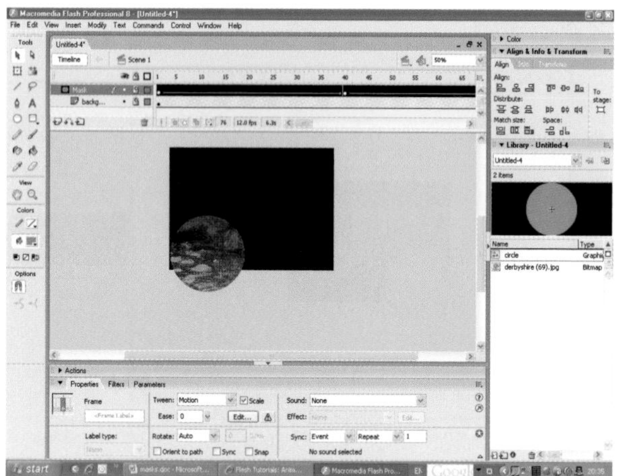

16. Preview by pressing Enter. Export the movie by clicking File > Export > Export Movie.

Morphing

Morphing is used to change one image into another using a seamless transition. Early films used a technique called cross fading to produce this effect. This technique began to be replaced by computer-generated morphing in the late 1980s. The quality of morphing has continued to improve ever since.

Research tip

Below is a link to a superb animation that morphs portraits of European women through the ages. See if you can find other examples.
http://www.saatchi-gallery.co.uk/blogon/mtvideobox.php?video_id=78.

Flash uses shape tweening to morph shapes. This tutorial shows:

- creating a shape tween
- how to export a Flash movie

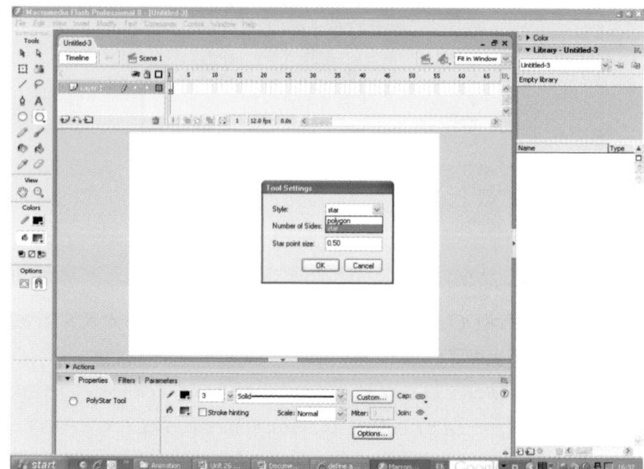

1. Choose the Polystar Tool on the toolbox. In the properties panel, click the Options button. From the Tool Settings window, choose Star from the Style list box, then select 5 sides.

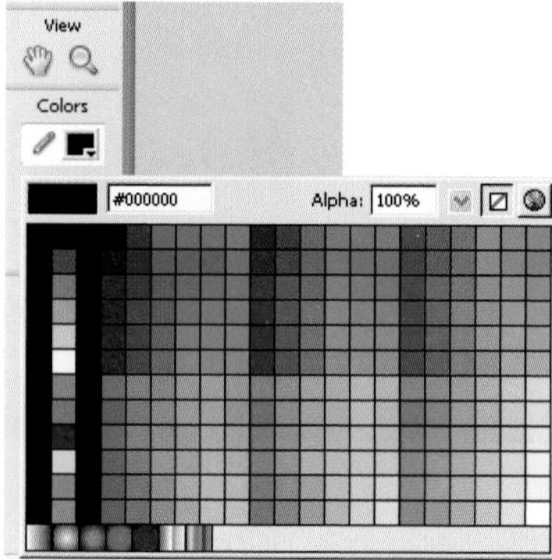

2. Click the stroke colour on the Toolbox and select 'No stroke'. (This is the small box with the red line through it. If you cannot see it, you may have accidentally deselected the polystar shape. Select the colour you want for the fill of the star.

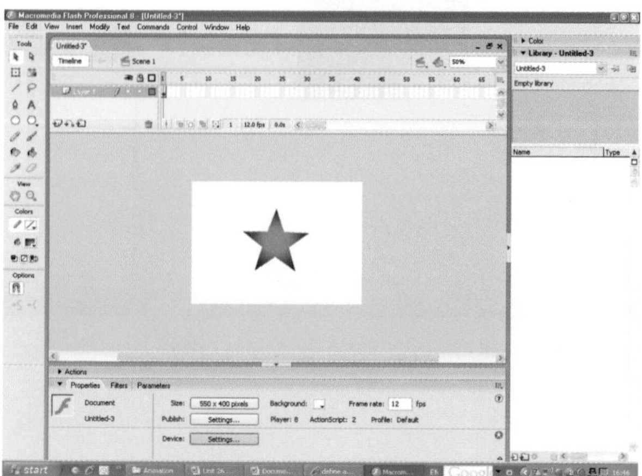

3. Now draw your star and position is where you want it, using the selection (arrow) tool.

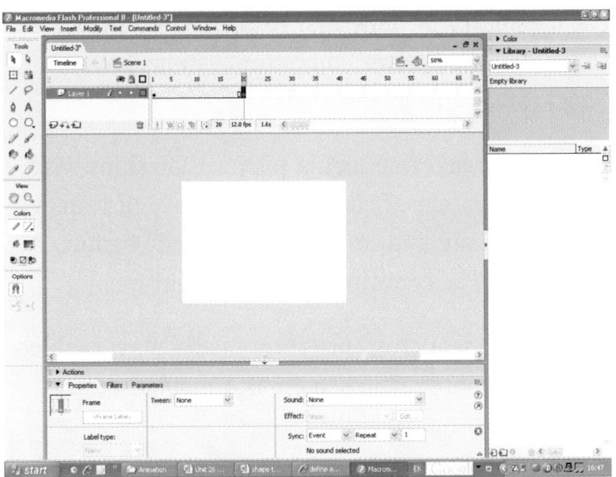

4. Select frame 20 on the timeline and press the F7 key to add a blank key frame.

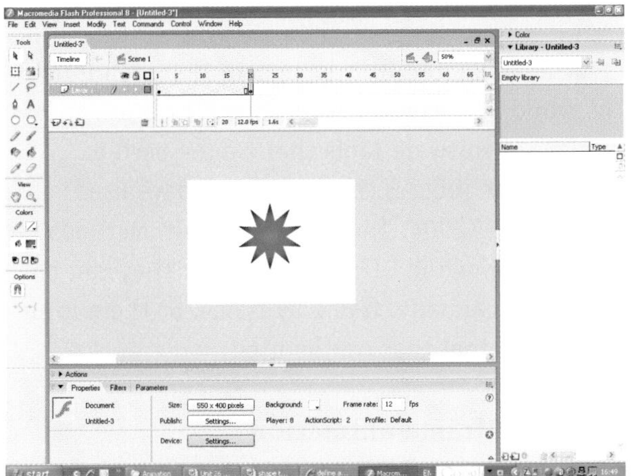

5. Draw another star, but choosing a different colour and 10 sides this time.

6. Select frame 40 on the timeline and press the F7 key to add a blank key frame. Then add another star, choosing a different colour and 15 sides.

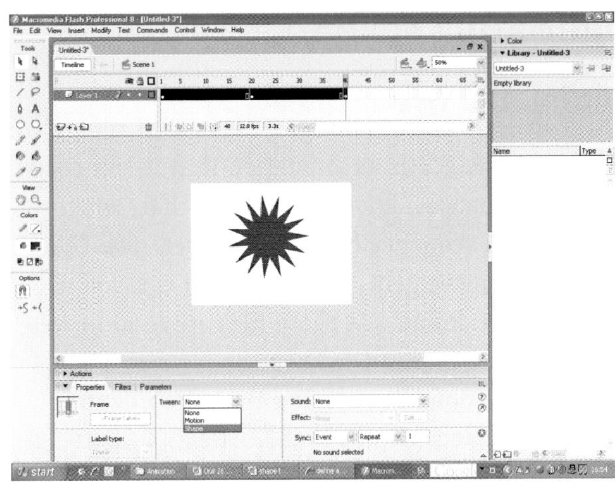

7. Select all the frames on the timeline, then in the properties panel, select Shape from the Tween list box. Press Enter to view your animation.

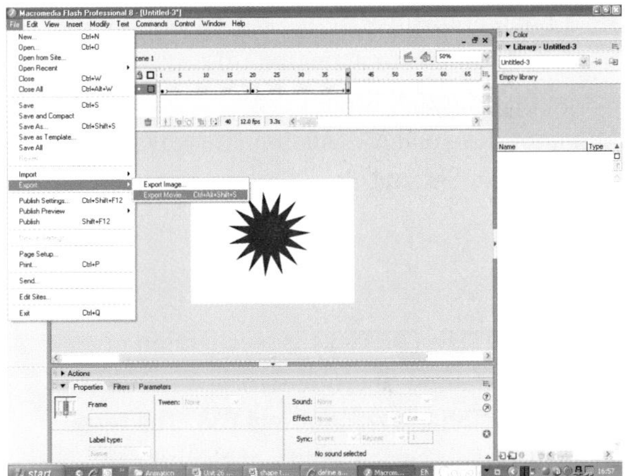

8. To export the animation, go to File > Export and then Export Movie. Type in a name for your file and click the Save button.

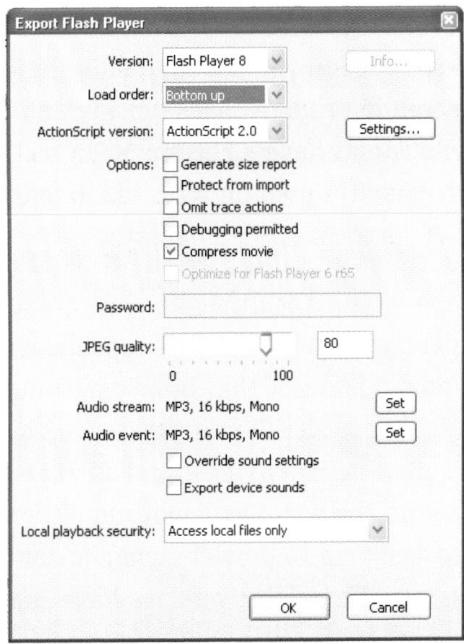

9. The Export Flash Player window opens. Click the OK button.

ANIMATION FORMATS

Animated GIF

An animated GIF is an animation that is composed of several images, known as frames, that, when played in a sequence by a web browser, give the illusion of movement. The animation is saved using a gif89a file format. As these files are used in web pages, it is important to keep the file size small. This can be done by reducing the colour depth (common colour depths for GIFs are 2, 4, 8, 16, 32, 64, 128 or 256 colours), or by reducing the number of frames in the animation. If the number of frames is reduced too much, the animation can become jerky. Therefore, a balance needs to be struck between file size and quality. There are a number of software packages that have the facility to create animated GIFs, including Adobe ImageReady, Ulead Gif Animator, easy Gif Animator, Macromedia (Adobe) Fireworks, GIF Construction Set and Jasc (Corel) Animation Shop.

Others

Dynamic HTML (DHTML) is a collection of technologies used to create dynamic websites, including HTML, JavaScript and CSS. The term 'dynamic' refers to the ability of the user to interact with content on the page.

Flash is a multimedia player that plays files with a .swf file format. It allows content to be played across a wide range of computer platforms and browser versions. It was originally designed with the web in mind. It loads quickly and most computer systems have a Flash plug-in installed. Flash is frequently used on websites to make an impact.

Shockwave is also a multimedia player, but is more powerful than Flash in that it is capable of offering many dynamic features that browsers cannot manage. It uses a .dcr file format created by Adobe Director software. Early versions of Director were around before the web was important. It was originally designed to provide dynamic content for CD-ROMs. Over time, later versions have supported more features for the web. Shockwave is used for more complex multimedia work than Flash or when web applications are required that are beyond the capability of browsers. It loads more slowly than Flash and fewer computer systems have a Shockwave plug-in installed.

QuickTime is a free media player that ships with all Apple systems. It supports a variety of formats including .wav and .mp3. A purchased version, QuickTime Pro contains additional features.

RealPlayer is a cross-platform media player which has additional features such as a playlist editor and CD burning capability.

ANIMATED GIFS

Features

Creating animated GIFs is a good, first step into the world of computer animation. There are a number of software tools that can be used to simplify the process. In this text, I have used Fireworks MX2004. There are two main methods for creating animated GIFs in Fireworks. They can be produced manually, frame by frame, or there is an automated tool that can be used.

Frame by frame animation

Open Fireworks and create a new file. I have chosen to create a file 300 pixels by 300 pixels with a transparent background.

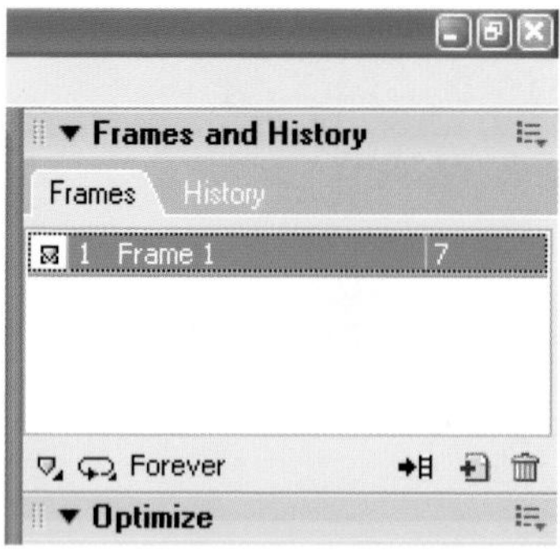

1. Open the Frames panel. (Window > Frames). A frame (Frame 1) will appear in the frames panel.

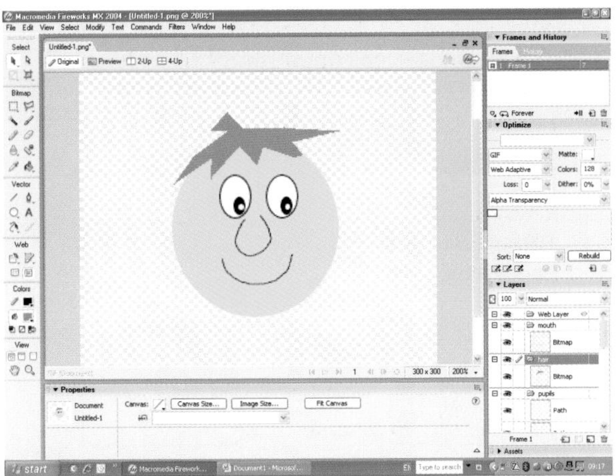

2. Draw an image of a face in Frame 1. Use layers to make it easy to change elements of the face on successive frames. Draw each element that you want to animate on a separate layer

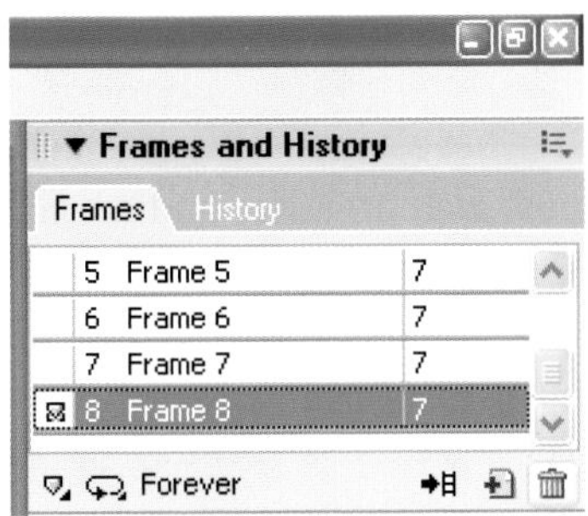

3. It would be very time-consuming to draw the image on each frame, so create a duplicate frame by dragging and dropping Frame 1 in the Frames Panel onto the New/Duplicate Frame button. It is located next to the Trash can at the bottom of the panel. Frame 2 should now appear. It is identical to Frame 1.

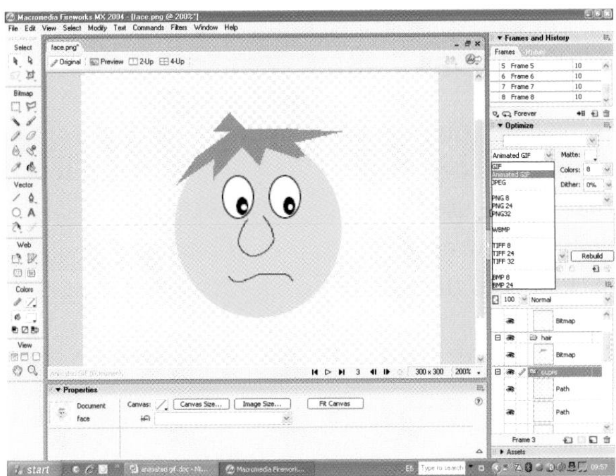

4. In Frame 2, edit any elements of the image you want to change. In the example, the mouth has been edited. Then create another duplicate frame as before. Repeat this method to create all the frames of your animation.

5. If you want to be able to see the changes you have made on each frame, there is an onion skinning option that allows you to see all your frames at once.

   Click on the button at the bottom, right-hand side of the Frames panel and choose from the options.

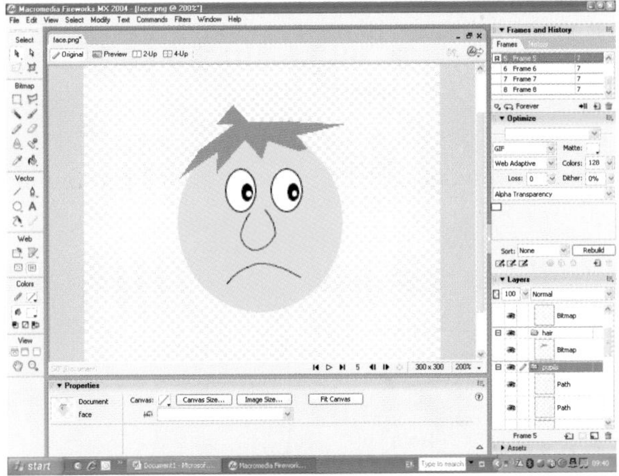

6. Once all the frames have been added, play your animation by clicking the Play button on the bar at the bottom of the drawing window.

   The speed at which individual frames play can be edited, on a frame by frame basis. In the frame panel, click on a frame to select it. You will notice that there is a number, usually 7, to the right of the frame number. This represents the play time in hundredths of a second. Double-click on the number and a box will appear that will allow the timing to be changed for that frame.

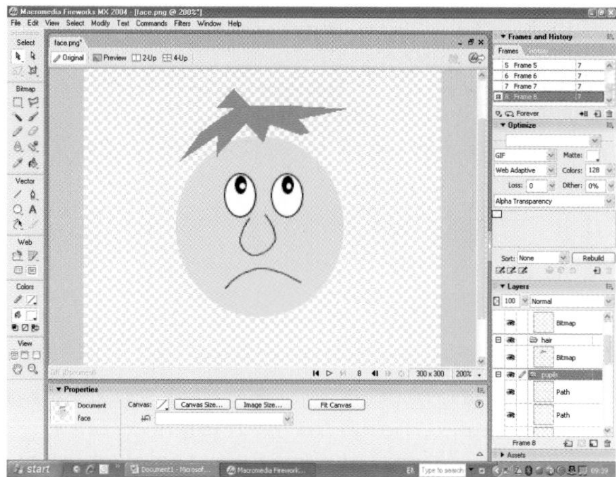

7. When you are happy with your animation, you will need to optimise and export it. It is good practice to save your image initially as a .png, so that if you decide to make changes to your animation at a later date, you have your original file with all the layer information intact.

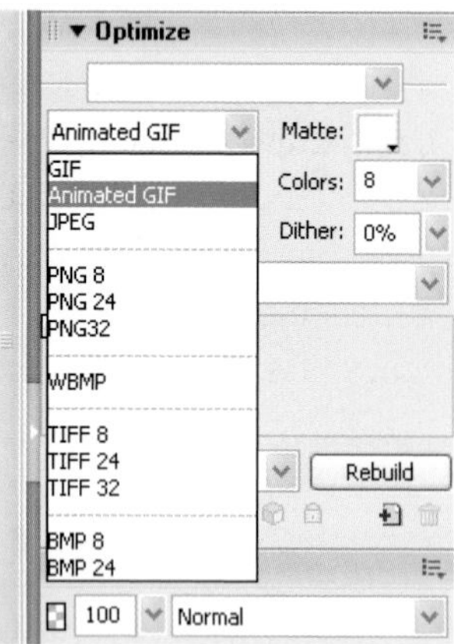

8. In the Optimize Panel, select Animated Gif. To reduce file size, you may wish to reduce the number of colours. In the example, the number of colours has been reduced to 8.

9. Go to File, then select Export. Give your animation a file name and save.

10. To test your animated GIF, right-mouse click on the file, then select Open with... and select your web browser.

Advantages

Animated GIFs have a small file size and will display in most web browsers and on most platforms. (Some early versions of web browsers did not support animated GIFs.) They will also play in PowerPoint presentations.

Limitations

Animated GIFS are limited to 256 colours, and therefore photographs cannot be successfully animated. In addition, the user cannot choose the frame at which the animation starts to play, or start and stop the animation from playing.

Alternatives

Instead of using the frame by frame method described above, Fireworks has an automated tool that can be used to create animated GIFs. Create a new document with a transparent background. Draw an object to animate.

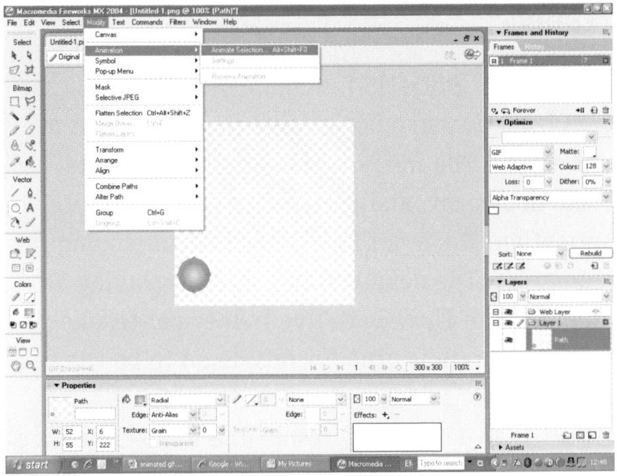

1. *Select the object to be animated. Go to Modify > Animation > Animate Selection.*

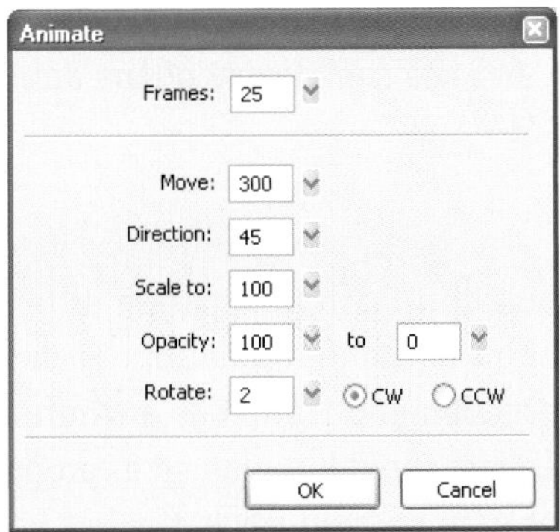

2. *Choose options from the Animate window, then click OK. Test and export as described for frame by frame animation.*

Instead of creating an animated GIF, a Flash animation can be created. Flash animations can be far more sophisticated than an animated GIF, but the file size is usually larger.

26.2 Be able to use software techniques used in animation

There is a wide range of software that can be used to create animations. In this section of the text, Flash 8 will be used to demonstrate many of the techniques that can be used in the production of computer animation.

TOOLS

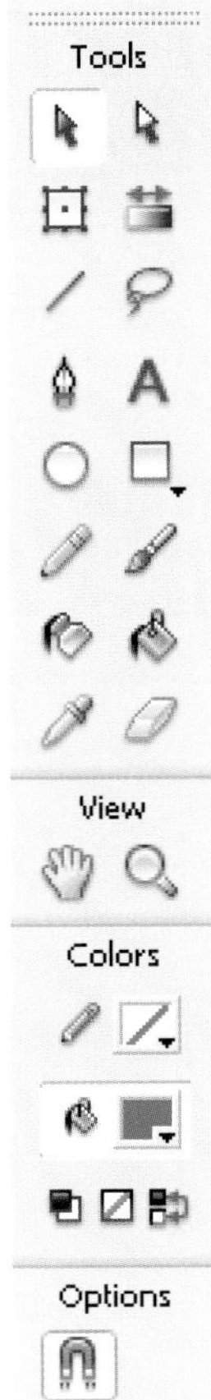

Before animating can begin, we must have an object of some description to animate. Usually, this involves drawing or importing an image or images. Flash contains a range of drawing tools. Talk to three different animators and each will have their own tool of preference and method of working. Some animators will begin drawing, using the oval tool and then deform the object into whatever shape they require. Others prefer to use the brush, pencil or pen tools. The important point is that you should invest time working with the various drawing tools to find a method that suits you. Freehand drawing is difficult with a mouse, and many animators prefer to draw in Flash using a digital tablet.

It is important to realise that when drawing an object, such as an oval or rectangle in Flash, two elements are created: the stroke (border) and the fill. When converting an object to a symbol, ensure that both the stroke and fill are selected, or you will find that you may only be animating the fill, leaving the stroke (border) behind!

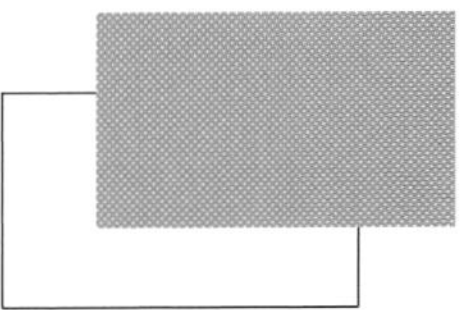

When selecting an object, to convert it to a symbol, use the selection tool (arrow tool) to drag a rectangle around the object to ensure that both the fill and stroke are selected.

A rectangle fill can be transformed into any shape you want. Click the selection (arrow tool). If the arrow is moved just outside a corner of the rectangle, a right-angle symbol appears. It is then possible to drag out the corner to change the shape of the object. If the arrow is moved just outside a side of the rectangle, a curve appears. This enables a curve to be added to the shape. Additional points can be added anywhere to the shape by holding down the Alt key.

Shapes can also be created by taking advantage of the way in which objects are drawn in Flash.

1. Draw an oval.

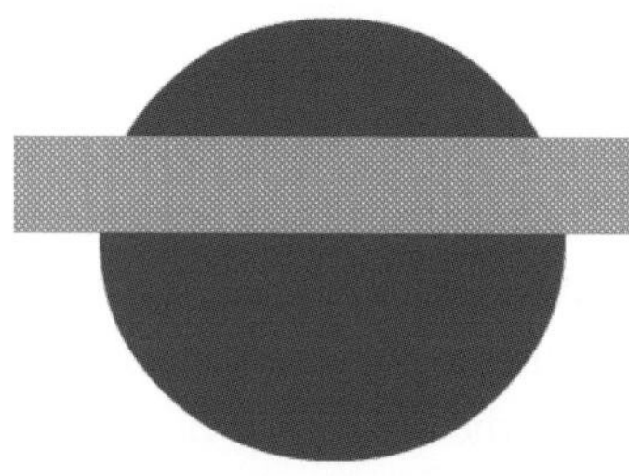

2. Select the rectangle tool. Change the colour. Draw a rectangle over the blue oval.

3. With the red rectangle selected, press the delete key on the keyboard.

Frames

A computer animation is composed of frames that are played in sequence to give the impression of movement. The frame rate is a property of the Flash document, and is set when creating the animation. It cannot be changed when playing the animation. The default frame rate for playing an animation in Flash is twelve frames per second. This frame rate is usually considered to be the best for animations designed for the web. Frame rates slower than 12 fps may result in a jerky animation. High frame rates can be processor intensive. Note that the appearance of the finished movie will be determined by two factors: the speed of the processor of the computer being used to view the animation and the complexity of the animation.

Layers

Layers are used in Flash to separate different elements of an image or animation. Each layer can be locked, hidden and viewed as a wireframe if required. Layers should be named appropriately, so that it is easy to keep track of what has been created on each layer. A separate layer is usually created to position Actionscript actions. When animating different elements in a movie, each element is created on a different layer. For example, if the eyebrows, eyes and mouth of a character are animated, the basic head shape, nose, ears and hair can be created on one layer. The mouth and each eyebrow and eye are created on different layers. This allows them to be animated independently. If a layer is locked, an object on that layer cannot accidentally be moved, edited or deleted. Special layers, known as action guide layers can be created when a custom motion path is required.

Controls/Tweening

Flash uses motion and shape tweening to speed up the production of animations. To produce a motion tween, an object is drawn in an initial key frame. The object is converted to a symbol. A later key frame is added and the object is changed in some way. The software creates the 'in-between' the two key frames.

In shape tweening, a shape is created in one frame. Another shape is created in a later frame. The software creates the frames in-between as before.

EVIDENCE ACTIVITY

P3 – M1 – M2

You have been asked to create a simple animation of a teddy bear face for a website for young children. Design two examples for the client. One should be an animated GIF; the other should be created using another format. Support your examples with notes that explain the features, advantages and limitations of each example. Include tables that compare the two different animation formats, and the two packaging or programming techniques used to create the animations.

Others

Buttons

Buttons can be used in a variety of ways in Flash. They can be created with rollovers, graphics, sounds or their own animations. They can also be invisible to create hotspots on a webpage or within a game.

When a button symbol is created, its timeline only has four frames (or states). These are Up, Over, Down and Hit. These can be used to determine how the button looks depending on mouse state.

Table 26.1

State	Description
Up	What the button looks like normally
Over	What the button looks like when the mouse hovers over it
Down	What the button looks like when it is clicked
Hit	This is the specified area over which the button acts

Buttons can be more useful than this, because in addition, Actionscript commands can be added to the different button states to create added functionality. For example, buttons can be used to play sounds or other media. They can be used to control the playback of an animation, or they can be invisible and used to create 'hotspots' in games. For example, when a player holds down a mouse button over a gun, it can be programmed to fire.

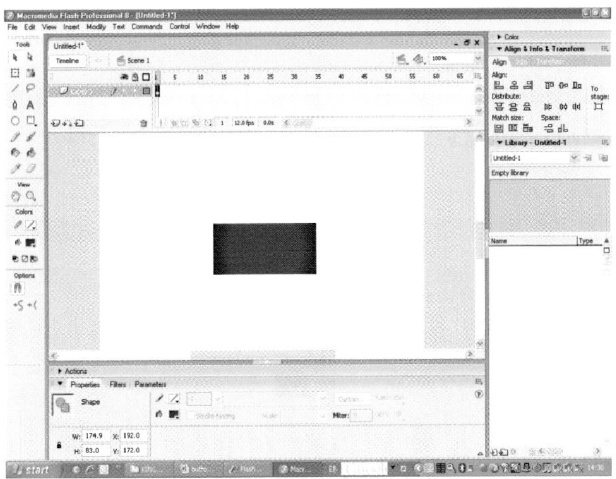

1. Use the rectangle tool to draw a button.

2. Right-mouse click on the button, then select Convert to Symbol.

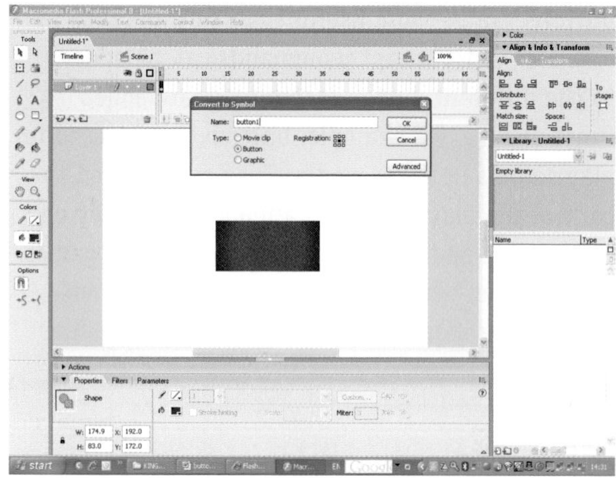

3. Choose Button, then type in a name for the button.

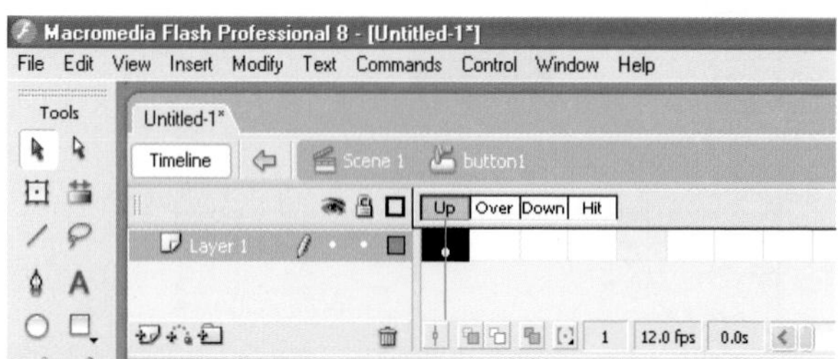

4. Double-click on the button to edit the button symbol. You should see four frames on the timeline: Up, Over, Down and Hit.

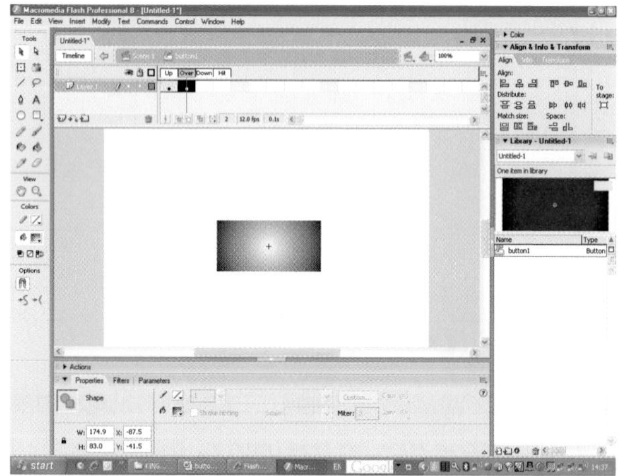

5. Click into the Over frame and create a key frame (F6). Now change the fill colour of the button.

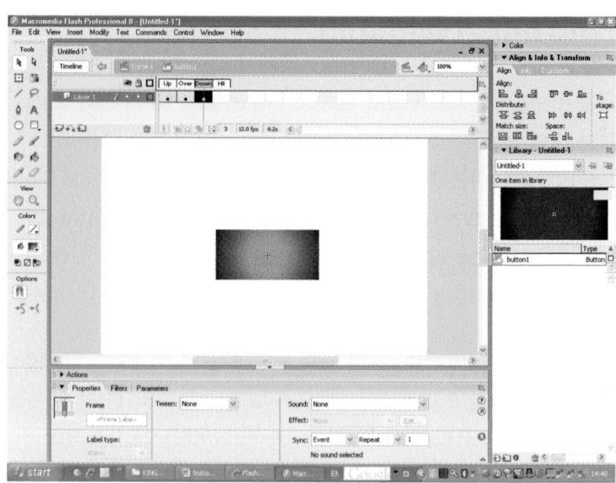

6. Click into the Down frame and create a key frame (F6). Now change the fill colour of the button. Leave the Hit frame empty.

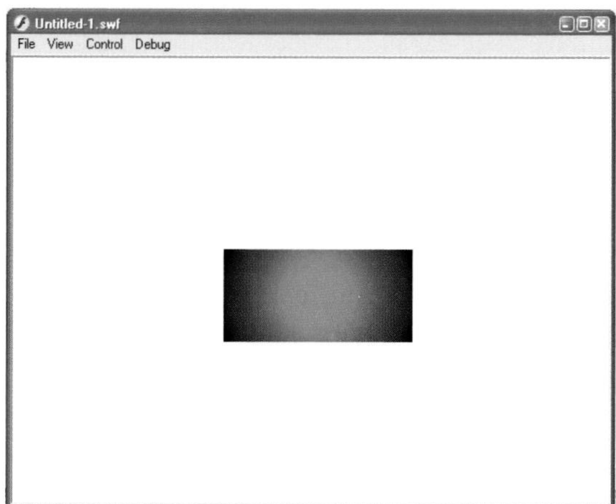

7. Press Ctrl+Enter to test the button.

Text buttons can also be created.

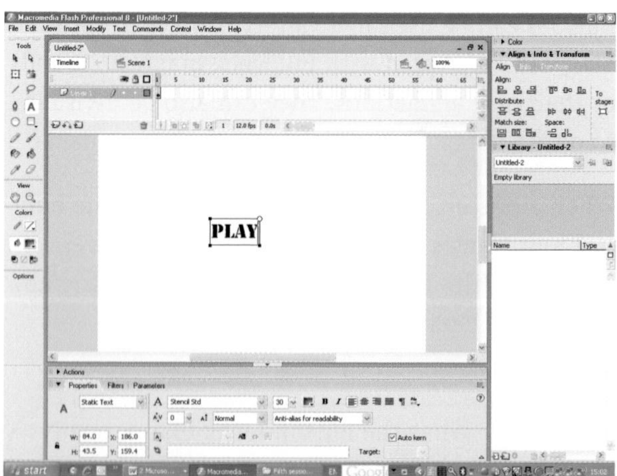

1. Select the Text tool and in the properties panel, choose the font and point size you want. Choose a colour for the text.

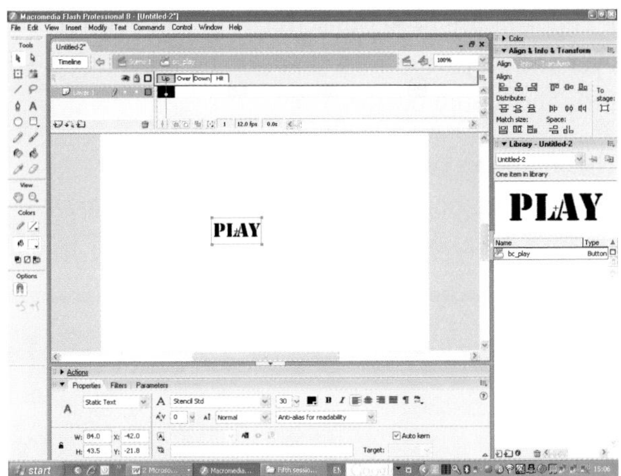

2. Right-mouse click on the text and select Convert to Symbol from the menu. Choose Button symbol and name button btn_play. Double-click on the button to edit it.

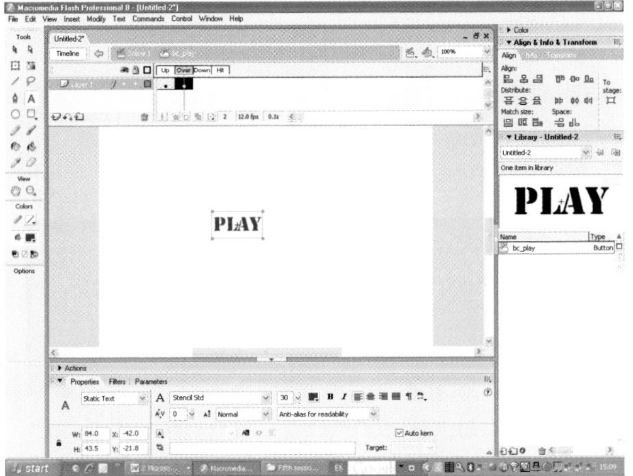

3. Click into the Over frame and create a key frame (F6). Now change the text colour of the button.

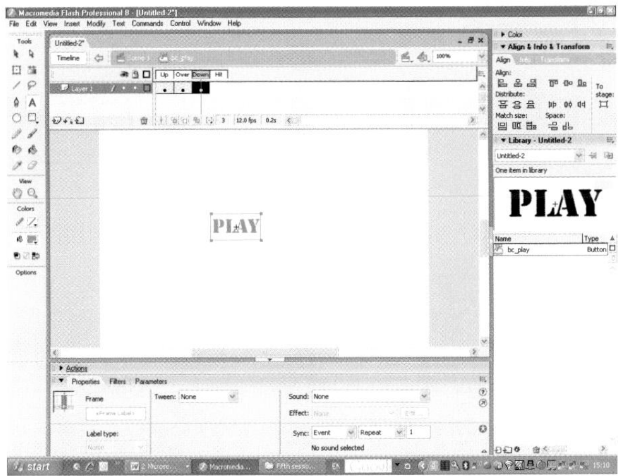

4. Click into the Down frame and create a key frame (F6). Now change the text colour of the button.

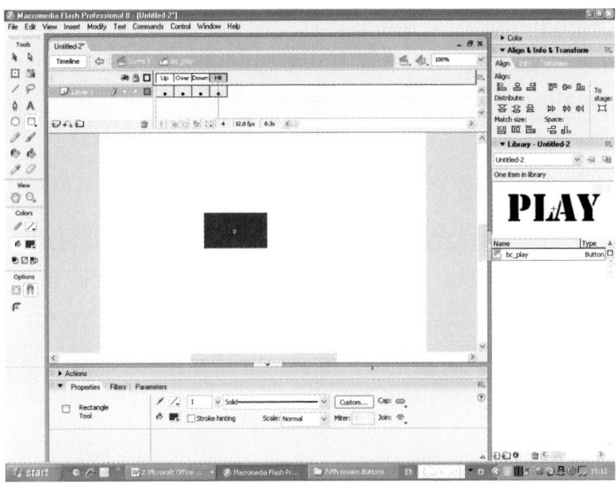

5. Click into the Hit frame and add a key frame (F6). Select the rectangle tool and draw a rectangle around the text. This will determine the area that will be affected by mouseovers or clicks.

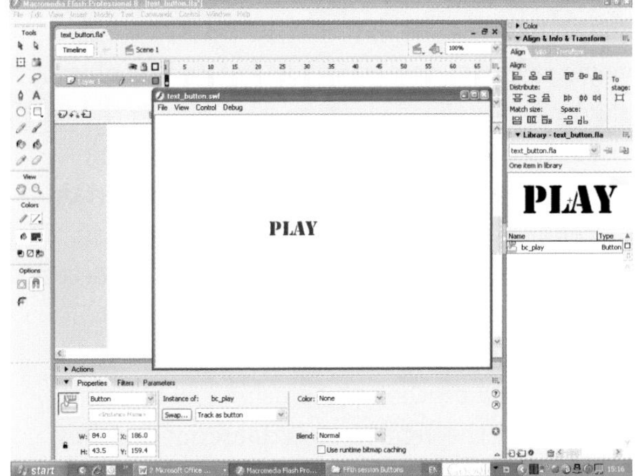

6. Press Ctrl+Enter to test the button.

Flash has a library of pre-built buttons. To use them, go to Window > Common Libraries > Buttons.

Library

Objects such as graphics, sounds, video and movie clips are stored in the library. Objects stored as symbols are only stored once in a Flash file, so help to keep the size of the file small. To add an object to the timeline from the library, just drag the object from the library to the stage. A preview window at the top of the Library panel makes it easy to check that the intended object is selected.

Symbols

Three types of symbols can be created in Flash: graphic, movie and button symbols. Graphic and movie clip symbols are frequently used interchangeably but movie clip symbols have their own timeline which is independent of the main timeline.

Integrating with other media such as sound

It is straightforward to add sound clips to a Flash animation. The clip is imported to the library. A new layer is created to position the sound clip on the timeline and the sound clip is dragged from the library onto the timeline.

Preloaders

Flash movies can begin playing before they have fully downloaded. Although this means that the viewer does not need to wait too long before beginning to watch the movie, this may cause problems with the synchronisation of the action and sound. Therefore, it may be better for the movie to completely download before it begins playback. A preloader can be used to give the user visual feedback while a movie is downloading.
It can also be set to start to play when a certain percentage of the movie has been downloaded. The scripting language, Actionscript, is used to detect when the movie has completely downloaded.
There are lots of examples of preloaders that can be found on the web. If using one of these, ensure that the version of Actionscript matches the version of software you are using. Examples of coding for many different examples of preloaders can be found on the web.

Scripts and script editing

Most animation software comes with an associated programming or scripting language. The scripting language for Flash is called Actionscript. It has similarities to JavaScript. It allows extra functionality to be built into movies such as associating actions with buttons, linking to URLs and loading other movies into a Flash movie. Actionscript 1.0 was released with Flash5 in 2000. Actionscript 2.0 was released with Flash MX2004. This was developed further in Flash 8. The language went through a major rewrite with the introduction of Actionscript 3 in 2006.

A common use of Actionscript is to add control over the playing of an animation by providing a Play and a Stop button.

The following tutorial, using Flash 8 will demonstrate how to implement this control over an animation.

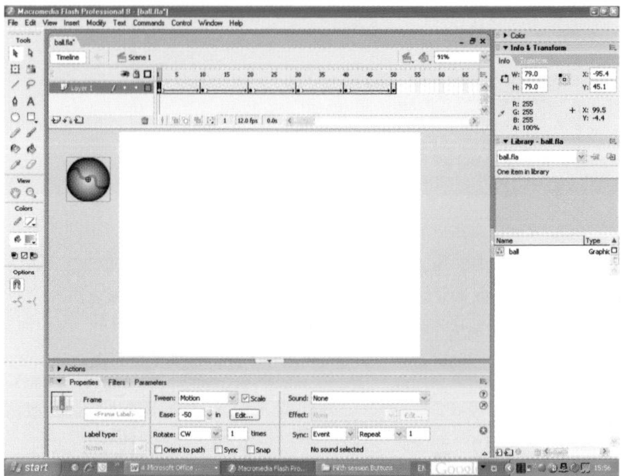

1. Either create an animation or open a flash animation file saved earlier.

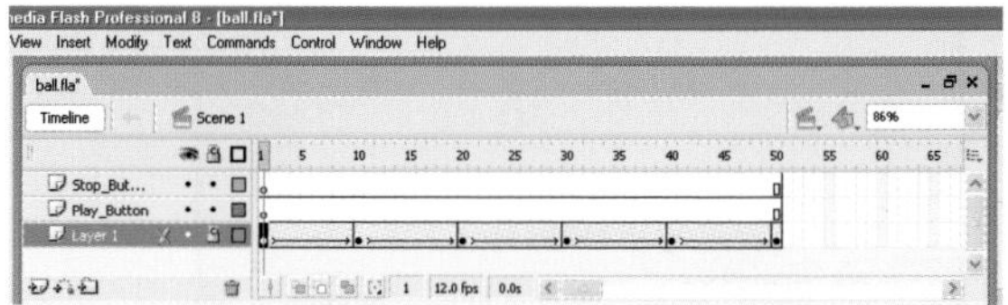

2. Lock the layers containing the animation. Add two new layers, one for each button. Name each layer appropriately.

3. Create a Play and a Stop button using techniques described earlier and place them on the stage. Name the Play button 'btnPlay' and the Stop button 'btnStop'.

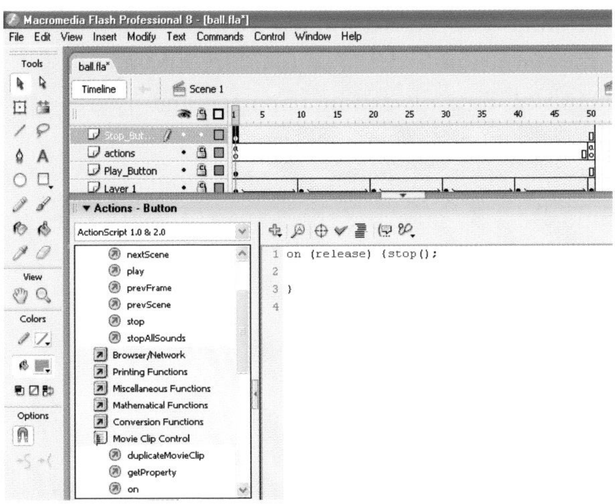

4. Select the Stop button on the stage. Press the F9 key to bring up the Actions window. Click Movie Clip Control > then 'on', then 'release', then scroll up to select Timeline Control > select 'stop'.

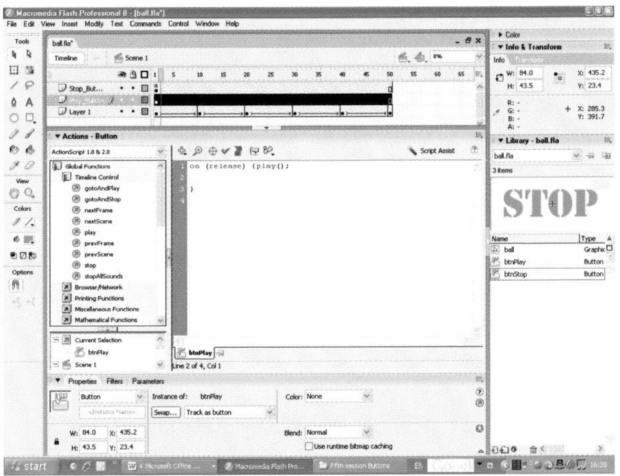

5. Select the Play button on the stage. Press the F9 key to bring up the Actions window. Click Movie Clip Control > then 'on', then 'release', then scroll up to select Timeline Control > select 'play'.

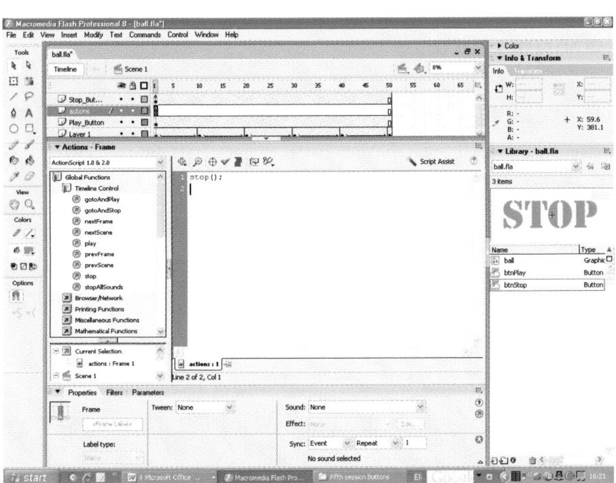

6. Add a new layer. Rename it 'Actions'. Select frame 1. From the Actions panel, select Timeline Controls > 'stop'.

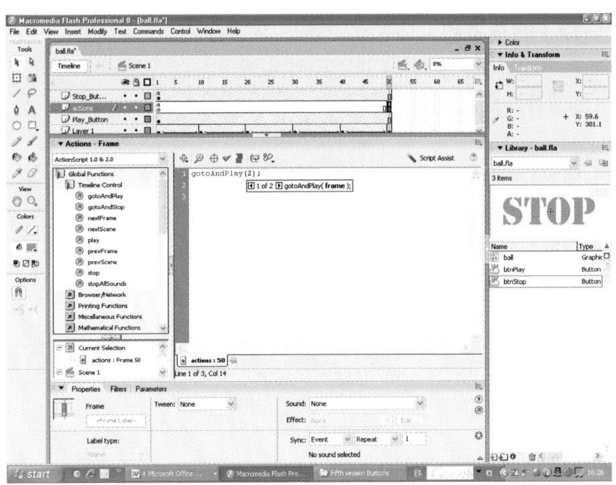

7. In the last frame on the Actions layer, add a blank key frame (F7). In the Actions panel, go to Timeline Control > GotoAndPlay(). Type the number 2 between the parentheses. When the movie reaches the final frame, the Actionscript will cause the movie to start again from frame 2, avoiding the stop action in frame 1.

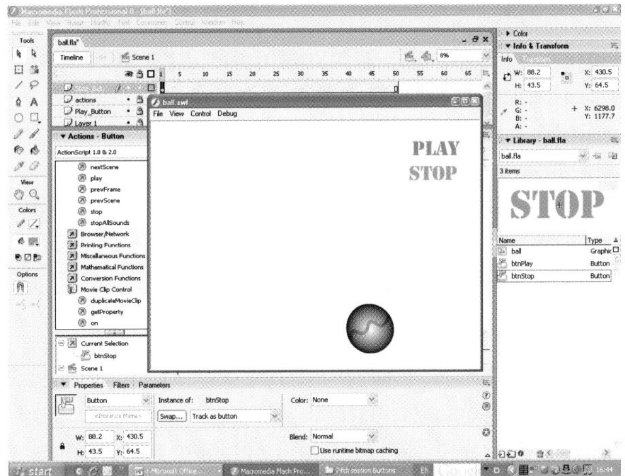

8. Press Ctrl+Enter to test the buttons. You should be able to start and stop the animation at any point. If there are any problems, an error message will appear. It is usually fairly straightforward to find the error, as the frame number and problem are usually contained in the error message.

EVIDENCE ACTIVITY

You have been asked to create a tutorial for animation students that describes how to use two different animation techniques. **(P4)**

SOFTWARE

Vector graphics

A vector graphic is held by the computer as a list of mathematical equations. Images are composed of simple geometric lines, polygons, curves and points to define their shape, location and properties. This method of storing images allows them to be resized, deformed and printed without degrading the quality of the image.

This makes vector graphics particularly useful where the same image needs to be produced in a number of different sizes, such as a logo. A similar image, saved as a bitmap is likely to have a larger file size. This is due to the vector image only needing to store mathematical instructions, while a bitmap holds information about the position of each pixel.

Flash is an example of a vector graphics program. When a vector image is displayed on a computer monitor, it is displayed as pixels due to the way in which monitors display graphics.

Bitmap graphics (Raster images)

A bitmap image is composed of small squares, known as pixels. Each pixel has a colour and position associated with it. Bitmaps are dependent on resolution. This is often displayed as dpi (dots per inch) or ppi (pixels per inch). Files with a .bmp extension are not compressed and can have very large file sizes. Therefore, many bitmaps are saved in compressed file formats such as .jpg, .png and .gif. Computer monitors normally display images at 72 or 96 dpi. Therefore images to be used on websites need only to be saved at this resolution. Higher resolutions will lead to larger file sizes and longer download times. Photographs are commonly stored as bitmapped images, as many different shades of colour can be incorporated into an image. When bitmap images are increased in size, extra pixels are created. This process is called interpolation. The program chooses colours for the extra pixels based on surrounding colours. This results in pixilation and the quality of the resulting image may be reduced. When the size of a bitmap is decreased, pixels are dropped; this also results in the quality of the image being reduced.

Although Flash is essentially a vector graphics program, it has limited support for bitmap graphics. Bitmaps can be imported and used as backgrounds. They can also be converted to graphic, movie clip, and button symbols and animated. By breaking them apart, they can be shape tweened.

Specialist software packages

There is a large number of programs available to the computer animator. They vary in cost from free to several thousands of pounds. The choice of software will also depend on the type of animation you want to create. Opposite is a list of some well-known programs.

MANAGING FILE SIZE

File size is an issue for animations produced for viewing over the Internet. One of the benefits of using a vector graphics program, such as Flash, for the production of animations is the resulting small file sizes. Importing bitmap images and soundtracks into Flash should be kept to a minimum as they will add to file size.

Balance against quality of image

If the animation is intended for viewing online, then importing images with resolutions greater than 72 dpi is pointless and will result in larger file sizes. It is a good idea to edit images so that they are the correct resolution and size before importing them.

Flash applies default compression settings to bitmaps when the animation is exported. For greater control over the quality of the individual bitmaps, they can be compressed individually, by clicking Options in the Library window, followed by Properties. Compression options can be selected. If Photo (JPEG) is selected, the quality can then be chosen. A value between 100 and 0 (with 100 being best and 0 being worst) can be entered. Click the Test button to see a preview and the resulting file size.

Table 26.2

3D Modelling and Animation	
Ray Dream Studio	• Produced by Fractal Design • commonly used to produce television advertisements, video games, architectural animations and special effects.
Bryce	• Produced by Daz 3 • commonly used to produce textured rendering and 3D environments
Maya	• Produced by Alias (Autodesk) • used for television and film animations, video and computer games
Blender	• Open source and available for a number of platforms • used for a wide variety of purposes including games and simulations
TrueSpace	• Wide use including games, animations, architecture
Lightwave 3D	• Produced by NewTec • used for modelling, animation and rendering television and film productions
3ds Max	• Produced by Autodesk • used for design visualisation, visual effects and game development
SoftImage XSI	• Used for television and film animation

Table 26.3

2D Animation	
Macromedia Flash	• Produced by Macromedia – now Adobe • 2D vector animation program used to create web-based animations, films, advertisements, etc.
Digicel Flipbook	• Used to produce 2D cartoons and animations
ToonBoom Studio	• ToonBoom produce a range of animation and storyboarding software from home to professional users

Use of special techniques

The following actions can be taken to reduce file size:

- Elements that are used more than once in an animation should be converted to symbols. Symbols are only loaded once on the viewer's system, reducing the downloading required. Modifying a symbol's properties allow you to customise the symbol without needing to produce a new one.
- Sound files can also be compressed individually. Select the sound clip in the library. Go to the Options button and select Properties. If the sound is a .wav file, it can be compressed by choosing mp3.
- The greater the number of frames, the greater the file size. Use key frames and tweening to reduce the number of frames.
- Use gradients sparingly.
- Minimise the number of fonts and font styles used.

ANIMATING FOR THE WEB

Special techniques

Animated rollovers can be created by adding a movie clip to the Over state of a button in Flash.

Animated GIFs can be inserted into the body of an email message. In Microsoft Outlook, go to the Insert menu, click Picture > then From File. Browse for, then select your animated GIF of choice. It will appear as a still image before it is sent. However, when it is received it will display in all its animated glory.

A number of websites allow users to create and customise e-cards online. Alternatively, they can be created from scratch using Flash, but require a knowledge of a server-side scripting language and an ODBC compliant database. For those that want to know more, a tutorial can be found at http://www.peachpit.com/articles/article.aspx?p=27138

Output devices

Flash contains a number of templates for use when designing output intended for mobile phones or PDAs. These can be found by going to File > New > Templates > PDAs.

Flash Lite is a run-time engine for supported mobile phones, PDAs and other electronic devices. It allows developers to provide those devices with streamed video and web content.

EVIDENCE ACTIVITY

P5

Create a web page that describes the factors that should be considered when creating animations for the web. Ensure your description includes examples of potential problems.

Monitor

The default size for a flash document is 550 × 400 pixels, but can be set as small as 1 × 1 pixels or as large as 2880 × 2880 pixels. When deciding on the size for a Flash movie, considerations such as whether the movie will be viewed inside a web browser window should be considered.

FILES

File types and features of each

Many different types of files may be used when dealing with graphics, sound and animation file types.

- The most common image file formats are .gif, .jpg and .png. These are file types used for images on websites. They have compression applied to them, reducing the time taken to download them to a viewer's browser.
- .bmp, .psp and .psd files cannot be inserted into web pages and need to be converted to one of the formats mentioned above.
- .wav is an uncompressed audio file format.
- More popular for web use is the compressed .mp3 file format.
- The native file format for Flash is .fla. Flash movies are compressed when they are exported and saved in a .swf format.
- Animations may also be saved in .mov (QuickTime) or .rm (RealAudio and RealVideo) formats.

Many programs have the facility to convert files (usually by exporting them) between different formats. In addition, software utilities may be purchased to perform this function.

It is important to check that the software you are using is able to import your files and export your finished animation in the format required by your client.

Working with graphics, audio and animations can create large numbers of files. It is important to have a sensible file management system for storing these files, to ensure that it is easy to find them when required. Many applications allow you to set up a default folder for saving your files. You could create subfolders to hold different types of assets or set up folders for different projects. Never forget the importance of keeping backup copies of your work. Little can be more irritating than discovering you have lost the pen drive with all your coursework on it the day before your assignment is due in. Even worse, losing a client's work could mean the sack!

26.3 Be able to plan, create and review an animation using digital methods

DESIGN

The design process begins with a user need or a project in mind. This may take the form of a script. The development of the design process involves the visualisation of the story, possibly by a writer, director or producer, followed by the production of a storyboard for the animator(s) to work from.

The style and genre of the movie needs to be considered. The style of drawings and choice of colours used for a horror animation will necessarily be different to the style used for a modern comedy.

How many backgrounds or locations will be needed? The script may need to be pared down in order to keep the project within reasonable bounds. The background should complement rather than distract from the story. Close-up shots should have simpler backgrounds. The background may be drawn much larger than the stage to simulate the appearance of movement in characters or the 'camera'. This is known as 'panning'. Other effects such as truck in can be used to create the appearance of a camera zooming in on a character.

The cast of characters needs to be drawn. Keeping the cast small can reduce the amount of drawing that needs to be done. Characters should be kept simple as animating complex character drawings can be extremely time-consuming. When drawing your characters, ensure that separate elements, such as legs, arms, mouth, eyes, etc. are drawn on different layers. This will ensure that it will be relatively easy to animate without having to redraw the entire character for each frame. (This is known as 'limited animation'.) In the animation industry, a **model sheet** is used. This is a reference guide for animators that shows a character from a variety of angles (known as a turnaround) and in a number of different poses. The purpose is to ensure that a team of animators working on a large project create drawings as close to the 'model' as possible. A **size comparison sheet** may also be used to show the varying sizes of characters when stood next to each other. This is to ensure that the sizes of characters are consistent with reference to each other in all shots.

Story boarding

The storyboard is used as a visual representation of the script. It breaks the story into scenes with individual shots. The storyboard can range from small thumbnail drawings to large boards. Drawings can be made on paper and then scanned, or drawn directly onto the computer.

The drawings should show how each shot is to be framed. This process will give a good indication of the amount of work that will be needed to complete the animation. Dialogue can be written under each drawing. At this point, design decisions should be made about the transitions that will be used between scenes.

The storyboard, saved as individual images can be imported into Flash and saved as a sequence of scenes.

Research tip

Find examples of storyboards and animations – www.storyboards.co.uk is a good starting point.

Timings

The production of an animatic allows the timings of the action in an animation to be developed. At its simplest, an animatic is a sequence of still drawings that has been imported into the animation program. Each image is framed as required. This might require the image to be moved to a different position on the stage, or scaled larger or smaller. Transitions, such as dissolves or wipes, may be added between scenes. Frames will be added to the timeline in each scene. The number required initially may be a rough guess. If the frame rate is 12 fps and the scene is estimated to last 3 seconds, then approximately 36 frames will be required. At some later point in development more frames may be added or deleted, depending on the amount of action and the effects required. In traditional animation, an X-sheet is used by the director and animator to keep track of the action at individual frame level. Effectively, it is a table where the director makes either specific or more generalised frame by frame timing notes for the animator.

Sound may also be added to the animatic. This will help to refine your timings. Import your sound files to the library. If using Flash, PC users should use .wav or .mp3 files. Add a new layer for your sound. Create a key frame where you want your sound to begin. Ensure that your key frame is highlighted, and then drag the required sound from the library onto the stage. It should be visible on the timeline at the correct position. Multiple sound files can be placed in a scene, either on the same layer or on different layers.

Key frames

Key frames are created in frames on the timeline when artwork is created or introduced. They are depicted by a black circle on the timeline. They are used to initiate a change in motion when creating motion tweens. If a key frame is created in a frame containing artwork or text, for example, in frame 1 and then another key frame is created in frame 20, the content of frame 1 will be copied to frame 20 and all the frames in between. The artwork will need to be moved or altered in frame 20 for any movement to occur.

Empty key frames (unfilled circles) can be created in frames that do not contain any artwork. When a new layer is added to a scene, a blank key frame is automatically added to the first frame on the timeline. When artwork is added to the frame, the blank key frame becomes a key frame and the circle changes to black.

Frame numbering and naming

As a default, frames on the timeline are referred to by number. This can create problems if you refer to frames by number in any Actionscript you write. You might refer to a particular frame when writing some Actionscipt. If you then delete or add frames, your script may then refer to the wrong frame. This problem can be avoided by naming particular frames and then referring to them in your Actionscript.

DOCUMENTATION

You will be required to produce documentation for the assessment of this unit. The development of an animation usually begins with a brief or a script. A brief will usually include a description of all requirements:

- the required product, its purpose and audience
- the format of the finished product
- the source of any images to be used
- naming conventions
- a target file size
- critical timings
- what storage medium will be used to distribute the product.

It is extremely important to ensure a high quality of documentation, as this will improve the likelihood that the product will fulfil its purpose. Documentation will also be used in the review purpose.

SOFTWARE

Appropriate for purpose

It may be the case that the software you use to create your animations is dictated by what is available in your centre or place of work. You will be required to justify its use. This is achieved by considering the brief and identifying the features and effects that are available in the software and can be used to meet the user requirements.

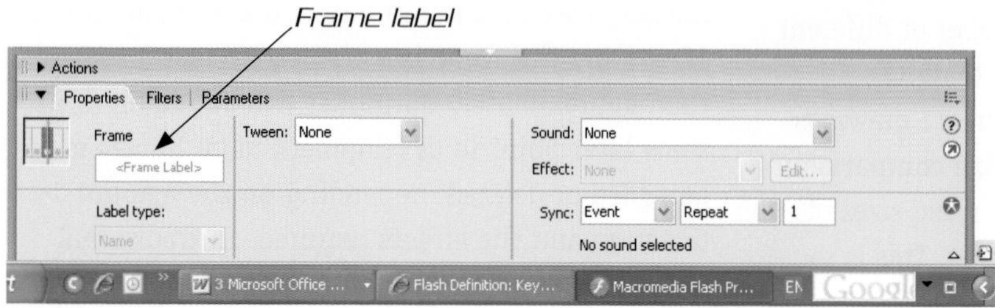

Figure 26.1

Use of tools

In general, the purpose of documentation is to allow someone to recreate a product if it is lost. Therefore, a list of the software tools used, with a description of how they were used is made as part of the documentation process. It is also an opportunity to show the breadth of your understanding of the software.

REVIEW

In many cases, the process of testing and review will be an iterative one. As the product is developed, problems may arise or it may become evident that the animation is developing a life of its own, rather than adhering closely to the original brief.

It is normal practice for regular reviews to take place to ensure that the project remains on track. These reviews may involve the client or may be 'in-house development team' reviews. Improvements may need to be made before the project can proceed to the next phase. The final product must be tested against the original set of requirements.

Does it meet the client's requirements? What are the measurables? Is the animation of the correct length, in the required format, the correct file size?

All the main elements of the animation should be tested. Refer back to the brief when designing your tests. Tests can be documented in a table, and the following headings might be appropriate: 'Purpose of test', 'Test results', 'Improvements necessary', 'Improvements made'.

Only when the client is happy with the product will the project be complete.

EVIDENCE ACTIVITY

P6 – P7 – M3 – M4 – D2

Design, create and review two different animations for particular purposes. The animations must be designed to be incorporated into web pages and will use both vector and bitmap graphics. Undertake a formal review of your animations and adapt and improve them, based on the outcomes of this review. Your solutions will need to be accompanied by the following documentation:

- the brief including all requirements
- design notes including a storyboard
- commented coding (if used)
- an explanation of techniques used to minimise file size
- evidence of testing.

Include evidence of at least one adaptation and improvement process which results from a formal review.

Evaluate the tools and techniques you have used to create the animations.

Glossary

AGP – Accelerated Graphics Port, used to assist graphics performance.

Analogue to Digital Converter – a device, normally an electronic integrated circuit, that converts a continuous analogue signal to discrete digital numbers.

ASCII (American Standard Code for Information Interchange) – a standard way of representing letters by using 7-bit binary codes.

Beta-testing – testing of software by people who represent end-users, rather than by software developers

Binary system – a number system which has only two digits, 0 and 1. It is useful for computers which work by being able to tell the difference between two states.

Bit – a binary digit with a value of either 0 or 1. It is the basic unit of data storage and data transmission.

Byte – abbreviation of 'binary term'. A byte is composed of eight consecutive bits that are capable of storing a single character.

Bluetooth – this is an industry specification for wireless personal area networks. Bluetooth allows the connection and exchange of information between devices including mobile phones and laptops.

Data sink – a device implementing the event interface to receive incoming events.

Database –a collection of information that is organised so that it can easily be accessed, managed and updated.

Digital filter – a digital filter performs mathematical operations on a digital signal to eliminate the unwanted bits of a converted signal. This is also known as reducing 'noise'.

ERM - Entity relationship model – diagrammatic method for understanding and explaining the relationship between the various data items to be stored within a program.

Hexadecimal system – often called 'hex' for short, this system has a base of 16 digits and it is easy to convert between hex and binary as 16 is a power of 2.

Iteration – repetition of data and processes within a computer application. Most conventional programming languages have several options for iterative code for a programmer to choose from.

Link protocol – the way in which data is transmitted from one node to another. The link protocol makes sure that the bits that have been received are the same as the bits that were sent.

Metadata - additional information that is stored within an image, such as: author, copyright notice, file size, date created and modified, resolution, colour mode, bit depth etc.

Multiplexing – also known as muxing. A process whereby multiple analogue message signals or digital data are combined into one signal

OOAD – Object-oriented analysis and design. A system based on objects and the collaboration between the various objects.

PCIe – PCI Express can support can support fast data transfers necessary for high-end graphics processing.

PCM – Pulse-code modulation – procedure that samples an analogue signal and converts the sample values to digital values.

Pixilation – when a picture appears to be constructed from small blocks of colour, as in Figure 24.15 (b).

Polish notation – or reverse Polish notation (RPN) refers to the way in which mathematical expressions are laid out in order to get the computer to perform the calculation in the correct order.

Programming language – any one of a vast number of languages used to control instructions to a computer.

Rasterising – preparing an image for printing by reducing the resolution.

Resistance thermometer – a temperature measurement where the resistance varies with the temperature. It is made out of platinum and has a resistance change of 0.385 ohms per degree centigrade.

Signal conditioning – translating the signal output by one device suitable for input into another device.

Sensor – a device which senses some aspect of its environment and converts it to an electronic signal.

Server – a dedicated computer that has been optimised to allow a controlled and shared use of applications and resources in a network. It also provides the connections.

Solenoid – a wire wrapped around a metallic core which produces a magnetic field when an electric current is passed through it. Solenoids can be used for many things in control systems, such as electromagnets, relay switches or to convert electrical energy into motion.

TFD - Transitive functional dependency – an indirect functional dependency where attribute X maps to attribute Y and attribute Y maps to attribute Z, to give attribute X maps to attribute Z.

Thermocouple – a temperature measurement where the voltage changes with the temperature. There are many different types of thermocouples, usually defined by the conductors used for the positive and negative electrodes.

TWAIN – the interface between a scanner or digital camera and image processing software.

Vector graphic – held by the computer as a list of mathematical equations. Vector graphics are excellent for drawings, particularly if they are to be resized.

Wi-Fi – this is a system that allows connection to the Internet. Wi-Fi networks broadcast radio waves that can be received by devices.

Wireframe – model composed of lines and curves.

Useful websites

www.atmforum.com

www.thewirelessdirectory.com

www.3gtoday.com

www.littlespringsdesign.com

www.openmobilealliance.org

www.standards.ieee.org

www.deviceforge.com

www.wikipedia.org

www.wisegeek.com

www.01vlog.com

http:/support.microsoft.com/kb/q110264

www.alice.org

www.clickteam.com

www.sxc.hu

Index

Pearson Education
Edinburgh Gate
Harlow
Essex
CM20 2JE

ISBN: 978-1-40586-805-1

Typeset in Great Britain by Tech-Set Ltd., Gateshead
Printed and bound in Great Britain at Scotprint Ltd., Haddington
Illustrations by Oxford Designers and Illustrators
Indexed by Richard Howard

Acknowledgments
Pearson Education would like to thank Eddie Allman for his advice and guidance in the compiling of this book.

In some instances we have been unable to trace the owners of copyright material and we would appreciate any information that would enable us to do so.

Picture Credits
The publisher would like to thank the following for their kind permission to reproduce their photographs:
(Key: b-bottom; c-centre; l-left; r-right; t-top)

Alamy Images: Jack Carey 101; Corbis Premium RF 138, 139 (background), 140; Nick Higham 5, 42, 43 (background), 44; Jupiterimages/Brand X 169; North Wind Picture Archives 173b; Design Pics Inc 4t, 10, 11 (background), 12; Carsten Reisinger 72, 73 (background), 74; Stock Images 75; **Alice Research Group, Carnegie Mellon University:** 108; **Celesco Transducer Products Inc:** 87t; **Corbis:** 73; image100 43; LWA/Dann Tardif/Blend Images 105; MM Productions 4tr, 11; Moodboard 139, 171; **DK Images:** 88; Gary Kevin 89l; Judith Miller/Cooper Owen 175; Stephen Oliver 86t; Karl Shone(c)Dorling Kindersley, Courtesy of the Museum of the Moving Image, London 173t; **iStockphoto:** 15, 25, 141, 144, 145t, 146; **Jupiter Unlimited:** Photos.com 89r; **PunchStock:** Stockbyte 145b; Westend61 104, 105 (background), 106; **Science Photo Library Ltd:** David Aubrey 170, 171 (background), 172; Adam Hart-Davis 174; Andrew Lambert Photography 86b

Cover images: *Front:* **Alamy Images:** Eye Candy Images

Picture Research by: Louise Edgeworth

Every effort has been made to trace the copyright holders and we apologise in advance for any unintentional omissions. We would be pleased to insert the appropriate acknowledgement in any subsequent edition of this publication.